# TO
# TEACH,
# TO
# HEAL,
# TO
# SERVE!

FIRST

ANNUAL ANNOUNCEMENT

OF

# THE AMERICAN COLLEGE

OF

## Osteopathic Medicine and Surgery.

———

1900---1901

———

A CHARTERED COLLEGE UNDER
THE LAWS OF THE STATE
OF ILLINOIS.

———

LOCATED AT
CHICAGO, ILLINOIS,
405 WASHINGTON BOULEVARD.

# TO TEACH, TO HEAL, TO SERVE!

## The Story of the Chicago College of Osteopathic Medicine

21041

### THE FIRST 75 YEARS
#### (1900–1975)

THEODORE A. BERCHTOLD

CHICAGO COLLEGE OF OSTEOPATHIC MEDICINE
CHICAGO, ILLINOIS

*Library of Congress Catalog Card Number:* 74-31540

Copyright © by Chicago College of Osteopathic Medicine
All rights reserved. Published 1975

Composed and printed by
The University of Chicago Printing Department

Printed in the United States of America

*"C.C.O.M. . . .*
*a professional college with assets of*
*human interest, dedication, and hopes and liabilities*
*inconceivable except in the minds, hearts, and*
*souls of determined, dedicated people."*

DR. SAMUEL V. ROBUCK

# TABLE OF CONTENTS

# AUTHOR'S FOREWORD

THE HISTORY of a 75-year-old osteopathic college is inextricably inter-twined with that of the osteopathic medical profession itself. Ever since the day in 1874 when a country doctor, Andrew Taylor Still, announced his new theory of osteopathy, and the subsequent founding in 1892 of the first college of osteopathy in Kirksville, Missouri, the battle for legal recognition and public acceptance by the osteopathic medical colleges and the os-teopathic medical physicians they graduated has been arduous and relent-less. It has been a warfare punctuated occasionally by encouraging victories for the profession, but far more often—until recent years, at least—a conflict of frustration and discouragement, of setback after setback, yet serving al-ways to rally the forces to press on more militantly than before.

If the fight for legal recognition and full professional equality in the state and local courts has been one of epic proportions by the osteopathic medical profession proper, it has been equally heroic on the part of the half dozen osteopathic medical colleges which have had to contend not only against organized prejudice and public ignorance, but also against the diploma mills, the quacks, and the charlatans who, dismally unqualified, brazenly set up practice throughout the land to becloud the reputations of the trained os-teopathic physicians who were battling prejudice and ridicule as well as the stubborn ailments besetting mankind.

In the determination to provide professional education and to send well-trained, qualified osteopathic physicians into the American communities (and, indeed, well beyond the continental borders), no institution has been more outstanding than the Chicago College of Osteopathic Medicine (known for so many years as the "Chicago College of Osteopathy.") At first glance, to one observing the year-to-year events of the college from today's vantage point, it is sometimes difficult to comprehend why the school's founders and early-day teachers and administrators suffered the woes they did. They were for the most part men of brilliant accomplishment, many with national, even international, reputations, men outstanding in the life and activities of their communities. Many not only had the D.O. degree, but the M.D. degree as well. They achieved startling results in their daily prac-tice. They were profuse in their contributions to professional journals. Yet they were refused admittance to medical hospitals, denied the privilege of even the most minor surgical performance (even vaccinating patients was prohibited).

Little by little, however, in one state after another, the bans have been gradually lifted, and today the profession is viewed with greater understanding and admiration than ever before.

The story of the Chicago College of Osteopathic Medicine is the story of one of eight small colleges which have helped to keep the ranks of the nation's osteopathic physicians filled. It was one of the earliest to establish professional standards and to upgrade, year after year, the entrance and performance requirements of those who sought to alleviate human ills under the aegis of osteopathic medicine. It is a story of struggle and perseverance against unbelievable odds, yet a struggle that somehow or other always found the men who could champion its cause and raise the financial means to keep the institution from extinction. It is, indeed, a success story in the best American tradition, a story of achievement not only in buildings and equipment, but of community and nation-wide medical service, and in sensitizing public awareness to the enormous potential of the osteopathic medical profession.

The writer has made no attempt to outline the history of osteopathic medicine, to give a detailed account of its origin and development. Such a task would extend far beyond the purpose and range of this undertaking. The intent is to present the history of a single school—the Chicago College of Osteopathic Medicine—and to confine itself to this objective insofar as possible.

THEODORE A. BERCHTOLD, M.A.

# ON BEHALF OF
# THE BOARD OF TRUSTEES . . .

Many years ago, the Board of Trustees of what was then the Chicago College of Osteopathy, declared that only a Board of Trustees which included lay as well as professional members would provide the balanced control and leadership needed to assure the growth and continuing development of the College. As the result of such thinking, the membership of the institution's trustees for many decades has included businessmen, industrialists, educators, civic leaders and alumni intensely interested in the important work this College is achieving in the community, the city, and the nation.

The diversity of the Board of Trustees has been one of the administrative strengths of the College. It has provided a broad perspective of leadership advantageous to the advancement of osteopathic medical education and health care delivery. I believe that horizons are wider, aims higher and intercommunication between campus and community more harmonious as the result of the constituency of CCOM's Board of Trustees.

As Chairman of the Board of Trustees, I am happy to express the deep satisfaction of our entire Board in being a part of CCOM's 75th anniversary observance. I know that even greater accomplishments will be ours.

ANDREW A. ATHENS
*Chairman*

# INTRODUCTORY NOTE

I T HAS been said that an institution is the lengthened shadow of a man. The Chicago College of Osteopathic Medicine is a montage of the lengthened shadows of many men. It seems fitting that on the 75th Anniversary of the founding of CCOM, we look again at the men who founded this institution, at the teachers and physicians who served so unselfishly during the critical early days of the college which today accounts for nearly thirteen per cent of all the osteopathic physicians who enter practice in the United States each year. This history of the College's first seventy-five years is a story told for the first time—a narrative that touches upon both the past and the future —on the yesterdays and the tomorrows—of an educational institution whose influence in the osteopathic profession continues to grow. Yet it is a story without a denouement—merely the occasion to pause briefly as the College prepares for the next two and one half decades to complete its first century of service to man.

THADDEUS P. KAWALEK. PH.D.
*President*

# CHIEF
# EXECUTIVE
# OFFICERS
# 1900
# TO
# 1975

J. MARTIN LITTLEJOHN, M.D., D.O.
1900–1913

CARL P. McCONNELL, D.O.
1913–1914

ERNEST R. PROCTOR, D.O.
1914–1917

GEORGE H. CARPENTER, D.O.
1917–1929

HARRY L. COLLINS, M.D., D.O.
1929–1936

RICHARD N. MacBAIN, D.O.
1936–1967

THADDEUS P. KAWALEK, PH.D.
1967—

# ACKNOWLEDGMENTS AND BIBLIOGRAPHY

I WANT to express my appreciation to a number of individuals for their help in making available documents, records, minutes of meetings, and journals—source materials without which this history could not have been written:

Dr. Thaddeus P. Kawalek, CCOM president, who placed at my disposal minutes of meetings held by the College's Board of Trustees. These provided information obviously available nowhere else.

Dr. Richard N. MacBain, former CCOM president, who turned over to me letters, notes, minutes of Board meetings and other early records, and who provided personal recollections of people and places during three informative sessions I had with him in his home in Tryon, North Carolina.

Dr. T. Edward Hall, London, England, staunch admirer of Dr. J. Martin Littlejohn, who furnished biographical information and forwarded copies of journals containing pertinent historical data. Dr. Hall knew some of the earlier faculty members, for he visited the College in the 1930's and became personally acquainted with some of its teachers and physicians.

Dr. and Mrs. A. P. Warthman of Detroit, Michigan, who supplied biographical material on the Littlejohn brothers, particularly David Littlejohn.

W. Lee Brooke, CCOM librarian, who not only gave me access to the files of journals in his charge, but who helped me dig out, from unsuspected closets and basement nooks, some of the very earliest catalogues and publications which a former librarian staff member with a sense of history had carefully wrapped and packaged for possible future use. (The fact that the wrappers crumbled and all but disintegrated while the contents were being extracted only heightened the anticipation of discovering what lay inside).

Ms. Barbara Peterson, associate editor of DO, who, at the national A.O.A. headquarters, placed at my disposal early professional journals and catalogues no longer on file in the CCOM library and who provided pleasant working space for my research; also Ms. Sophie Born of Ms. Peterson's staff, who helped me round up many of the materials I needed, including microfilms, and whose cheerful cooperation never flagged.

Mr. Al Wykel, reference room supervisor at *Chicago Today* who permitted me to examine clippings and photos from the files of the old *Chicago Herald-Examiner* and the *Chicago American*.

Mrs. Janice Lewis, who, as *Chicago Daily News* librarian, extended me the same courtesies with regard to clippings and photos under her jurisdiction.

Doctors Samuel V. Robuck, W. Fraser Strachan, Martin C. Beilke, W. Don Craske, and Otto F. Gursch, former CCOM faculty members, who granted me personal interviews and provided colorful background information on persons and events.

Prof. William H. McNeill of the history department of The University of Chicago, who read the manuscript and offered helpful suggestions.

Dean Robert A. Kistner and Dr. Norman J. Larson of the Department of Osteopathic Principles and Practice, for their suggestions and comments.

Dr. Grace E. Clunis, CCOM alumna who provided interesting information on some of the women faculty members in the 1920's.

Mrs. Dorine Kenney, Director of the Chicago Osteopathic Hospital Volunteer Department, who forwarded memorabilia (reports, photos, scrapbooks) pertaining to women's activities at the College and Hospital during the earlier years.

Earl C. Kubicek, CCOM Vice President for Planning and Development, who maintained an interested eye in the progress of my research and writing and who was always ready with helpful advice and counsel.

I hope I have not inadvertently omitted the names of others, but if I have, I ask their forgiveness.

I am indebted for much of my source material to the files of the *Journal of the American Osteopathic Association,* the *Osteopathic Physician,* and the *Forum of Osteopathy*. Other important publications included the early catalogues of the American College of Osteopathic Medicine and Surgery, the Littlejohn College and Hospital, and the Chicago College of Osteopathy. There were also issues of the *Boston Osteopath* (published by the Boston Institute of Osteopathy); the *Cosmopolitan Osteopath,* (published by the A. T. Still College, Des Moines, Iowa); the *Journal of Osteopathy* (published by the American School of Osteopathy, Kirksville, Missouri); the *Bulletin and Journal of Health* (published by the Littlejohn College and Hospital); the *Chicago College of Osteopathy Alumni Bulletin;* the *National Cyclopaedia of American Biography* (for material on David Littlejohn); the *Reflex* and the *Osteon* (yearbooks published by CCO and CCOM); reports issued by the President of CCO and CCOM from year to year; and miscellaneous pieces of literature issued by the College.

T. A. B.

# 1

# THE PROFESSIONAL CLIMATE
# IN 1900

Wʜᴇɴ three Scottish brothers—John Martin Littlejohn, James Buchanan Littlejohn, and David Littlejohn—arrived in the United States with some 153,000 other Scotsmen and Britons during the middle years of the 1890's [1], there were 122 regular schools of medicine in existence. They were designated as "allopathic schools," with a total enrollment of 21,400 students and were the only institutions in the United States recognized as being qualified to train physicians and surgeons. Competing with these allopathic schools, however, were 21 homeopathic schools, with an enrollment of 1,802 students, and 18 so-called osteopathic schools of assorted sizes and merits. The latter enrolled approximately 1,700 students, many of whom did not even have a high school education. In addition to these, there were six eclectic schools with an enrollment of 500 [2].

All but the recognized allopathic schools were generally regarded as training grounds for "cults." A practitioner of the healing arts not possessing an M.D. degree was automatically categorized as a member of a cult. This included the osteopaths, the homeopaths, the chiropractics, and eclectics. There were many others, however, who had no formal affiliation whatever and conducted their business strictly as independents. The medical profession obviously looked with disdain upon all these competing institutions and practitioners—often, it must be admitted, with considerable justification. The belief then, and for many decades, persisted that only those displaying the familiar framed M.D. diploma were qualified to treat the physical and mental ills of humanity, and the medical profession fought fiercely to thwart any attempts of competing schools to win legal recognition or public acceptance.

Andrew Taylor Still's announcement, on June 22, 1874, of a new method of treating disease, caused a stir in the medical world. Still believed that the human body was a vital mechanical organism, with all its parts structurally and functionally coordinated. Disease or other toxic conditions occurred when resistance in the body tissue was lowered and the circulation of the blood impaired. The body, he maintained, must be considered *as a whole;* it had its own curative powers and the ability to manufacture its own remedies against disease if the structural relationship was normal, environmental conditions favorable, and nutrition satisfactory. Osteopathic manipulation—an important element in Still's method of treatment—was required to stimulate mechanically the organs of the body to resume their proper functions, restore the normal blood flow, and cause the body organs to adjust to their natural relation with each other [3].

The climate for the practice of osteopathic medicine in the State of Illinois in 1900 when the Littlejohns contemplated establishing a college in Chicago was especially forbidding. J. A. Egan, M.D., secretary of the Illinois State Board of Health in Springfield, tersely summed up the official attitude toward osteopathy in a letter to A. B. Shaw, secretary of the Still College of Osteopathy in Des Moines, Iowa. Wrote Mr. Egan:

> . . . In reply [to a letter of July 9], I beg to say that *no college of Osteopathy is recognized by the Board,* but that each applicant for license to practice 'any other system or science (than medicine or surgery) of treating human ailments, who does not practice operative surgery' is required to pass an examination by the Board. See marked copy of the Medical Practice Act enclosed [4].

The Illinois Medical Practice Act, passed by the state legislature in 1899, stipulated, in part:

> The examination of those who desire to practice any other system or science of treating human ailments, who do not use medicines, internally or externally, and who do not practice operative surgery shall be of a character sufficiently strict to test their qualifications as practitioners. All examinations provided for in this Act shall be conducted under rules and regulations prescribed by the Board, which shall provide for a fair and wholly impartial method of examination. PROVIDED, that graduates of legally chartered medical colleges in Illinois in good standing *as may be determined by the Board,* may be granted certificates *without examination* [5].

It was in such a climate that on May 21, 1900, the three Littlejohn brothers founded what was to become the first recognized school of osteopathic medicine in Illinois: The American College of Osteopathic Medicine and Surgery, the forerunner of the present Chicago College of Osteopathic Medicine.

[ 2 ]

### REFERENCES

1. *Historical Abstract of the U.S., Colonial Times to 1957.*
2. *The Boston Osteopath,* April, 1901, p. 83 (Published by the Boston Institute of Osteopathy.)
3. Modern osteopathic medicine, of course, utilizes the manipulative treatment to complement *all* the presently known modalities in providing care for an ill patient.
4. *The Cosmopolitan Osteopath,* Oct. 1900, p. 20. (Vol. 5, No. 3)
5. *Ibid.*

# 2

# THE FOUNDERS: A FAMILY MATTER

RARELY have three members of a single family exerted as much influence upon a profession as did the three Littlejohn brothers. Born in Scotland, educated at the University of Glasgow, they emigrated to the United States in the 1890's. The osteopathic profession is under an immense debt to these three men for the status it now enjoys and owes a great deal to the talents, skills, and foresightedness of these three sons of a Scottish minister.

## JOHN MARTIN LITTLEJOHN
### (1865–1947)

John Martin Littlejohn, oldest of the three, was born in Glasgow, February 15, 1865. At the age of 16 he entered the University of Glasgow to study theology, but devoted much of his time to the arts, Hebrew and oriental languages, as well. He left the University before graduating, but was ordained in 1886. After spending some time teaching, he returned to the University in 1889 to continue his studies. It is very probable that during the three-year interval he was away from the University, he studied physiology and anatomy, for his familiarity with these two subjects, revealed a few years later, can be explained in no other way. The University records show that he received his Master of Arts degree in 1889, his Bachelor of Divinity in 1890, and his Bachelor of Laws in 1892.

After a brief stay in Londonderry, Northern Ireland, Littlejohn sailed for the United States late in 1892 and, at the age of 27, enrolled as a Fellow in Columbia University where he studied political philosophy, political economy and finance. In the summer and fall of 1893 he was back in Europe for a brief time to study medieval culture. Upon his return to Columbia he continued his deep interest in the thinkers of the Middle Ages and wrote his doctoral dissertation on, "The Political Theory of the Schoolmen and Grotius [1]." In 1894 he received his Ph.D. degree from Columbia.

Littlejohn's scholarship was instrumental in his obtaining the appointment as President of Amity College at College Springs, Iowa. Amity College was a co-educational institution specializing in the liberal arts. Thus in 1894, at the age of 29, Dr. John Martin Littlejohn became one of the youngest college presidents in the United States. After serving four years as the college's chief executive officer he resigned in 1898, largely because of fragile health. The trustees of Amity College were reluctant to accept Littlejohn's resignation and when they at last acceded to his wishes, passed the following tribute which appeared in the minutes of their meeting: "We recognize in Dr. J. M. Littlejohn one of the ablest ministers and ripest of scholars, and as an educator he has no superior. A refined gentleman, a true Christian, his influence has always been on the side of right and the best interest of education, his aim in life being to lift up and stimulate the educational interests of the whole community [2]."

Dr. Littlejohn's physical ills, particularly involving his neck and throat, led him to begin a series of visits to Kirksville, Missouri, where the founder of osteopathic medicine, Dr. Andrew Taylor Still, was demonstrating the healing theories he had so startlingly announced more than twenty years earlier. Under Dr. Still's personal treatments, Littlejohn's health was restored. He was so impressed with Dr. Still's philosophy of healing that he moved to Kirksville and took up the study of *osteopathic medicine*. Later he described his conversion:

> Being an enthusiast in the study of anatomy and physiology and myself a sufferer, and exiled from my native land by the medical profession on the ground of ill health, I was fascinated by Still's ideas and then and there accepted the philosophy of his system, that based the foundation of his treatment of disease upon the medicine chest of the human body, and laid the foundation for the prescription of remedies in the adjustment of the body structure, to normalise the production, distribution, and application of these remedies in the cure of disease [3].

In 1898 Littlejohn enrolled as a student in Dr. Still's American School of Osteopathy (ASO) in Kirksville, but as early as 1897, while he was still undergoing treatment by the "Old Doctor," he was giving lectures on physiology in the school [4]. It was not long after he had enrolled that he was appointed Dean of the Faculty and Professor of Physiology, two positions which gave him quick professional stature.

On October 27, 1898, Littlejohn addressed a graduating class of the American School of Osteopathy. In his talk he indicated the tremendous

hold which osteopathic medicine now had on him and his determination to
further its objectives and aims. He told the graduates:

> I think that Osteopathy will stand if it is in the hands of the proper men
> and women, and if it takes the true stand in regard to the other sciences.
> Osteopathy sets aside medicines in the same sense of drugs, but it cannot
> afford to set aside anything else. Osteopathy is certainly an independent
> school of medicine and need not fear to stand side by side with other
> schools, first to rival and finally to outrival them, if she adheres to anatomy,
> physiology, pathology, diagnosis, hygiene, surgery, obstetrics and chemis-
> try, substituting Osteopathic therapeutics and practice for the old school
> theory and practice of medicines. Everything that medical science has
> achieved is ours, if we take it. If you and I are to be simply bone-setters and
> when we come to deal with vital diseases or with surgical cases, have to call
> in an M.D., then we had better acknowledge that we are only part of a
> profession and take a back seat [5].

It was during these few years at ASO that Littlejohn initiated, as he wrote
later, the osteopathic research movement. Working in partnership with Dr.
A. T. Still, he conducted a series of experiments on animals during the
winter of 1898–1899. Using an old barn for his laboratory, he made minute
examinations of the heart, lungs, and spinal cords of dogs "subjected to
experiments under anaesthesia," producing lesions and attempting to correct
them. Following these projects, at Dr. Still's suggestion, he experimented on
the use of morphine, quinine, iron, and arsenic with animals to prove that
such substances were foreign to the body and "produced detrimental instead
of beneficial effects." Also at the behest of the "Old Doctor," Littlejohn
conducted experiments on the lymphatic system in order to demonstrate the
organism's capacity to flush the lungs in case of pneumonia [6]."

Although he was not unhappy in his work at ASO, his insistence that
"physiology is the gateway by which this immense field of Osteopathy is to
be entered," rather than blind allegiance to the theory that manipulation and
anatomy were the sole basics, brought about opposition to his views. He was
determined to establish a school of his own after he graduated. Receiving his
D.O. degree from the American School of Osteopathy in Kirksville in 1900,
Littlejohn moved to Chicago and, with his two brothers, James and David,
founded the school now celebrating its 75th anniversary.

During these early years of the college, Littlejohn, evidently not satisfied
with the many degrees he already held, studied medicine at Dunham and
Hering medical colleges in Chicago and earned an M.D. degree to add to his
impressive collection [7]. He edited from 1900 to 1907 *The Journal of the
Science of Osteopathy,* and wrote many books and papers, including *The Science*

*of Osteopathy* (1902); *Treatise on Osteopathy* (1903); *Theory and Practice of Osteopathy* (1907); and *The Fee System* (1907).

Littlejohn returned to England in 1913, settling at Thundersley, Essex, to found the British School of Osteopathy. He continued his teaching and osteopathic activities until his death on December 8, 1947.

The papers and speeches of J. M. Littlejohn contain not only his views regarding osteopathic theory and practice, but a definite philosophy as to the purpose and aims of osteopathic education. It is in this area, as well as those others in which his talents as an anatomist, surgeon, and teacher were so forcefully demonstrated, that he contributed significantly to the advance of professional osteopathic medical training.

As a professional osteopathic physician and educator, he never abandoned his firm belief that osteopathic medicine must be an *independent system or science of healing.* He insisted that the members of his faculty share that belief, and he maintained that osteopathic education must everlastingly stress research "from the strictly osteopathic points of view, rather than attempting to expand our efforts in study in the regular medical colleges [8]." "A college," he explained, "if it means anything in the field in which it is located, is a research center; a field of investigation as well as a place for education [9]." He added, "The best teachers are those who do not live in a cloister of physical anatomical and physiological laboratories, but dig deep into the mines of human experience [10]."

He urged that the doors of the country's hospitals be opened to osteopaths so they could study the countless cases there in order to "widen our views and get a clearer basis for generalization in regard to our therapeutics," and "to make the basic foundation of our education as wide as possible so that we may not fall into narrowness or bigotry [11]."

Dr. Littlejohn lamented that disreputable schools then in operation were "dragging down our system." He told the delegates attending the AOA convention in Kirksville in 1901:

> We have several schools in Chicago that graduate Osteopaths without seeing them, professing to give by mail or otherwise in a few weeks or even days the principles and practice of this great system. Some of them claim that graduates of the present school are behind them in this. There are men and women practicing Osteopathy or pretending to do so, who know nothing about it and are misrepresenting us to the laity and the scientific world. Unless we can come to the help of our science in this respect, much detriment will be done to our system [12].

He believed that osteopathy could be properly taught only in osteopathic colleges. "The osteopathic college," he insisted, "must exist in fact, not in the office of a medical college [13]." Furthermore, "The extensive pharmacology and materia medica of the symptoms of other schools by themselves would throw little light upon Osteopathic methods [14]."

As an educator, Littlejohn reminded the osteopathic profession that it was indebted to the colleges of osteopathy for three important developments: (1) for the supply of practitioners; (2) for the elevation and maintenance of standards of qualification; and (3) for a basis upon which legislative enactments must rest." (15) Consequently, he argued, the profession should support its colleges at every turn.

There are specific ideals which an osteopathic college must uphold, Littlejohn wrote: "The college should not be a mere commercial enterprise . . . proprietary projects for money making and professional business getting . . . the ideal school should not be conducted for profit; and in fact if it is conducted in the proper manner and spirit it will cost money far in excess of the fees paid into the college treasury [16]." Further: "Colleges should be more than merely quiz classes. They should be centers for laboratory, hospital, dispensary as well as didactic instruction [17]." Too many schools, he held, were merely quiz sessions for students preparing to take the farcical State Board examinations "which after all test no more than student memory and professional quizzing ability [18]."

What of teacher qualifications? Littlejohn was quite specific: "The colleges must be manned by teachers of wide educational equipment, training in pedagogic methods and the student spirit. . . . Practical experience joined to laboratory experience is the best foundation for successful instruction. The practical teacher who gives part of his time to instruction and the balance to practice will make the best teacher [19]."

Littlejohn divided an osteopathic college teaching body into three groups: (1) the practical teachers who deal with surgery, and the principles and practice of osteopathy; (2) the laboratory and science teachers who devote most of their time to the laboratory and research work; (3) the younger men who serve as assistants, and whose time should be devoted to research in some field of anatomy, physiology, chemistry, pathology, and at the same time to clinical work in hospital, dispensary and school clinics [20].

While he was a champion of upgrading entrance and performance requirements in osteopathic colleges, he believed that a four-year course for *all* students should not be mandatory. However, he insisted that no student be admitted without having completed a high school course which emphasized physics, chemistry, and biology. He supported both the 3-year and 4-year programs offered by the Chicago College, explaining that the three-year program would be adequate for the graduate who would practice merely as an osteopathic physician, but that a four-year program should be required of any student planning to practice as both physician *and* surgeon.

"The future of osteopathy depends on the colleges and their teachers," Littlejohn emphasized time and time again. "The profession should take the schools by the hand; encourage them in their arduous work; hold up their hands in the effort to make osteopathy a system deserving of perpetuation; and encourage prospective students to take up the study of osteopathy [21]."

John Martin Littlejohn was superbly equipped in intellect, background, and experience to establish a school which would adopt and apply the principles he so strongly believed were vital to the profession and its educational institutions [22].

## JAMES BUCHANAN LITTLEJOHN
### (1869–1947)

James Buchanan Littlejohn, second of the three founding brothers, was associated with the College almost continuously from the date of its founding until his death in 1947. When John Martin, the oldest of the three, returned to England in 1913, James took over many of the administrative duties and held fast to the course which the brothers had charted for the college in 1900.

Like his brother, James was born in Glasgow, attended the University of Glasgow where he earned his M.D. and Ch.M. degrees. He then emigrated to the United States in 1894 and, like his brother before him, became interested in the work of Dr. Andrew Taylor Still.

James apparently began to practice medicine in Chicago in 1895. It was some time later that he enrolled in the American School of Osteopathy in Kirksville where he received his D.O. degree in 1902, two years after he had collaborated with his two brothers in founding the American College of Osteopathic Medicine and Surgery in Chicago. During his stay in Kirksville he was listed as a surgeon on the staff of Dr. Still's hospital, obtaining the experience which qualified him later to define surgery as "the application of mechanical principles for the relief of disordered functions and structures when such disordered functions and structures pass beyond the control of physiological principles [23]."

His professional career is studded with honors and achievements. In 1904 he was elected President of the Associated Colleges of Osteopathy, a federation he had helped to organize in 1901 to set up standards for the profession's training institutions [24]. In 1906 he agreed to serve as Chairman of the Teachers Committee of the Associated Colleges. In 1908 he was re-elected President of the Associated Colleges and he continued his campaign for establishing and maintaining uniformly high standards for the training and education of osteopathic physicians.

He was one of the early backers of the three-year college program for osteopathic colleges. In 1904, the AOA at its national convention in St. Louis passed the following resolution: "Moved that the report of the Committee on Education be recommended by the association, with the further recommendation that the time be extended to September, 1905, as the date *when the requirement shall be enforced for a three-year course in the schools* [25]."

Littlejohn strongly supported the adoption of the three-year program, even though he realized that the expanded course would put serious pressure on the smaller colleges with their limited budgets. He appealed to the delegates: "I ask that you stand by the vote that was taken by this assembly . . . I do not believe there is any man or woman in this hall that would want to pull down the standard which we raised [26]." He wholeheartedly supported the four-year curriculum which was later offered by the leading osteopathic colleges.

Yet, accompanying his espousal to improve and maintain high professional educational standards, he had a great understanding for the individual case. He declared: "There ought to be some provision for a worthy candidate to enter the portals of the profession who in his earlier days was denied the privilege of a college or high school training. It is not fair to make one live the best half of a lifetime before entering on such a professional career [27]."

On another occasion he remarked: "I believe that any school that cannot teach the subjects sufficiently to allow a person to pass at the end of their school term, as is done in the other schools, should be prodded up or go out of the school business. The time is coming when we will do that, and I believe that is a thought in advance for the educational committee to consider next year [28]."

Littlejohn was pleased when professional osteopathic publications supported the drive for higher standards in the schools. He wrote *The Osteopathic Physician:*

> I am glad to see the stand *The Osteopathic Physician* continues to take in the battle for increase in the course of study. It is surely essential for the correct progress of Osteopathy. It is the united effort that succeeds, and I am fully convinced from the strong stand taken by the profession . . . that it will continue to stick together as a substantial unit in the future on this subject. Is it not fair for the schools which have taken this stand to suppose that those members of the profession who indorse the three-year course will show their basic approval by throwing their support to the colleges? If the friends of higher education will support it, now the chance is before them, by sending new students to the schools which have made sacrifices

by setting out upon a three-year course—even with some of the oldest and richest schools opposing the innovation—it will help to make the three-year course a prompt success [29].

As a member of the College faculty he taught surgery, obstetrics and pathology and became nationally known as a skilled surgeon as well as an outstanding college administrator. On one occasion he performed an operation in Minneapolis which won great acclaim. The *Minneapolis Journal,* announcing the incident in 1905, reported:

> A surgical operation of great interest was witnessed today by the Minnesota State Osteopathic Association at the Lawrence sanatorium, Ninth Avenue S. Dr. James B. Littlejohn, of Chicago, operated on Lilian E. Walker, the eight-year-old daughter of G. W. Walker, of 1600 Twenty-second Avenue, N., for congenital displacement of the hips. The operation belongs in the same class as those of Dr. Lorenz, the Austrian orthopedic surgeon, about which so much has been written. Dr. Littlejohn, who is a famous surgeon, has been doing much of this kind of work quietly and is regarded by many as surpassing the Austrian in skill. So important was this case considered that a special meeting of the state association was called to witness it. It was a bloodless operation and the patient had been prepared for it. . . . About 100 physicians witnessed the operation [30].

After he had established himself in Chicago, Littlejohn attended the Kent College of Law and earned an LL.B. degree, obtaining legal knowledge which, he no doubt felt, would be helpful to him as a college administrator. He also contributed many articles to professional publications and for a time edited *The Bulletin and Journal of Health.*

During his active career with the college he helped to establish, he served as a member of the Board of Trustees, Vice President, Dean of the Faculty, Head of the Department of Surgery, Secretary, teacher and consultant. James Littlejohn's final years as an active member of the faculty were the early 1930's when his health began to fail and brought about his gradual withdrawal from professional activities. One of his great disappointments was his inability to attend the dedication of the new teaching hospital in February, 1947, and he forwarded his personal regrets in a letter to Dr. Paul van B. Allen, then president of the College's Alumni Association.

There are a number of former CCOM faculty members who still vividly remember Dr. James Buchanan Littlejohn. Among them are Doctors William F. Strachan and Samuel V. Robuck, both now retired. They were profuse in their praise of Littlejohn's professional skills which, they quickly add, were matched only by the great understanding and affection he had for his students. He had a special gift, they recall fondly, for making his students feel important—by placing them on a level with himself. Even when he entered a patient's room with an intern, they remember, Dr. Littlejohn insisted that the intern precede him into the room. He then painstakingly explained to the intern, step by step, his technique in examining and treating the patient. Kind, courteous, and friendly, he was respected and admired by everyone. The esteem in which he was held by the college and hospital staff alike is legendary [31].

When Dr. James Littlejohn died in his home in Chicago on May 21, 1947 at the age of 78, just a scant seven months before his renowned brother John passed away in England, alumni of the school mourned: "Doctor Littlejohn's death meant the loss of a close personal friend and teacher to many graduates of the Chicago College. . . . [32]" And the *Journal of the American Osteopathic Association,* communication medium for the profession, left little doubt that it and the osteopathic physicians it represented, shared the feeling expressed by Dr. Leonard V. Strong, Jr., when he wrote: "There are few men who quietly and without acclaim have exerted as profound an influence on the development and standards of osteopathy as did James Buchanan Littlejohn [33]."

Doctor of Medicine; Doctor of Osteopathy; Master of Chemistry; Fellow of the Royal College of Surgeons (England); Life Member of the British Medical Association; member of the Illinois Bar Association and many other organizations, James B. Littlejohn had in common with his brothers the brilliant professional and educational qualifications so vital for launching and directing a school which was to rank second to none in its professional status.


## DAVID LITTLEJOHN
### (1876–1955)

David Littlejohn, youngest of the three brothers, was active in helping to establish the College and guide the institution through its infant years. It was not too many years after its founding, however, that his professional interests took him away from the campus to other fields where he won prominence as a public health physician and administrator.

David was born in Glasgow, Scotland, on September 24, 1876, where he attended the public schools. He then studied at the College of Science in Kensington, London, from 1891–1892, and at the University of Glasgow, Scotland, from 1893 to 1896. While studying at the University, he also served as an instructor in chemistry at the Western Medical School of Glasgow. Finally, in 1896, he sailed for the United States as had his brothers before him.

Littlejohn lost no time in continuing his studies upon his arrival in

America. He earned a Ph.D. degree at Amity College, Iowa, then an M.D. degree at Central Michigan College in St. Joseph, Michigan, where he also taught sanitary science. He studied at Dr. Still's American School of Osteopathy in Kirksville, Missouri from 1898–1900, and received his D.O. degree from that institution in 1900.

Shortly after helping his brothers launch the Chicago College in 1900, he took up the study of law and received an LL.B. degree from the Dearborn College of Law of Chicago in 1904. While serving on the faculty of the Chicago College, he also taught at the Dunham and Hering Medical College in Chicago. In 1906 he opened a private practice in Chicago which he maintained until 1910. He apparently also had an office in Pontiac, Illinois, since *The Osteopathic Physician* for May, 1907, carried a display advertisement announcing that D. Littlejohn, M.D. and D.O., was successfully treating alcohol and drug addicts and invited osteopathic physicians to write for full particulars [34]. In 1911, David was in Bridgman, Michigan, where for the next six years he maintained a private practice.

In 1917 he enlisted in the U.S. Army and was commissioned a 1st Lieutenant in the Medical Corps. After completing basic training at Ft. Riley, Kansas, he was sent to Camp Beauregard, Louisiana, as a member of the 39th Division, placed in charge of sanitation, and given an assignment as instructor in gas defense. Later he was promoted to the rank of Captain and he sailed for France in 1918 with the 39th Division as division medical gas officer. While in the combat zones, he conducted important studies in the handling of gas casualties. After the signing of the Armistice, Littlejohn became sanitary inspector for the 1st Replacement Division at St. Aignan, France, returning to the U.S. in April, 1919, when he was honorably discharged with the rank of Major.

Upon his return to civilian life, Littlejohn's interests were concentrated in the field of public health. It was in that area that he would win national recognition. From 1919 to 1922 he was in Ishpeming, Michigan, where he organized the city's health department, serving as its director. From 1923–1925 he performed similar organizational and administrative work in Bluefield, West Virginia, then for eight years served as director of communicable diseases for the West Virginia State Department of Health.

During the period 1933–1936, he organized and directed the county health department at Midland, Michigan, and from 1936–1944, directed the operations of the Chippewa County Health Department at Sault Ste. Marie, Michigan. His outstanding work in public health at county, city and state levels, resulted in an invitation from prestigious Wayne County, Michigan, to organize and direct its health department and where his work would, of course, encompass Detroit, the nation's fifth largest metropolis.

During his many years as a public health administrator, he wrote many articles for medical and public health journals. A partial list of titles selected from these include: "The Functions of a Public Nurse," (*Michigan State Medical Journal,* August 1, 1923); "The Relation of Health Officer to Physician," (*West Virginia State Health Bulletin,* January, 1925); "Control of Communicable Diseases," (*West Virginia State Health Bulletin,* January, 1926); "The State's Responsibility for Adequate Health Program," (*Hospital Social Service,* XX, 1921); and "Preventative Medicine, Its Evolution, Present Status, and Future Possibilities," (*West Virginia State Health Bulletin,* January, 1923) [35].

His work in the field of public health and sanitation resulted in many honors and invitations to join various organizations, both professional and social. He was a Fellow of the Society of Science, Letters and Arts (London), a member of the American and Michigan medical and public health organizations and other professional groups. Yet he found time for service clubs, serving as president of Lions Clubs in Charleston, West Virginia, Sault Ste. Marie, Michigan, and Dearborn, Michigan. In 1931 he was district governor of Lions International in West Virginia.

David Littlejohn died in Detroit on May 25, 1955, survived by his wife and three children [36].

During his brief career as a member of the Chicago College faculty he taught physiological chemistry, histology, and diseases of the nose and throat. He also conducted classes in toxicology, where his students studied the various varieties of poisons, their symptoms and treatment, along with the physical chemical characteristics of the principal poisons confronted by mankind.

Littlejohn served as Secretary of the College during its earliest years, but by 1904 his name was no longer on the faculty roster. The 1904–1905 college catalogue indicates that he had been succeeded as Secretary by his brother, James B. Littlejohn. It is apparent that David Littlejohn's interests now lay elsewhere [37].

In view of his early withdrawal from the Chicago scene, what can be said of his contributions to the College he helped found? Of great importance, obviously, is the fact that he, along with his two brothers, provided solid "family" prestige and momentum to an institution whose existence was sorely needed to counteract the deplorable work of the fly-by-night diploma mills and the disreputable "osteopathic" training centers operating throughout the land. Moreover, his work as teacher and administrator was tremendously important to a school starting from scratch in a field where integrity, such as that represented by the Littlejohn family, offered the only assurance of ultimate success.

## REFERENCES

1. Grotius, of course, was the noted 17th century jurist and statesman who codified international law, while the Schoolmen were prominent medieval university philosophers and theologians.

2. *Journal of Osteopathy,* March, 1898, p. 489. (Published by the American School of Osteopathy, Kirksville, Missouri)

3. Quoted by T. Edward Hall in "The Contributions of John Martin Littlejohn to Osteopathy," London, 1952.

4. This would substantiate the belief that Littlejohn had studied anatomy and physiology during his final years in Europe, but there is no personal confirmation of this in his papers or recorded remarks.

5. From his address, published in the *Journal of Osteopathy,* December, 1898, pp. 325–329.

6. Related by J. Martin Littlejohn in a by-line article in *The Osteopathic Physician,* December, 1908, pp. 11–12. (Vol. 14, No. 6).

7. These two medical colleges originally operated as two independent schools: the Dunham Medical College, named after Carroll Dunham, M.D., and the Hering Medical College, named after Constantine Hering, M.D. The two institutions were "named in commemoration of two eminent practitioners and teachers" and they were medical schools "graduating students in the homoeopathic system of medicine." Later, Dunham College became incorporated into and absorbed by Hering Medical College. ("The Osteopathic Blue Book," London. 1956? 1957?)

8. From an address delivered at the AOA national convention in Kirksville, Missouri, in 1901, and published in the *Journal AOA,* September, 1901.

9. *Journal AOA,* January, 1908, pp. 217–222. (Vol. 8, No. 5).

10. *Ibid.*

11. *Journal AOA,* September, 1901. (Vol. 1, No. 1).

12. *Ibid.*

13. *The Osteopathic Physician,* September, 1902.

14. *Ibid.*

15. *Journal AOA,* January, 1908, pp 217–222. (Vol. 8, No. 5).

16. *Ibid.*

17. *Ibid.*

18. *Ibid.*

19. *Journal AOA,* January, 1908, pp. 217–222. (Vol. 8, No. 5).

20. *Ibid.*

21. *Journal AOA,* January, 1908, pp. 217–222.

22. One of his students, Dr. Flora Y. Swengel, said of him: "Dr. J. Martin was a great teacher, but I never seemed to know how or what to ask him, lest I make a mistake. I think the distance between my brain power, education and ability, and his, was just too great." (In a letter to Dr. R. N. MacBain, September 7, 1968).

23. *Bulletin and Journal of Health,* March 15, 1912. (Vol. 5, No. 3).

24. He had served as Vice President in 1903–1904, having been elected to that post at the national AOA convention in Cleveland in the summer of 1903.

25. *Journal AOA,* September, 1904, pp. 43–44. (Vol. 4, No. 1).

26. *Ibid.*

27. In an address to the delegates attending the AOA convention in Minneapolis, Minnesota, August, 1909.

28. In an address at the national AOA convention in Denver, Colorado, August, 1905, before the Committee on Education. Quoted in the *Journal AOA,* October, 1905, p. 69.

29. *The Osteopathic Physician,* August, 1904, p. 13. (Vol. 6, No. 3).

30. Reprinted in *The Osteopathic Physician,* July, 1905, pp. 12–13. (Vol. 8, No. 2).

31. Dr. Flora Y. Swengel, a graduate of the Class of 1908, wrote of Dr. Littlejohn later, in a letter to Dr. Richard N. MacBain: "Dr. J. B. was a great surgeon and a wonderful teacher. He somehow made us want to ask questions and helped us understand the answers. He was usually quick to answer, but always seemed relaxed. I cannot remember that anyone ever went to sleep in his class; we were too afraid of missing an interesting point. I thought he could do more things at once than anyone I ever knew."

32. *CCO Alumni Bulletin,* July, 1947. Dr. Littlejohn at the time of his death resided at 5689 Ridge Street, Chicago. He is buried in Acacia Park Cemetery on Irving Park Road, Chicago.

33. *Journal AOA,* June, 1947, p. 529. (Vol. 46).

34. *The Osteopathic Physician,* May, 1907, p. 9. (Vol. 2, No. 5).

35. *National Cyclopaedia of American Biography,* Vol. 43, p. 380.

36. David Littlejohn was married three times. In 1899, while a member of the faculty at the American School of Osteopathy (ASO) in Kirksville, Missouri, he married Miss Mary Forbes, the sister of Mrs. William Smith of Kirksville. Mrs. Smith's husband was Professor of Anatomy at the Kirksville school. The marriage to Miss Forbes was officiated by the Rev. James Littlejohn (David's father), and Dr. J. Martin Littlejohn, his brother (who had received a divinity degree in Scotland and was for a short time a minister in County Londonderry, Northern Ireland, in 1892). A newspaper report of the marriage stated that "The wedding was very quiet, only the families of the contracting parties, together with Dr. and Mrs. C. E. Still and little daughter Gladys, and Misses Blanche Still and Ethel Soles, being present." The report added that "An elegant breakfast was served, and Dr. and Mrs. Littlejohn left on the 10 o'clock train for a short trip to Chicago and other points in Illinois." David Littlejohn's first wife died in Chicago a few years later, and the body was taken to Kirksville for burial. In 1904, Littlejohn married Miss Mary Elizabeth Avery of Pontiac, Illinois; they were divorced in 1913. On Dec. 18, 1913, he married Miss Sadie Kremer, daughter of a Coloma, Michigan, contractor, and three children were born of this union: Avery, Imogen Lucile, and Olive Ethel.

37. Yet David Littlejohn continued to be listed, from time to time, as a member of the College faculty. The 1908–1909 catalogue listed him as a bona fide member of the teaching staff specializing in ear, nose and throat, and his office location was given as Room 1315 in the Masonic Temple in Chicago.

# 3

# THE EARLY YEARS: 1900–1913

ON MAY 21, 1900, the State of Illinois, through its Office of the Secretary of State, issued a Certificate of Incorporation authorizing the establishment of "The American College of Osteopathic Medicine and Surgery." It was the humble predecessor of today's prestigious Chicago College of Osteopathic Medicine.

Three individuals signed the application for the original charter: John Martin Littlejohn, James Buchanan Littlejohn, and Edith M. Williams (Mrs. James B. Littlejohn). David Littlejohn was named as one of the four members of the Board of Directors.

Adhering firmly to the principle emphasized frequently by J. Martin Littlejohn as one which should govern osteopathic schools, the new college was organized to operate "Not for Profit". The charter stated that the school's management was to be vested in "a Board of four directors, to be elected annually," and listed the four members of the original Board: John Martin Littlejohn, James B. Littlejohn, David Littlejohn, and Elizabeth W. Littlejohn [1].

The purpose of the school was stated firmly. It would be "a College of Osteopathic Medicine, Surgery and Obstetrics, the object of which shall be to discover, formulate and teach the improved methods of surgery, obstetrics and the treatment of diseases in general so as to systematise and place on a scientific basis the osteopathic methods of healing and treating diseases and conditions of the body; to impart this scientific system of healing to the medical profession, and others attending this College."

In order to fulfill the College's objective, the founders announced that: (a) "This College shall maintain a standard of requirements for entrance equivalent to that laid down by the American Association of Medical Colleges, shall teach such sciences and arts as are usually taught in reputable medical colleges and in addition the science of osteopathy in all its branches; and members of the medical profession graduated from reputable colleges shall be allowed to complete the courses, both practical and theoretical, in osteopathy and on the completion of such courses, shall be entitled to receive the diploma in osteopathy"; (b) "This College shall be and represent an independent medical school or system or method of healing or treating diseases and conditions of the body, said College using, applying and teaching the osteopathic theories of diagnosis and therapeutics, surgery and obstetrics so as to maintain the same as an independent system or science of healing"; and finally (c) "This Corporation shall not be conducted for profit but shall be solely conducted as an educational institution, with annexed infirmary, as the Board shall determine, in accordance with the laws and constitution of the state of Illinois." The College was empowered to confer degrees and diplomas "upon all those who shall have attended the prescribed course and passed examinations satisfactory to the faculty in each and every branch required to be taught and studied in the course. . . ."

The groundwork was laid!

On Monday, September 3, 1900, in small leased quarters in a house at 405 West Washington Boulevard, the American College of Osteopathic Medicine and Surgery officially opened its doors to students for the first time. Four students enrolled for the opening term as a staff of five instructors awaited them [2]. When the College's first announcement catalogue for 1900–1901 came off the press, the brochure regretfully reported that its faculty had not yet been selected, stating that "Arrangements have been made for several members of the Faculty but as the complete arrangements are not yet made, announcement will be made later of the full list of the Faculty." In all probability, however, the small faculty group included the three Littlejohn brothers, Mrs. Edith W. Littlejohn, and Dr. Carl Philip McConnell who had been a faculty associate of the Littlejohns at the American School of Osteopathy in Kirksville [3].

The announcement catalogue stipulated that students admitted for instruction must be capable of writing good English, and demonstrate a familiarity with arithmetic, United States history and geography, physics, and Latin. The College offered two programs: (1) a two-year course, adequate for meeting the requirements in most states at the time; and (2) a four-year program "in which every branch and department of medicine and surgery required by all the states in the Union and in foreign countries will be taught," including osteopathic principles, techniques, diagnosis, and practice, these latter subjects being substituted for "pharmacy and materia medica and therapeutics of the other schools of healing." The College tactfully stated that it "does not antagonize any one or any system, but claims the right of establishing under constitutional guarantee an independent and complete system of healing against which no discrimination can be made."

[ 20 ]

Clinical facilities—available because of the college's location in a large city—were described as "unsurpassed" and every student was promised the opportunity for "a varied experience in the treatment of a great variety of cases." To provide this variety was the giant Cook County Hospital just a few blocks from the school's location on West Washington Boulevard. An additional facility, attached to the College itself, was a "first class infirmary" specializing in surgery and providing "surgical patients with the best nursing care that can be furnished anywhere." The school's administrators made it clear that "students are not allowed to treat the Infirmary patients."

Tuition for the regular two-year course was $300, with half the amount payable at the beginning of each ten months' course. In order to attract as many students as possible, the catalogue happily described some of the many advantages which Chicago offered, chief among them the modest living costs: "Good board can be secured in the city for from $4.00 per week and up. The cost may be reduced by renting rooms and making arrangements for clubbing, etc. Board is as cheap in a large city as in a small town, the accommodations and facilities are better, the streets and sanitary conditions, etc., are much superior to those found in the smaller towns."

While the College was anxious to attract an adequate number of students to assure its survival and growth, its founders were nevertheless determined that there be no misunderstanding as to the fundamental reasons for having established the new Chicago osteopathic college. Osteopathy, they explained, was based on Dr. Andrew Taylor Still's theory that "the body is a mechanism, delicately constructed, finely adjusted, built on the principles of order and continuity and operated by the laws of physics, chemistry, and physiology, such as we find embedded in the human organism [4]." They asserted that osteopathy represented an independent system of healing, yet admitting that "all the worthy sons and daughters of Aesculapius are true physicians and surgeons [5]." It was a system, they maintained, that must be taught with care, and to help provide some of the thousands of qualified practitioners that were needed to demonstrate the new healing art, the American College of Osteopathic Medicine and Surgery came into being. The College would "present a complete course, including everything that is embraced in the new Osteopathic system." Yet it was a system with rigid qualifications, for "None but a perfectly trained and thoroughly skilled hand shall deal with the body."

In June, 1901, the College graduated its first class: a group of three students, two of whom had received osteopathic medical training elsewhere before entering the Chicago school and who had therefore been enrolled as "advanced students."

All too soon there was a need for larger quarters. Some time during the spring of 1901 the College moved to a new location at 334 West Monroe Street. Announcement of the location shift was reported in a letter written by J. Martin Littlejohn to the *Cosmopolitan Osteopath,* a monthly publication issued by the S. S. Still College of Osteopathy and Infirmary in Des Moines, Iowa. The publication acknowledged the letter as follows:

> We are pleased to learn by a letter directly from Dr. J. M. Littlejohn that their college work has been moved from 405 West Washington Boulevard to 334 West Monroe Street, Chicago, Illinois, and now numbers twenty-four students enrolled. Dr. Littlejohn reports a pleasant prosperity, which is enjoyed by osteopaths wherever they are thorough and worthy [6].

An increase in enrollment from a total of three students to twenty-four within a single year indicated that the new college was off to an encouraging start.

The College began its second year (1901–1902) in the three-story brick building at 334 West Monroe Street. A basement provided additional space. The faculty had added some new names, including that of Dr. H. Stanhope Bunting who taught "Practice of Osteopathy" and who became widely known in the profession. The three Littlejohn brothers remained active in their combined teaching and administrative roles. During this year a husband-and-wife team of osteopathic physicians established their practice in Chicago. These two individuals were to have a profound effect upon the development of the college. They were Dr. George H. Carpenter and his wife, Fannie, both of whom had been graduated as D.O.'s from the S. S. Still College, Des Moines, Iowa, in June, 1901.

At the end of the College's second year, twenty-one diplomas were awarded.

The modest success of the College during its first two years evidently stimulated competition, for in 1902 a group of osteopathic physicians headed by Dr. William McClelland and his wife, Bessie (also a D.O.) applied for a charter to operate a rival institution under the name "The Chicago School of Osteopathy." The charter was granted October 9, 1902, and listed, in addition to the McClellands, the name of Dr. J. Frederic Farmer, A.B., D.O.

The purpose of the school was given as "The investigation, advancement and teaching of Pure Osteopathic Therapeutics." The school was to "Maintain a standard of requirements for matriculation and course of study conforming to the requirements of the Associated Colleges of Osteopathy [7] and the laws of the State of Illinois. The course of study to comprise a period of two years of four terms of five months each." The school, the charter application indicated, would "be conducted solely as an educational institution with annexed Infirmary and clinical facilities as may be deemed necessary." The Board of Directors consisted of the three charter applicants. The school's address was listed as No. 34, The Hampden, 3853 Langley Street, Chicago.

The career of the rival institution was short-lived. One year following its founding in 1902, the school merged with the American College of Osteopathic Medicine and Surgery (ACOMS) administered by the Littlejohns. Students of the Chicago School, if they chose to remain, were given full credit for work completed in the school which the McClelland group had founded [8].

The merger resulted in the retention of some of the faculty of the McClelland school and their transfer to the staff of the Littlejohn institution. Among these was Dr. William McClelland himself, who not only taught anatomy, psychology and physiological neurology, but who became Assistant Manager of the merged institution. Dr. Edith Williams Littlejohn was named Manager, succeeding Dr. James B. Littlejohn in that position. Dr. Littlejohn had been both Manager and Treasurer, now continued as Secretary and Treasurer.

In 1903, when the American College of Osteopathic Medicine and Surgery opened for its fall term, it was in another location, this time at 495-497 West Monroe Street, a block from Madison Street between Loomis and Laflin streets. The catalogue stated:

> The College building, which is used for the first time this year, has been secured permanently by the trustees. It is much larger and better adapted in every way for the purpose than the previous one. It is a large four-story stone and brick building, with a two-story brick annex. It has been thoroughly renovated and remodeled, having six class rooms, 18 treating rooms, laboratories, and dissecting rooms in addition to a surgical room, reading room for students, waiting room for patients, offices, etc.
>
> It is thoroughly equipped with all the requirements for a modern scientific College, is heated with steam and every room is well lighted by electricity, ventilated, and opens on the outside.

The description of the new quarters continued:

> The Clinical facilities of the College furnished by location in the center of a large city are unsurpassed, and every student will have two terms of practice in the diagnosis and treatment of a large variety of cases.
>
> The College is located between the hospital center and the city center, so that there is abundant clinical material. Cook County Hospital, one of the largest institutions of its kind in the United States, is within easy access to the College. The clinics, autopsies and operative work are open to our

students, and they are required to attend during the fourth term and in the post graduate course.

A stereopticon and X-ray apparatus has been added to the College apparati for demonstration and lecture illustrations.

The College infirmary for the treatment of patients is located at the College building.

A note to the College's program for 1904–1905 announced that an athletic program had been adopted and that "we never do things by halves; the Superintendent in charge is one of the best in the States." (He was a Mr. Slater, a graduate of the University of Illinois).

During these early years of the century, the struggling osteopathic colleges were faced with serious problems, one of them being the need for winning the support of the profession. As the schools attempted to formulate guidelines for their work in order to gain acceptance, no college spoke out more positively and clearly than did the young Chicago institution. Drs. John Martin Littlejohn, James Buchanan Littlejohn and others of the faculty preached the necessity for sound education time and again, either through talks before professional groups or through papers published in professional journals.

Dr. Carl P. McConnell, outstanding ACOMS faculty member who had been elected President of the American Osteopathic Association in 1904, was one of the pioneers who established sound guidelines for osteopathic education. Speaking before the New York Osteopathic Society in December, 1904, McConnell warned of the pitfalls facing the profession and the need for the colleges to "teach and crystallize osteopathic thought and theory." Later in the year he wrote in the *Journal AOA:*

> There is an alarming amount of apathy in the osteopathic profession. . . . I cannot but feel the osteopathic profession is not doing the best possible. . . . Unless the colleges replace some of the "frills and furbelows" with good, common, hard sense of osteopathy, they will teach the profession out of existence. . . . The very basic principles of osteopathy have barely been scratched.
>
> Our colleges, the backbone of the profession, are not developing osteopathy as they should or can. How much original work has been done? Even the mechanics of technique has not been worked out, to say nothing of the thousand and one clinical, physiological and laboratory experiments that are awaiting us. . . . Are we going to leave our imprint on future science? We can if we but will [9].

On another occasion he wrote:

The future of osteopathy. . . . is going to be what the colleges make it. If they will be careful whom they matriculate, thorough in their instruction, then, now and forevermore, osteopathy will be assured of the dignity of a school of medicine (in fact THE school of the healing art).

Now, two years of ten months each gives a good start but we all know that it is not enough. . . .

It is evident that the course to pursue is to equip our colleges to meet any and all legitimate legal requirements. If we are not going to be a school of medicine on an equal footing with other schools our destruction is clearly mapped out [10].

The *Journal of the American Osteopathic Association* hammered constantly on the importance of the osteopathic colleges to the profession. In 1904, the *Journal* in a ringing editorial, stated:

The practitioners of osteopathy have an interest in the colleges of their profession that is a real and vital one. Indeed, so closely interwoven are all our professional interests that the elevation of one raises all, the degradation of one lowers all. The colleges exist to make practitioners. If they graduate educated men and women of good character, who are properly qualified to enter society and perform well the duties of physician, the profession will be elevated and strengthened by this constant influx of new blood. If, on the other hand, for any reason, the colleges should send out ignorant, immoral or incompetent physicians, the general standard of the profession is lowered and weakened, and if this process is continued, the profession will ultimately fall into disrepute, and in the course of time become extinct [11]."

The osteopathic profession, concluded the *Journal's* editorial writer, must insist that the colleges "maintain a standard both ethical and educational —for matriculation as well as graduation."

Many schools, most of them small, of course, sprang into being to help the cause. But the mortality rate of osteopathic colleges during the early years of the century was high. Many of the schools should never have opened their doors. They were inadequately financed, poorly administered, and woefully lacking in facilities and equipment. When, in 1904, the Ohio College of Osteopathy in Chillicothe failed, *The Osteopathic Physician* commented:

Another school that ought never have been founded is now no more. Another eloquent lesson is taught by this fiasco. . . . that the promiscuous founding of mushroom colleges, without adequate financial backing and lacking in every advantage as to location, etc., is not only a tactical blunder, but it is getting to be a crime against the profession [12].

The journal lamented the fact that good students were left stranded by the closing of these "mushroom colleges," many of which were founded by a single D.O. or by a small group of D.O.'s more to "glorify their personal esteem and vanity" than to turn out trained osteopathic physicians in significant numbers.

The American College of Osteopathic Medicine and Surgery recognized the pitfalls, sidestepped them as best it could and struggled on behind its staff of determined administrators and faculty.

In May, 1906, after nearly five years of activity, the College was subjected to its first blast of criticism when Dr. Charles C. Teall of Weedsport, New York, representing the American Osteopathic Association, visited the campus to inspect the school's facilities. He subsequently submitted a report to his headquarters sharply censuring ACOMS. His report, published in the October, 1906, issue of the *Journal of the AOA* read as follows:

> The school building is a large dwelling house with a detached two-story building in the rear, and is very well adapted to the use· intended. It is shared in common with the College of Medicine and Surgery, they using it in the forenoon and having some work in the afternoon. This made it difficult to identify the osteopathic students, and in one class at least there were students from both schools. Just how far this union extends I have not found out. On the schedule in the post graduate course there is one hour to the 'practice of medicine.' With the exception of laboratory work in histology and pathology, work does not begin until 1 p.m., and one class has work extending from 7 to 10 p.m. in anatomy and chemistry. At no class I attended was there a roll call, which rendered it very difficult to identify students.
>
> Instructors seemed to be changed frequently in the midst of work. This, with the employment of students, cannot be but prejudicial to good work, for instructors should be of experience and a ripe scholarship.
>
> The laboratories seem well equipped for the ordinary work. Dissection was over for the year, but the medical end was still at work. The clinics were plentifully supplied and are presided over by various practitioners. The examinations by students, as well as instructors, were not as full and complete as needed. The discovery of a lesion which might cause trouble generally ended the examination. Things seem to run rather loosely, as if no one was at the head.
>
> In the forenoon, students are required to visit various hospital clinics. The benefits derived are problematical, outside of what might be seen of strictly medical procedure. This, with the combining of the medical school under one roof, as well as mixed classes, would seem like a contaminating influence. The instructors, outside of Drs. Littlejohn, were not of a class to insure the best results. With two exceptions, the instructors were M.D.'s, while three were undergraduates. Under such conditions the emphasizing of osteopathic principles could not be expected to be very strong. "Broad Osteopathy," a science embracing everything, was talked by the president of the senior class, when introducing me, at a short talk before them. I have

asked for a statement in writing as to the relations existing between the College of Medicine and Surgery; the extent of joint classes and instructors. In answer to this inquiry, I have the following from J. B. Littlejohn:

"Regarding the question of association with the College of Medicine and Surgery to which you refer, let me say there is none. The College of Medicine and Surgery has rented the use of the building and has no other relation to our college whatever. The college represents a system of medicine which has been very friendly toward our college and ourselves, and we did this to help them out of a difficulty. Regarding the common instruction, all of the classes, namely, chemistry and histology, are taught by our teachers, and the students of the other school were allowed to attend. This is as far as the relation exists."

It is of interest to note that some of the faculty of the A.C.O.M. & S. are also of the faculty of the medical college. All of this comes very near to 'dangerous entangling alliances,' and the student could easily assume that osteopathy and medicine were on most harmonious terms [13].

The report of Dr. Teall not only drew a quick response from Dr. James B. Littlejohn, Secretary and Treasurer of ACOMS [14], but a long, vigorous denial of Dr. Teall's charges by Dr. J. Martin Littlejohn, President of ACOMS. Here is his explanation and defense as published in the *Journal AOA* for December, 1906:

Editor of the *Journal of the AOA*

I am very sorry that it is my duty to enter my protest against some statements in the report of the inspector of colleges, Dr. C. C. Teall, published in the Appendix to the *Journal of the A.O.A.* for October. For six years past we have been loyally trying to uphold the banner of osteopathy in this college. We have had to meet medical tyranny in many forms and above all to contend against a registration law that places osteopathy with the mongrel breed of know nothings. Ours has been an uphill fight, but everywhere we have maintained our stand upon the basis of the chartered idea, an independent physiological system of healing. We have been taunted again and again with teaching medicine by men who know not of what they were speaking because they have never visited our college. At the present time we have a faculty that will bear favorable comparison with any osteopathic college, from the standpoint of educational qualification, experience in teaching and loyalty to the charter thought of the college.

Instead of the inspector coming to us and giving us a word of encouragement to help us in bearing aloft the banner of osteopathy, he comes with cold water on this shoulder and insinuates that we are disloyal to osteopathy and incompetent to teach. Although Dr. Teall excludes myself and my brother from his condemnation of inefficiency, I resent none the less the imputation against my loyal colleagues. Such things as these do not help osteopathy. Misrepresentation cannot bring any gain. All our faculty and students, when they read the report, will know that it is not true.

Let me point to a few facts (1) "The building is shared with the college of medicine and surgery." The secretary of the college replied to Dr. Teall's query and yet *doubting this* statement Dr. Teall says "just how far this union extends I have not found." Dr. Teall was told there was no union. There was no mixing of students. In chemistry and histology some of the students of the College of Medicine and Surgery received special permission to attend our classes under our own professors. And yet when Dr. Teall knew this he gets a fling at the college when he says, "the medical end was still at work." There was no medical end. He was not sent to inspect the College of Medicine and Surgery and to our college there is no medical end. (2) Dr. Teall says there was no roll call. In some classes there is, and in others there is not probably a roll call. But each one keeps a roll, marks his roll, hands it to the assistant secretary each day and signs the roll of the faculty after each lecture. If Dr. Teall wanted to know what was done, he could have inspected the roll of every class and the record of every lecture, clinic, demonstrations from the first day of the session.

When he was told about these he did not want to examine them. (3) Dr. Teall says "instructors seemed to be changed frequently in the midst of work." I do not know what he means. If he means that our instructors were changed during the course of the term or year work that is absolutely false. We have kept in the main our instructors from the very opening of the college, adding year by year new members from the ranks of our graduates. (4) Dr. Teall states that we employ students as instructors, three of the instructors he says were undergraduates. One of these, our teacher in biology, is a certified teacher in Great Britain, certified in science under the South Kensington, London, governmental board, and a teacher for over fifteen years. Another, our teacher in chemistry, was a high school teacher of chemistry for years and acknowledged by everyone as an excellent teacher. Dr. Teall spent five minutes in this class of chemistry. (5) Dr. Teall says "the instructors, outside of Drs. Littlejohn, were not of a class to insure the best results. With *two* exceptions the instructors were M.D.'s, etc."

I wish to call Dr. Teall's attention to positive misrepresentations. Excluding myself and my brother there were nine M.D.'s on our faculty; of these, six were supplying the material for our class in post-graduate work on comparative therapeutics. The other three are our own graduates who completed a medical course after graduation for the sake of surgery. When these materials were supplied I conducted a two-hour class of osteopathic therapeutics in which I compared the osteopathic theory and practice with that of the other systems and told why ours was better.

This class Dr. Teall never visited although I was present and held my class. Instead of *two* osteopathic graduates as instructors, excluding my brother and myself, there were seventeen D.O.'s pure and simple, actually engaged in the teaching work of the college as regular instructors when Dr. Teall was here. I would be willing to put these against an equal number anywhere for experience, ripe scholarship and loyalty to osteopathy.

Dr. Ford has been teaching regional anatomy in this college for six years and I consider him an ornament to the anatomical science, as well as a loyal osteopathic friend. There were but *two* M.D.'s teaching at the time Dr.

Teall was here. Theoretical pathology was taught by Dr. Griffiths, a graduate in arts and medicine, and an accomplished teacher.

Laboratory and research pathology was taught by a D.O. Dr. Teall says "under such conditions the emphasizing of osteopathic principles could not be expected to be very strong." He also says the examination of the clinics was not complete. He visited my clinics on Monday when I examined two patients, a report of which is in our clinic record taken down during the clinic. For an hour I talked on the lesions, their significance, the line of treatment and the possible benefit, demonstrating the mechanical basis of the lesions found and their treatment. Then I turned the patients over to the demonstrators who show the students how to treat in the treating room. Our students examine each patient, get a history and report to the public clinic. Then we examine and demonstrate in public.

Was Dr. Teall in a position to say whether we taught osteopathically or not? My class in osteopathic technique, diagnosis and manipulation was meeting twice a week and he never visited it. He spent less than twenty minutes in my class on the principles of osteopathy and less than fifteen minutes in my class on the practice of osteopathy. During the last year I gave to my students thirteen hours a week on the principles, practice and technique of osteopathy and comparative osteopathy. And it is not medicine either as my students can testify.

Dr. Teal says there was a class scheduled in the fourth year practice of medicine. Yes, the Supreme Court of the State of Illinois has decided that the practice of osteopathy is the practice of medicine (see catalogue of school 1905–6, p. 10–12). "As the materia medica, theory and practice of medicine are taught by the particular school to which they belong, so is the osteopathic system representing an independent method of healing diseases, taught and applied according to the osteopathic theories of diagnosis and therapeutics, surgery and obstetrics, so as to maintain the same as an independent system or science of healing." "And as the independent and distinctive system, as our definition makes clear, osteopathy includes all that is commonly included in the field of the practice of medicine, namely, diagnosis, therapeutics and surgery, from its own distinctive standpoint. It is not the practice of medicine by drugs." (Catalogue, p. 14).

I am sorry that Dr. Teall was not generous enough to give one word of commendation. I protest against the wholesale denunciation of my colleagues, some of whom have been years in osteopathic practice. We did not parade anything for display. Dr. Teall came at the close of a long and tedious year of work. We were near the close of the ninth month of work. It may be some of us were fagged, but I know that we are as loyal to osteopathy as our critic. I feel satisfied that our condemnation will bring us more friends than otherwise, because those who know us best, know that we have not hesitated to spend our time and money in defense of osteopathy and even in research work that the world has not yet even heard of.

In regard to the hospital clinics that Dr. Teall thinks of doubtful value and tending to mixing with medical students. A schedule is made out of clinical work in surgery, eye, skin, heart and diagnostic clinics at the

County Hospital where the students can see a variety of operations and acute cases not seen anywhere to better advantage in this country. They have the privilege before and after the public clinic of examining the cases for lesions. During the first three years of the college existence I personally took the students and examined with them all the cases. During that time I was privileged to act as assistant to Dr. Duncan. Since then I have not been able to spend the forenoon of each day on account of other work but this does not limit the field of usefulness in seeing and examining these cases.

We have tried to secure our place which belongs to us by right to share in conducting the county clinics but so far have been unsuccessful, largely through the apathy of the osteopathic profession. The time is coming when we will have our share in the examination and treatment of all cases in the county of Cook. Till that time comes we can use the facilities offered to splendid advantage for our students. I remember when Dr. Teall graduated from Kirksville he solicited the help of the Drs. Littlejohn to get admission to these clinical facilities of the Chicago hospitals, and at that time Dr. Teall did not despise the day of small mercies.

As a college we realise that we have failures and we are trying to improve on these. The college, like the system, is young. We are not incompetent, dishonest or disloyal to osteopathy. Any reasonable counsel is welcomed and the good will and fellow feeling of osteopaths is asked in helping us to make this college a center to represent osteopathy. The clinics conducted by us free of cost as a labor of love gives us cases that amply repay the time expended in developing and extending the osteopathic field here.

In justice to osteopathy I ask you to give this statement a place in the *Journal of the A.O.A.* Our faculty sends its loyal greetings to all honest and straightforward osteopaths.

J. Martin Littlejohn
President

Chicago, Illinois, November 28, 1906 [15]

Earlier in the year, the Littlejohns had filed a request with the Illinois Secretary of State asking for authorization to increase the membership of the college's Board of Directors from four to six. The request was granted in a charter amendment dated July 10, 1906, and the 1906–1907 school term opened with a Board of Directors listing as its members Dr. J. Martin Littlejohn, Dr. Edith Williams Littlejohn, Dr. James B. Littlejohn, Elizabeth W. Littlejohn (mother of the Littlejohn brothers), Judge J. M. Longenecker (the college's attorney), and John H. Lucas.

The faculty had grown to a total of 39, including five clinic instructors [16]. Listed on its roster were such individuals as Dr. Harrison H. Fryette who taught physiological neurology and was to win a wide reputation for his studies in the anatomy of the nervous system and as the inventor of an "articulated spine." [Dr. Richard N. MacBain, president emeritus of CCOM, recalled that Dr. Fryette was a tall, handsome, distinguished looking man who attracted some of this country's well-known figures to his practice. Among these was the world famous opera star, Mme. Galli-Curci who, in appreciation, assisted the osteopathic colleges in their financial problems by staging benefit performances for them. Another of his patients was W. Ogden Armour, meat packing magnate, who personally assisted the development of CCOM with financial support. Dr. Fryette, Dr. MacBain recalls, was the first CCOM graduate to become president of AOA (1919–1920)].

Others included W. Burr Allen, who taught descriptive anatomy, mental and nervous diseases, and served as Dean of the College from 1913–1917; and Walter Elfrink, a specialist in dietetics and frequent contributor to osteopathic publications. Dr. Elfrink was to serve for many years as Secretary of the Illinois Osteopathic Association. Dr. Blanche Mayes Elfrink, his wife, was also a member of the faculty and later became head of the Department of Obstetrics.

In the fall of 1906, Dr. James B. Littlejohn thought it timely to send out word that, in response to many requests, the American College of Osteopathic Medicine and Surgery would offer a special post-graduate course beginning January 14, 1907. The course was designed primarily "for those desiring the three-year diploma" and would "consist of all the usual branches taught and be practical in its character and of such a scope as to make it specially valuable to those who have already had work in these branches."

The course would also "be so arranged as to cover, among other subjects, work on the eye and ear, nose and throat, special and clinical pathology, X-radiance, a broad and practical course on the theory and practice of osteopathy, comparative therapeutics and hospital training."

Once again the availability of the Cook County Hospital as a superlative center for case studies was emphasized. Dr. Littlejohn noted: "Facilities are offered for attendance at the Cook County Hospital, the largest of its kind in the United States. Here students have an actual opportunity to see hundreds of bed-side cases of all kinds, examples of all cases of skin and venereal diseases, in fact, bringing one in close touch with everything pertaining to disease and surgical work of all kinds [17, 18, 19]."

By means of such post-graduate courses and the adaptation of its curriculum to the needs of the times, the American College of Osteopathic Medicine and Surgery steadily widened its influence and reputation. The College's adjustability to new circumstances as they developed extended even to its name. In December, 1908, the *Journal of the American Osteopathic Association* carried the following paragraph:

Dr. Littlejohn announces that the name of the American College of

Osteopathic Medicine and Surgery has been changed to the Littlejohn College and Hospital. This eliminates the word "medicine [20]."

James B. Littlejohn, recounting the early history of the school later on, wrote:

> The question of recognition of the College by the State Board of Health was being considered and in order to obviate some difficulties as to the name it was changed in 1909 to The Littlejohn College and Hospital, by which it was known until 1913 when the work of the College was suspended [21].

Documents in Cook County and Illinois State offices indicate that the name change was agreed upon by the school's Board of Directors at a meeting held on October 4, 1908. A report of this meeting, typed on the College's official stationery and on file in the Cook County and the Illinois Secretary of State offices, reads:

> At a special meeting of the Board of Directors of the American College of Osteopathic Medicine and Surgery held on the 4th day of October, 1908 after due notice the following resolution was adopted—
>
> Resolved that the articles of incorporation be amended so that the name of the College be changed to "The Littlejohn College and Hospital"; and that section 2, paragraph (c) be amended by inserting the words "Hospital and Training School for Nurses" after the words "annexed infirmary" so that the section would read. . . . "with annexed Infirmary, Hospital and Training School for Nurses. . . ."

The report was signed by J. Martin Littlejohn, President, and James B. Littlejohn, Secretary, and officially filed by the Illinois Secretary of State on January 9, 1909.

Although there was now a change in name, there was no change in the College's intent as originally announced in 1900. The college would continue to stress teaching and methods of healing in conformity with the College's philosophy that osteopathy is an independent system of healing diseases and conditions of the body, and would continue to teach osteopathic theories of diagnosis and therapeutics, surgery and obstetrics so as to maintain osteopathy as an independent system.

At this point, however, there was some concession to advances in medical practice. The Littlejohn College admitted that its courses would include not only surgery and surgical medicine but such subjects as anesthetics, antiseptics and antidotes. The use of antiseptics and antidotes, Dr. J. M. Littlejohn acknowledged, involved the use of drugs, a practice considerably at variance with the original teachings of Dr. A. T. Still, osteopathy's founder. Drugs, Dr. Littlejohn said, were "as much drug when used by the osteopath as when administered by the allopath, hence it is not right for us to say we do not use drugs, but using them it is proper that we should have the degree that indicates their use, though limited to osteopathy [22]."

While this sort of thinking obviously represented a liberalization of earlier osteopathic teachings, Dr. Littlejohn defended his interpretation of osteopathic practice on the grounds that "the osteopath must be the complete physician [23]." The use of drugs must be limited, he admitted, but it was imperative that the osteopathic physician know the properties of drugs, their use and their effects. The thoroughly qualified osteopathic physician, Dr. Littlejohn maintained, "must be a family physician as well as obstetrician," and the osteopathic colleges must turn out graduates who can fulfill this broadened range of usefulness.

In a speech before the Associated Colleges in 1909, he said:

> If osteopathy is to be established as a theory and practice—if its principles are to be demonstrated and if the profession is to be perpetuated, these ends must all be promoted through schools or colleges devoted to osteopathic research, education, and clinical demonstration. . . .
>
> I want to see osteopathy and the osteopathic profession absolutely independent of every other system. Our first duty is to protect our system in order to maintain our identity. It is the order of the day—the puzzle of the A.M.A.—the study of the Homeopathic societies and colleges, how to take osteopathy and make it a part of themselves. Why? They see that we have the public ear, that we have the faculty of getting students for our colleges. They envy us our success. They grudge us our students, and attempt to proselytize in order to swamp us. Their stock argument is that the D.O. is only one half a physician. He has only part of the physician's rights. Come to us and we will make you a full-fledged physician and surgeon. The problem of the professional schools is how can we meet this successfully. We can not meet it by dissension among ourselves—jealousy one towards the other among schools and their disciplines. . . . What the colleges need is reorganization, lengthening and strengthening of the courses [24].

He agreed with Dr. Carl P. McConnell that "our school courses should be equal to or better in all necessary respects than any of the schools of medicine not only for the salvation of osteopathy as an independent system but for legal standing as well." Wrote Dr. Littlejohn:

> Osteopathy is built on the rockbed foundation of biology, chemistry, physiology and anatomy, but these must be imbibed by the student and elaborated by the practitioner and professor from the osteopathic standpoint. . . . If the foundation is properly laid it will not be necessary for the osteopathic practitioner to round out his curriculum in a medical college [25].

These, then, were the principles which the Littlejohn College would extol as it continued its work under its new name.

On June 15, 1909, the *Bulletin and Journal of Health,* a monthly publication of the College, appeared with the college's new name and the accompanying explanation: "Formerly the American College of Osteopathic Medicine and Surgery." The college remained at 495-497 West Monroe Street for the 1909–1910 term. Later in the year the first catalogue bearing the title "The Littlejohn College and Hospital" was distributed and it announced that the fall term would begin September 15. The catalogue's cover stated that the College offered complete three and four year courses, had ample clinical and laboratory facilities, was located in the medical center of America, had attached to it a hospital and dispensary and, in bold type, a TRAINING SCHOOL FOR NURSES IN CONNECTION.

Chief administrators were J. Martin Littlejohn, President; James B. Littlejohn, Secretary and Treasurer; and Rolla R. Longenecker, Attorney. These three were also members of the Board of Directors, of course, and serving with them as trustees were Edith W. Littlejohn, Elizabeth W. Littlejohn, and John H. Lucas, thus making a total of six. The faculty roster listed, in addition to such well-known D.O.'s as Harrison H. Fryette and Walter E. Elfrink, the names of Grace D. Watts, embryology and biology; M. Lychenheim, hydrotherapy; Ernest R. Proctor, Director of the Department of Clinical Practice, a specialist in pediatrics and organizer of the institution's first free children's clinic; Andrew A. Gour, medical gymnastics; and Chester H. Morris, clinic instructor and a 1905 graduate of the college. All of these were to remain closely associated with the college's development and growth for many years; several of them would contribute immeasurably to the survival of the college itself.

The opening year for The Littlejohn College, and the tenth since its founding as the American College of Osteopathic Medicine and Surgery in 1900, was accompanied by trouble from an unanticipated quarter. During the year an inspector, representing the Carnegie Foundation for the Advancement of Teaching, visited the eight reputable osteopathic schools then operating in the United States and charged that all of them were "reeking with commercialism." The inspector's report alleged that all the osteopathic institutions were of a "mercenary character" and that their catalogues were "a mass of hysterical exaggerations." The report read, in part:

> The eight Osteopathic schools now enroll more than 1,300 students, who pay some $200,000 annually in fees. The instruction expended for this sum is inexpensive and worthless. Not a single full-time teacher is found in any of them. The fees find their way directly into the pockets of

the school owners or into school buildings or infirmaries that are equally their property. No effort is anywhere made to utilize prosperity as a means of defining an entrance standard or developing the "science" . . . Granting all that its champions claim, osteopathy is still in its incipiency. If sincere, their votaries would be engaged in building it up. They are doing nothing of the kind [26].

The report continued:

> In no case has a competent osteopath made a failure in his attempt to build up a paying practice. His remuneration, counted in dollars, will be greatly in excess of what he could reasonably expect in most other lines of professional work. . . . The average osteopath has a better practice than ninety of every hundred medical practitioners. . . . A lucrative practice is assured by every conscientious and capable practitioner [27].

The report also took some of the medical schools to task, particularly those operating independently of a university or college. A medical college, the report stated, "is essentially a department of a university and should not exist independent of it," and it urged that there be but one medical institution in any one city. While the inspector charged many of the allopathic schools with mediocrity or downright ineptitude (some of which should be eliminated), he reserved his most savage criticism for the osteopathic colleges.

In December, 1909, the Carnegie inspector visited the Littlejohn College and if criticism of the college in 1906 by Dr. Teall had caused consternation, the brutal denunciation of the Littlejohn College by the investigator caused dismay, then downright anger. The Carnegie analysis of the College was recorded by the inspector as follows:

> LITTLEJOHN COLLEGE OF OSTEOPATHY. An undisguised commercial enterprise. Entrance requirement: Nominal. Attendance: 75. Teaching staff: 43. Resources available for maintenance: Fees, and income from patients. Laboratory facilities: Practically none. At the time of the visit some rebuilding was in progress, in consequence of which even such laboratories as are claimed were, except that of elementary chemistry, entirely out of commission and likely to remain so for months; but "teaching goes on all the same." Class rooms were practically bare, except for chairs and a table. Clinical facilities: beds, mostly surgical—which can be of little use. The Littlejohn Hospital, a pay institution of 20. It was claimed, too, that "medicine and surgery are taught in the school" and color is lent to the statement by the presence on the faculty of physicians teaching materia medica, etc. [28]

The American Osteopathic Association and the osteopathic colleges fought back vehemently. In counterattacking, the AOA immediately uncovered the Carnegie inspector who had filed the report. He was identified as Abraham Flexner, a brother of Dr. Simon Flexner of the Rockefeller Institute for Research. This in itself, the Association indicated, would preclude an impartial survey of the osteopathic colleges. Nevertheless, the *Journal of the AOA* advised certain reforms:

> Let us profit by this scathing rebuke of Abraham Flexner. Let the schools do their part, teach high ideals rather than the reverse. Let the practitioners send to the schools a fine body of men and women. . . .
>
> Just as literature used by the practitioner has no right to be other than educative, so the catalogues of our colleges have no right to hold out financial success of the practitioners of osteopathy as an inducement to men and women to enter its walls. It is not right to ask the faithful, ethical practitioners to carry such a load as that imposes upon them [29].

The Littlejohn College stoutly denied the charges which Flexner had filed with the Carnegie Foundation. At the 1910 AOA national convention in San Francisco, Dr. E. R. Proctor, of the school's faculty, read a paper which Dr. J. M. Littlejohn had prepared but which he was unable to present personally. The reply made by Dr. Littlejohn to the charges stated in part:

> This College and Hospital is chartered for the express purpose of systematizing and placing on a scientific basis the osteopathic methods of healing and treating disease and conditions of the body. . . .
>
> To complete our system, we believe that surgery is a field to which the osteopathic principle is equally applicable as to the rest of the field of healing; and that any other adjustive measure in line with the body structure, composition and relations fall within the province of our system.
>
> This College believes that the only way in which recognition can be secured is by placing the osteopathic system on an independent basis of equality with other schools of medicine, thereby establishing a system so complete and comprehensive that the practitioner is qualified to deal with all conditions of disease. . . .
>
> We hereby express our determination to support as we always have in the past, such legislative action as will define the osteopathic system to be Osteopathy as taught and practiced in the legally incorporated and reputable Colleges of Osteopathy [30].

The vitriolic attack by the Carnegie inspector upon The Littlejohn College and Hospital had no effect, happily, on the college's continuing growth. Dr. James Littlejohn, as secretary and treasurer, wrote the *Journal of the AOA* that the school was prospering. Under the heading "Plans and Prospects of our Osteopathic Colleges," Dr. Littlejohn's letter appeared as follows:

> The Littlejohn College and Hospital are in a flourishing condition. The new College building is complete and is admitted by all to be up to date and convenient in every particular. The laboratory facilities are perfect and the apparatus for the same has been thoroughly renovated and increased so

that no institution can claim any superiority in that direction.

The trustees have taken a more pronounced position on the question of the curriculum. They have adopted the four year course as the standard in emphasizing the completeness of the course and the necessity for such a course. This College was the first to offer a four year course, and has made it heretofore optional, but now makes it essential.

The standard of entrance is the same as that required by the Association of Osteopathic Colleges and the American Medical Association, viz., a high school certificate, or a certificate from the department of public instruction in the state equivalent to a four year high school curriculum.

The hospital has been crowded and the trustees are considering the question of enlarging the same. The clinical facilities have been adequate, all types of disease and conditions being represented. Osteopathic, Gynecologic and Surgical as well as such special types as Ear, Nose and Throat and Eye cases have been abundant.

The year [1909–1910 school term] has been very pleasant and auspicious. Much of the work was done under some difficulty, while the new building was progressing, but student, teacher and patient seemed to vie with one another to make things more pleasant [31].

The "new College building" mentioned in J. B. Littlejohn's summary became a reality for the 1910–1911 school term. The college was now located at 1420–1422 West Monroe Street—its fourth site since opening in 1900. The Littlejohn Hospital was nearby, at 1408–1410 West Monroe.

To publicize the institution's new location, the College issued a special announcement brochure prior to the beginning of the 1910–1911 term. The introductory paragraphs informed the reader:

> This special announcement is issued for the purpose of making it known that the Littlejohn College will be permanently located in its new building at the opening of the school year of 1910–1911. Located in this instance meaning that everything and everybody necessary for the successful conducting of college work will be on hand on the morning of September 12, and that on the following morning the full curriculum will be in force as outlined provisionally on pages 29–32.
>
> We have never been, nor are we now, believers in sending out an elaborate picture book, in the form of a catalog, yet from the very fact that but few of those to whom a copy of this brochure is sent will perhaps ever have opportunity of seeing our new building, it seems necessary at this time to include a photographic reproduction of the building, as well as detail floor plans, together with a picture of the Littlejohn Hospital [32].

The faculty of 64 listed at least a dozen individuals who were to become prominent not only in their professional field but as administrators or teachers in the College: the Littlejohns; W. Burr Allen, Professor of Osteopathic Technique; Harrison H. Fryette, Associate Professor of Osteopathic Technique; Grace D. Watts, Professor of Embryology and Associate Professor of Clinical Gynecology; Walter E. Elfrink, Professor of Dietetics and Applied Physiological Chemistry, and his wife, Blanche Mayes Elfrink, Associate Professor of Obstetrics; Chester H. Morris, Clinical Instructor of Osteopathy; Andrew A. Gour, Professor of Medical Gymnastics; [He was a specialist in corrective gymnastics, aggressive by nature and only too willing to take on Dr. Morris Fishbein on behalf of Osteopathic medicine when the latter attacked the profession through the medium of the *American Mercury Magazine.* Dr. Gour issued a vehement reply to Dr. Fishbein in *Pearson's Magazine* for June, 1924.] Also Ernest R. Proctor, Associate Professor of Pediatrics; Fred Bischoff, Clinical Instructor of Osteopathy, and later Secretary of the Board of Trustees with a well earned reputation for financial acumen; Mary H. Connor, Professor of Pediatrics, and a number of others.

The brochure said of its faculty members: "Each one is actively engaged in teaching, as per schedule, else he is immediately dropped and his successor appointed."

The new four-story building provided the most satisfying facilities the college had yet been able to offer. Constructed of brick and stone, with a basement, the building had excellent sanitation, heating, lighting and ventilation to make it truly "a big, comfortable scientific home."

One the first floor were the dispensary, the waiting and treating rooms, as well as a number of offices. On the second were the library, the junior and senior class rooms, a dispensary, clinic room and dark room. On the third were freshman and sophomore class rooms, a dispensary, treating rooms, and laboratory. Four additional laboratories were on the fourth floor. In the 50' × 100' yard in the rear was a two-story brick annex housing the anatomical laboratories, demonstrating rooms and museum.

The brochure carefully explained that "The buildings and equipment of the college and hospital are owned solely by members of the college corporation and the college is in no way a commercial enterprise but rather an institution of learning, incorporated 'not for profit.' It is an educational institution conducted without financial gain where men and women may be thoroughly trained as osteopathic physicians and surgeons."

The Littlejohn Hospital, an adjoining two-story brick building at 1408-1410 West Monroe, could accommodate twenty patients. There was also an outpatient dispensary and clinic department for examining and treating patients who came to the hospital directly from their homes.

A facility in which the institution took great pride was the training school for nurses which admitted girls "of good moral character" over 20 years of age and who "possess a good English education in the primary branches so as to make them intelligent nurses, accurate reporters of cases and educated representatives of the profession." Girls who successfully passed a probationary period were admitted to an extensive training program [33].

Each student applying for admission to the Littlejohn College was required to submit evidence "of good moral character" and present a certificate of attestation signed by two physicians in good standing in the state where the applicant resided. Only high school graduates or individuals able to present certificates stating that they had successfully passed examinations covering a complete four-year high school program, or certificates attesting that they had successfully passed the Regents' Entrance Examination in the State of New York, were admitted.

The college year consisted of 36 weeks, and the training program covered four years. Tuition was $150 a year, and board and room could be obtained near the College for amounts ranging from $15 to $25 per month [34].

The Littlejohn College stressed that Chicago was the logical center for the leading osteopathic college of medicine in the world, and that "We propose to strive to be that College!" In support of that vow, the Littlejohn College continued its efforts to elevate osteopathic educational standards.

Dr. Harrison Fryette, recognizing the enormous task the osteopathic colleges faced in obtaining recognition equal to that of the medical schools, announced that the time had come for all top-flight osteopathic schools to adopt the four-year program. He said, "If we are to become a complete and independent system of therapeutics, our educational qualifications must be second to none. In order to get legal and popular recognition of the kind we want and deserve we must have as thorough a college course as any system . . . the degree of D.O. seems far more practical for us under the circumstances than the degree of M.D., which would be misleading and have no better standing than the former, if the former was backed by as good or better educational qualifications[35]."

Dr. Carl P. McConnell supported the expanded college program wholeheartedly, but urged that more clinical experience be offered. At the annual AOA meeting in San Francisco, Dr. McConnell told the delegates:

> I am in favor of such a course (the 4-year program) provided the extended time is given over to teaching the student osteopathy, not merely marking the time by rehearsing medical work for the student to meet the questions of some medical Board of Health. In my opinion the weakest point in an osteopathic education is the lack of sufficient clinical training and experience [36].

These men were typical of the leaders who were charting the course of the College. They were in the forefront in setting the high standards which other osteopathic colleges later adopted.

During this period in the history of U.S. osteopathic medicine, considerable controversy arose as to whether the teaching of the use of drugs in osteopathic colleges should be permitted. At the 1911 AOA convention, the Littlejohn College received considerable criticism for its stand on drugs. Dr. Edgar S. Comstock, a graduate of the College who later became Secretary of the Board and served in that position for many years, wrote the *Journal of the AOA* to defend the school's position. Comstock wrote that in some patients the presence of "elements that go to make up the body economy are lacking. These elements, I believe, must be supplied in some form or other . . . and this may be done in food form or in some prepared substance, which might be termed medicinal, but which, nevertheless, serves the purpose."

He declared that the Littlejohn College stressed structural maladjustments as the underlying causes of many of the patients' ills, but that at Littlejohn "We must all believe in the administration of anaesthetics when necessary, the use of antidotes in poison cases, the use of antiseptics, the value of dietetic procedure, and other methods physiological, all of which seem to me to be osteopathic." He continued:

> It is and has been the aim of Littlejohn College and Hospital to so prepare its graduates as to force the State Boards of Health to recognize every osteopath to be as well prepared and as fully equipped as any graduate of any medical college . . . Littlejohn College has been fighting, is fighting, always will fight for equal requirements, equal or better education and equal recognition with the "regulars," and whatever course it has pursued, it has been with this object in view [37].

The *Journal of the American Osteopathic Association,* determined that osteopathy remain an independent healing science and that it should shun any practices which would render osteopathy indistinguishable from the general practice of medicine, found fault with such policies as that described in a *Littlejohn College Bulletin:*

> If there is any virtue in drugs at all, osteopaths ought to avail themselves of it. There can be no question but that drugs have been over-rated. All doctors admit that. But neither can there be any question but what there are times when properly selected drugs are useful [38].

Dr. J. Martin Littlejohn assuaged the *Journal's* fears that the Littlejohn College may be acting "outside the bounds of osteopathic practice" by writing the publication that the College had never believed in or taught the use of drugs as medicinal agents, nor had the school ever claimed that "the physician schooled in drugs is the only learned and adequately equipped practitioner." He wrote:

> In fact, it has taught just the opposite, that the osteopathic system is an

independent system of therapy, that the osteopathic practitioner is a physician just as truly as any other physician of any school and as such is entitled to equal rights and privileges. The only recognition it has ever given to medicine has been . . . the antiseptics, anaesthetics and antidotes of surgery and toxicology, and these only when used in *compliance with the principles of adjustment* [39].

Dr. Carl P. McConnell, osteopathic pioneer, perhaps summed it all up neatly when he wrote in *The Osteopathic Physician:*

> No one questions anesthesia, antidotes, asepsis, parasiticides and opiates in rare instances. But why make a bug-a-boo of rare cases? Osteopathic technique, plus hygiene, diet, hydro-therapy, sanitation, rest cure, environmental considerations, and the like constitute a tremendous work. . . . We are young, very young. What osteopathy needs beyond everything else is a little rest from the numerous attempts to define its limitations [40].

The Littlejohn College, always advocating the necessity for research, was delighted when, in 1911, it received reports that the trustees of the American Osteopathic Association Research Fund were planning to establish a research institute and that the chances were good that it would be located in Chicago.

The College's *Bulletin and Journal of Health* for July 15, 1911, reported:

> We have been given to understand that it is the intention of the trustees of the Research Fund to locate the Institute in Chicago, provided that sufficient encouragement is received from local sources. It is held that on account of its central location, Chicago is the logical place for such an undertaking.
>
> It is therefore up to the osteopaths of Chicago to get busy and give this enterprise all the support possible. It will mean much to Osteopathy to have such an institution in actual operation and it will mean more to the osteopaths to have this osteopathic center in our midst.
>
> Unfortunately the news of this intention on the part of the Institute Trustees did not become public in time for any concerted action on the part of Chicago osteopaths before the convention. Some definite movement should be inaugurated however, at the Convention or immediately afterward [41].

Not until several years later, however, did the Research Institute's plans materialize in Chicago.

REFERENCES

1. Elizabeth W. Littlejohn, who is listed as one of the four directors, was the mother of the Littlejohn brothers. Five officers were listed for the Board of Directors in the 1900 *Announcement Catalogue:* J. Martin Littlejohn, President; T. J. Anthony, Vice President; David Littlejohn, Secretary; James B. Littlejohn, Treasurer and Manager; and Judge J. M. Longenecker, Attorney.

2. *CCO Reflex,* 1922.

3. Dr. McConnell was not only one of the great pioneers of the College, but an osteopathic physician whose talents became internationally known. His papers on the osteopathic lesion became classics in their field. Dr. Edith Williams Littlejohn, wife of James B. Littlejohn, was an outstanding osteopathic physician in her own right. She taught constitutional and renal diseases in the College.

4. Quoted in the *Announcement Catalogue for 1900–1901.*

5. The College accepted women on an equal footing with men from the very beginning, believing, as did Dr. Andrew Taylor Still, that women were just as capable as men in the practice of osteopathy and thus antedating Women's Liberation Movement demands by many decades. As a matter of fact, some of the nation's leading osteopathic physicians were, and are, women practitioners.

6. *The Cosmopolitan Osteopath,* June, 1901, p. 232. (Vol. 6, No. 5).

7. This federation of osteopathic colleges was formed in 1898 when representatives of six osteopathic schools met in Kirksville, Missouri. In 1900, a follow-up meeting was held in Chicago, and by 1901, the organization, known as The Associated Colleges of Osteopathy, had a membership of 13 schools. The Associated Colleges set up minimum standards for these institutions and in 1902 established professional qualifications as well as a uniform professional curriculum. The name of the organization was later changed to "The American Association of Osteopathic Colleges." By the end of World War I, only six schools remained of the thirty which had been active at one time or another during these years.

8. In May, 1903, ACOMS reported that it had 54 students enrolled. At a January commencement in 1903 the College had graduated nine. *The Osteopathic Physician* announced: "The American College of Osteopathic Medicine and Surgery graduated nine doctors this commencement at Steinway Hall, Chicago. Dr. J. M. Littlejohn delivered a masterly address vindicating the principles of Osteopathy." The names of the nine graduates accompanied the announcement. (*The Osteopathic Physician,* February, 1903, p. 5).

9. *Journal AOA,* Vol. 5, 1904, p. 364.

10. *Journal AOA,* November, 1902, p. 355.

11. *Journal AOA,* November 1904, p. 134. (Vol. 4, No. 3).

12. *The Osteopathic Physician,* November, 1904, p. 11. (Vol. 6, No. 6). The osteopathic diploma mills, of course, were not concerned with ethics, since they sprang into existence to turn out practitioners quickly and in volume—at a handsome profit. The Metropolitan College of Osteopathy in Chicago, for example, advertised in a New York publication that it offered "a home study course in osteopathy which insures the equivalent of college training." The AOA termed the school an outright "quack institution". (*Journal AOA,* October, 1905, p. 91, Vol. 5).

13. *Journal AOA,* October, 1906, p. 21. (Vol. 6). Dr. Teall's report had been included as part of the "Official Report of the Proceedings of the American Osteopathic Association" issued at the close of the 1906 national AOA convention in Put-in-Bay, Ohio, August 6–10.

14. Dr. Littlejohn was also serving as Chairman of the AOA's "Committee of Teachers" at this time. In 1908 he was elected President of the Associated Colleges of Osteopathy.

15. *Journal AOA,* December, 1906, pp. 167–169. (Vol. 6).

16. *A.C.O.M. & S. Announcement Catalogue for 1906–1907.*

17. *The Osteopathic Physician,* December, 1906, p. 12. (Vol. 10, No. 6). It should be remembered, of course, that ACOMS had had a four-year course in active operation since its founding in 1900, and since 1904 the three-year program urged by the Associated Colleges of Osteopathy. A fourth year of study was offered for those planning to become osteopathic surgeons.

18. In addition to these facilities, the Drs. Littlejohn had established a sanatorium at the corner of 76th Street and Saginaw Avenue in an area known as "Windsor Park" on Chicago's south side.

19. An example of the shady practices prevailing during this era is an incident described in *The Osteopathic Physician* for May, 1906: "Dr. J. Sullivan Howell, the Chicago M.D. who used to use so much space in the Chicago papers advertising himself as an Osteopath and who occasionally confused his identity with Dr. Joseph H. Sullivan [a member of the ACOMS faculty, outstanding practitioner and a loyal friend of the college for many years] owing to the similarity in names, has been the subject of a fraud order in the United States Post Office, which has cut him off from the use of the mails in exploiting himself and his health schemes. Recently he has been giving health horoscopes, "Osteopathy" and other things by mail, it is said, under the name of the Astropathic Institute. Perhaps our profession can apply the same federal medicine in other localities to keep the name of osteopathy from being smudged under false pretenses." *The Osteopathic Physician,* May, 1906, p. 13. (Vol. 9, No. 5).

20. *Journal AOA,* December, 1908, p. 183. (Vol. 8, No. 4).

21. *1929 CCO Reflex,* pp. 62–63.

22. From an address, "Osteopathy and Its Colleges" by Dr. J. M. Littlejohn at an open meeting of the Associated Colleges of Osteopathy in Minneapolis, 1909, and published in the *Journal AOA,* February, 1910, pp. 220–228. (Vol. 9, No. 6).

23. *Journal AOA,* February, 1910, pp. 220–228. (Vol. No. 6).

24. *Ibid.* Dr. Louisa Burns defined the osteopathic physician admirably when she said, "If the osteopath is the true physician, he will be thoroughly fitted to do the best thing possible in every conceivable circumstance of human suffering." (*Osteopathic Physician,* July, 1915, P. 15).

25. *Journal AOA,* February, 1910, pp. 220–228. (Vol. 9, No. 6). It was a common practice for a D.O. to study for an M.D. degree as well—in order to assure his right to practice without interference from state or local officials. Licenses for D.O.'s at this time severely restricted their rights as medical practitioners.

26. *Journal AOA,* July 1910, p. 503. (Vol. 9, No. 11).

27. *Journal AOA,* July 1910, pp. 503–504. (Vol. 9, No. 11).

28. *The Osteopathic Physician,* September, 1910, p. 4. (Vol. 18, No. 3).

29. *Journal AOA,* July 1910, p. 504, (Vol. 9, No. 11).

30. *Journal AOA,* September, 1910, pp. 47–48. (Vol. 10, No. 1).

31. *Journal AOA,* June, 1910, p. 443. (Vol. 9, No. 10). At the Commencement Exercises held on June 3, 1910, nineteen graduates received their D.O. diplomas from Dr. J. Martin Littlejohn.

32. *Bulletin and Journal of Health,* August 15, 1910. This monthly publication of The Littlejohn College and Hospital was published from 1908 to 1913.

33. *Bulletin and Journal of Health,* June 15, 1911, page 26.

34. The Hudson College of Osteopathy and Electro-Mechano-Therapy in Union Hill, New Jersey, was offering a full course in osteopathy for only $7.50! The course was reported to run from two weeks to three months, and a diploma "good in any state" was promised on completion of the course. In West Hoboken, Henry Behm was arrested and jailed for fleecing Mrs. Ellen Moore of Weehauken of $2,150—her life savings—to "found and incorporate a school of medicine and osteopathy in New York." In Chicago, the American College of Mechano-Therapy was flooding the country with advertisements announcing that it taught osteopathy by mail, but in small print explained that the school was in reality teaching Mechano-Therapy, something much better than osteopathy. *The Osteopathic Physician,* bitterly denouncing the school, commented: "It is a burning shame that the newspapers of the country can be utilized to promote this kind of fraud. . . . It is a pity that the A.M.A. instead of spending time fighting osteopaths, does not devote

some effort to clean up these notorious correspondence course schools. (*The Osteopathic Physician*, February, 1911, p. 8 Vol. 19, No. 2). These schools were typical of the type of competition that the reputable osteopathic schools faced, and the almost hopeless task of exposing them and putting them out of business.

35. *The Osteopathic Physician*, February, 1910, p. 1. (Vol. 17, No. 2)
36. *Journal AOA*, November, 1910, p. 134. (Vol. 10, No. 3)
37. *Journal AOA*, September, 1911, p. 670. (Vol. 11, No. 1)
38. *Journal AOA*, September, 1911, p. 673. (Vol. 11, No. 1)
39. *Ibid.*, October, 1911, p. 728. (Vol. 11, No. 2)
40. From his article "Osteopathy and Drugs" published in *The Osteopathic Physician*, May, 1911, pp. 9–10. (Vol. 19, No. 5)
41. *Bulletin and Journal of Health*, July 15, 1911, p. 10. (Vol. 4, No. 7)

# 4

# 1913: REORGANIZATION—AND A NEW NAME

In 1912–1913 important events occurred which would give further direction and impetus to the college. It was a good time for reevaluating the school's objectives and aims, for its principal founder, Dr. J. Martin Littlejohn, announced his intention of returning to England and help organize the British School of Osteopathy. With his departure, only James B. Littlejohn and his wife, Edith, would remain of the original founding group. David Littlejohn, one of the three founding brothers, had withdrawn from the school in 1906 to concentrate on his private practice, then move on to other areas.

Late in 1912, a small group of Chicago osteopathic physicians, responding to an invitation from the owners of the Littlejohn College and Hospital, met in the office of Dr. Carl P. McConnell to discuss plans for the school's reorganization and expansion. Included in the group were Fred Bischoff, faculty member who for many years was to serve as treasurer of the college corporation and who won national recognition for his work with the American Osteopathic Association; Edgar S. Comstock, who was to serve either as Dean or Secretary of the school from 1913 to 1924; Ernest R. Proctor, who was to become the first Dean of the Faculty, then serve for many years as a member of the Board of Trustees, and who won the gratitude of the entire Chicago south side community by opening a free children's clinic in 1918; and Dr. Charles A. Fink, who later was elected Vice President of the Chicago College of Osteopathy Corporation.

In February, 1913, a second meeting was held, attended by a larger number of interested osteopathic professional men, and in March, a third session at which time a permanent organization was effected and a Board of Trustees chosen. By this time more than sixty osteopathic physicians had become interested in the project. The first Board of Directors, a group of

[ 45 ]

seven, was comprised of Dr. Carl P. McConnell, President; James B. Littlejohn, Vice President; Edgar S. Comstock, Secretary; Fred Bischoff, Treasurer; and Grace L. Smith, George H. Carpenter (later to become President of the College); and W. Burr Allen.

Of particular significance at the February meeting was the decision to abandon the name "Littlejohn College and Hospital" and adopt, in its place, the name "Chicago College of Osteopathy."

Reorganization, of course, meant a new charter, and accordingly an application was filed on March 1, 1913, with the Illinois Secretary of State for an amended document. The application was filed by the State on March 9; it had been signed by Dr. McConnell, President, and Rolla R. Longenecker, Attorney.

The revised charter stated that the object of the new corporation was to "establish and maintain an educational institution in Illinois as a college to investigate, teach and advance the science of Osteopathy," and that "This corporation shall be conducted not for profit, but solely as an educational institution with power to maintain and establish a general hospital, clinics, training school for nurses, laboratories for original investigation, and such other establishments in connection therewith as may become necessary." It also authorized an increase in the Board of Trustees membership from six to seven.

While there was now a change in name and administration, and a new seven-member Board of Trustees, the goal of the new College remained the same as the one which had guided the old: "to investigate, teach, and advance the science of osteopathy." The Chicago College of Osteopathy, new in organization but veering not at all from its original purpose, was destined to become one of the most important osteopathic training centers in the world.

In reporting the important events which led to the reorganized institution, one of the trustees wrote: "The move is entirely non-commercial. Every dollar we take in will go back to the College. We have no desire to antagonize any other institution. We have the buildings, equipment and an organized osteopathic faculty. Buildings and equipment are valued at over $75,000. There will be several paid instructors, as those in anatomy, physiology, laboratory, etc., who devote all or nearly all of their time to teaching. These will be men of ability and experience [1]."

At its meeting on March 1, 1913, the Board of Trustees of the newly created Chicago College of Osteopathy (CCO) instructed the President and Secretary to arrange for a five-year lease covering the use of the Littlejohn College and Hospital facilities. The rental fee would be $30,000 for the five-year period and was to cover the use of all facilities on the Monroe

Street site. There would be "an option to renew the lease upon a new valuation of the said property to be leased by this corporation, and said lease shall be dated to begin July 1, 1913 [2]."

On March 8, the trustees met again (at the Boston Oyster House in Chicago) and agreed to pay the five-year rental of $30,000 in 36 monthly installments of $450 each, followed by 24 installments of $575 each.

Of foremost concern was a qualified and trained faculty. Considerable discussion took place as to faculty recruitment and responsibilities. The Board minutes of the meeting describe the procedure:

> It was suggested that the course of study be divided into departments with a professor at the head of each department, and that the associate professors, teaching in each department, be under the supervisor of that department. That the professor and associate professors of each department meet not less than once each month to discuss the work and method of instruction for the coming month [3].

The trustees recommended that, if possible, a special lecturer be procured each week during the school year to give a popular lecture to the entire student body. They ruled also that during the College's first year, beginning in September, "the course of study shall be three years, with an optional four-year course," but beginning in September, 1914, and thereafter, "the course of study shall be four years and no less."

The availability of "clinical material," especially for "skin and venereal diseases," was of some concern. Someone suggested that "cards be placed in the lodging houses and with the Salvation Army for such material," and Dr. F. J. Stewart, Professor of Surgery, offered to conduct these clinics. Problems such as these indicated only too clearly the situation confronting the new college.

The creation of the Chicago College of Osteopathy had some notable immediate results. It not only marked the activation of a new and expanded center for training osteopathic physicians, but it also acted as a catalyst to bring together, in a common cause, the osteopathic practitioners of the Chicago area and the State. It was particularly helpful in uniting the work of the Chicago Osteopathic Society and the Illinois Osteopathic Association, two groups whose activities, when they did not overlap, were frequently antagonistic. Moreover, the College helped to eliminate much of the coolness that existed among osteopathic physicians connected with the College and those not associated with the school, since it invited (and with happy results) a greater number of D.O.'s to participate in the work of the center. As a matter of fact, the entire profession looked with approval upon the new Chicago college.

No organization was happier than the AOA. Its education committee commented:

> Your committee (Education) is pleased to note that in the reorganization of the Littlejohn College of Osteopathy as the Chicago College of Osteopathy, it has received the support of the entire profession in that city, insuring a large and capable faculty. This blending of the active profession with the educational field is one which is much to be desired in all of our educational centers, and this example is to be highly recommended [4].

Osteopathic publications, such as *The Osteopathic Physician,* allocated space generously in describing the new Chicago school. The issue for April, 1913, devoted its entire first and second pages to this important news development, but in reporting the event, the publication stated that "The Chicago College of Osteopathy has been chartered by the State of Illinois as a corporation 'not for profit,' thus making the 'not for profit' principle the corner stone of the new institution," and that "The basic principle of the school will be to spread every dollar of its funds on osteopathic education [5]."

Dr. J. Martin Littlejohn, who was still in Chicago at this time and who had devoted so many years to the school, was highly nettled at the impression given by the article that the 'not for profit' principle was something new for the school. With some vexation, Dr. Littlejohn wrote *The Osteopathic Physician:*

> Permit me to say a few words about your statement in the last issue regarding the new college of osteopathy. You do not say, but what you say creates the impression that this new college represents a new principle, as this is your cue, namely, "not for profit." The college that this new college succeeds, or rather continues, the Littlejohn College, formerly the American College of Osteopathic Medicine and Surgery, was founded in May, 1900, on the non-profit principle and was conducted on that principle during its entire existence.
>
> No profits ever accrued to anyone. I worked for eleven years as head of the institution and gave two hours a day or more to teaching and never drew a cent out of it. One-half of the equipment of the college and the hospital represents time, money and labors I spent in building up for osteopathy an institution representing absolutely the non-commercial in osteopathic education. My physical strength could not any longer stand the strain.
>
> I am glad to see the consummation of unity and harmony in the establishment you announce. For this I hoped earnestly during the passing years. If I am not there it is because, like one greater than myself, I "laid down my life" in trying to establish a foundation upon which such a college might be built; and I helped to hold the fort until the greater developments you announce were rendered possible. From the field of my rest in the

faraway I shall look with eagerness to see the prosperity of this movement
for the perpetual upbuilding of osteopathy, that we all love [6].

It was a touching valedictory by one of the truly great men of American and
British osteopathy, and by a man who, more than any other single individual,
etched upon the pages of the school's history the solid principles upon which
today's internationally-known Chicago osteopathic center was built.

On April 5, 1913, Dr. Ernest R. Proctor was appointed Dean of the
Faculty by the Board of Trustees—the first to hold this position in the
reorganized institution. Accompanying the appointment was the Board's
recommendation that a change in the corporation's by-laws be made to
permit the election of a Dean of Faculty each year at the regular March
meeting, the appointee to serve for a period of one year, and meet with the
trustees as an ex-officio member of that body.

In June, the Littlejohn College as such graduated its last class, awarding
degrees to thirteen departing seniors. On July 1, the new organization took
over the control of the College and the new era began.

As the College prepared for the September term, Dr. Carl P. McConnell,
President, thought it proper to state again what lay behind the reorganization and to outline the course which the College would take. He said:

> The Chicago College of Osteopathy, an organization composed of a
> large number of the Chicago osteopaths, has for its only purpose the
> promoting and developing of the science of osteopathy. We feel that local
> and state conditions demand an organization that presents a solidarity for
> both offensive and defensive welfare. All interested parties have mutually
> and thoroughly agreed that the only feasible solution of the peculiar local
> conditions that have confronted us for many years is the promulgation of
> the present organization [7]. This step has been taken after mature deliber-
> ation and which we believe will prove a credit to not only the Illinois
> osteopaths but to the profession at large.
>
> We realize our responsibilities, knowing full well that they are many.
> But with our thorough unification we believe they will be satisfactorily
> met. We have no factional ax to grind. Neither do we purpose to an-
> tagonize any society or institution. Osteopathic teaching, development and
> advancement will be our endeavor [8].

The Chicago College of Osteopathy had a distinguished teaching staff as it
began accepting students for the September term. The roster included the
names of some of the foremost osteopathic physicians and surgeons in the
country. Dr. Carl P. McConnell was the head of the Department of Osteopathy, Theory and Practice; his colleagues in that department were Dr.
Charles A. Fink, Osteopathic Principles; Dr. Harrison H. Fryette, Osteopathic Technique; Dr. Frank C. Farmer, Diagnosis and Clinics, (an as-

sociate of Dr. McConnell up until he entered the military service during World War I); Dr. Fred Bischoff, Clinic Demonstration. Dr. Ernest R. Proctor was in charge of obstetrics in the Department of Gynecology, and Dr. James B. Littlejohn was head of Surgery. Dr. Walter E. Elfrink directed the Department of Dietetics; Dr. F. J. Stewart, the work in Skin and Venereal Diseases. Dr. H. W. Maltby was the No. 1 man in Orthopedics.

There were other well-known practitioners such as: George H. and Fannie Carpenter; Grace L. Smith; W. Burr Allen; H. R. Holmes; Edgar S. Comstock; J. C. Groenewoud; Jesse R. MacDougall; Bettie Hurd and Chester H. Morris (Clinical Demonstrations); Jessie O'Connor (Embryology) for some years Vice Chairman of the Board of Trustees and respected by her male colleagues as being sensible, reliable and levelheaded and a valiant promoter of "women's rights"; Andrew A. Gour (Corrective Gymnastics); Blanche Elfrink (Obstetrics) [8a]—all of them well known in local, state, and national professional circles.

In its *Announcement Catalogue* the College stated:

> The Chicago College of Osteopathy, in every one of its departments, will be of standard excellence. Its teaching power, both in its faculty and equipment, will be the highest attainable. Its post-graduate department will be of the kind-in its clinical, lecture and laboratory features-which the practicing osteopath has most ardently longed for and which, thus far, he has not been able to obtain anywhere at any price. . . .
> The Chicago College of Osteopathy will encourage investigation, and the progress that springs inevitably from it. These influences are all powerful in forming the professional character, the broadness, the intelligence, and the power of the future practitioner [9].

Fifty students reported for classes when the 1913 fall term opened, "the largest ever enrolled in a Chicago osteopathic college."

The Board of Trustees was committed to doing its utmost to attract students to the new college. It recommended that 1,000 letters be sent to osteopathic physicians in Iowa, Illinois, Wisconsin, Indiana, Michigan and Ohio, urging them to supply the College with the names of prospective students (primarily high school graduates). Later the College awarded scholarships to high school students who wrote winning essays in area-wide competition. The scholarships granted half-tuition rates to the recipient, provided that he remained at CCO for the full four-year program. A field recruiter was also authorized, with the agreement that he would receive a ten per cent commission for all students enrolled through his efforts.

As if to lend impetus to the work of the reorganized teaching institution, the Research Institute, which the College was so eager to welcome to the city, opened its doors in 1913. The osteopathic physicians of Chicago and the State of Illinois had been determined to have the research center located in the Midwest, preferably in Chicago.

To provide quarters for the center, the Chicago Osteopathic Association and the Illinois Osteopathic Association purchased a large private home at 122 South Ashland Boulevard for $20,000. The home and lot upon which it stood was valued at between $35,000 and $50,000; the property was available at the lower price only because apartment houses, factories and shops were extending into the area so as to "render it undesirable a residence for people of means [10]."

The huge stone mansion stood on a lot 50 feet wide and 145 feet deep. It had been built by General Fitzsimmons, a well-known Chicago engineer and civic leader, and had 11 rooms on the first and second floors. There was also a basement and attic. The home was illuminated by both gas and electricity and had a ventilating system which was a rarity at the time. At the rear of the lot was a 25' × 50' brick building which its buyers said would "make splendid quarters for the animal experimental department [11]."

The building, purchased by the two osteopathic organizations, was presented to the Research Institute as a gift to help celebrate the 85th birthday of Dr. Andrew Taylor Still, founder of osteopathy. It was, fittingly, named "The A. T. Still Research Institute," and not long after the original purchase, the Institute purchased an additional facility—a four-unit apartment building which adjoined the Fitzsimmons mansion. This structure provided the Institute with three additional floors and basement. It had been renting for $3,000 a month.

The Chicago-based A. T. Still Research Institute began its work under the direction of Dr. Wilborn J. Deason, a graduate of the American School of Osteopathy in Kirksville. Deason, a nose, ear and throat specialist, had directed research at ASO from 1911 to 1912, and he became totally dedicated to this branch of osteopathic activity. One of his students at ASO wrote later that "The elimination of all possible sources of error seemed to be a religion with him [12]." He became well known for his textbook, *Physiology: General and Osteopathic,* a work which the *Journal of the AOA* characterized as "readable practical, scientific, and above all else, osteopathic [13]." It was published in Kirksville.

[As to his extra-curricular activities, Dr. Deason is remembered by his colleagues as a big game hunter, with the Atlas Club members sharing the kills from his hunting expeditions in Canada.]

The A. T. Still Research Institute became closely allied with the work of the Chicago College of Osteopathy. It was staffed primarily by faculty members from CCO and these included Drs. Carl P. McConnell, Fred Bischoff, Blanche Elfrink, E. R. Proctor, E. S. Comstock, A. A. Gour, Grace L.

Smith, Frank Farmer, and Harry L. Collins. Dr. Collins held both D.O. and M.D. degrees and specialized in surgery. [He joined the staff of the college in 1920 and was Chairman of the Board of Trustees in 1929 when the institution was merged with the Osteopathic Foundation of Colorado. His title then was changed to that of President of the College. When the merger was dissolved in 1936–1937, Dr. Collins again became Chairman of the Board.]

Only a year after the founding of the Institute, Dr. McConnell was appointed Dean of the Institute's post-graduate department [14]. Dr. Deason, the Director, became closely associated with CCO during the Institute's regrettably short career in Chicago.

Early in 1914, Dr. Louisa Burns, brilliant research worker from the Pacific College of Osteopathy, joined the Still Research Institute and, later in the year, Dr. C. M. Turner Hulett of Cleveland joined the Institute staff as "Manager". His functions were largely to raise endowment funds among the laity [15]. This permitted Dr. Deason to devote more of his time to his laboratory and research work.

The Chicago College of Osteopathy graduated its first class in June, 1914, awarding diplomas to 27 seniors. Eight of them had completed the four-year program and were thus qualified to practice surgery. The *Journal of the American Osteopathic Association* was quick to praise the policies of the new school. Wrote one of its editors:

> One commendable feature about this school is that it will not permit any of the members of its faculty to run outside classes for remuneration as it demands that the members of the faculty give the students in their class room work the best instruction which they have to impart. While the college regrets to give up Dr. McConnell as its President, due to his association with the Research Institute work, he still retains his position as the head of the Department of Osteopathic Theory and Practice, and hence the student body will not lose his valuable instructions.
>
> The Secretary announces that the prospects for the coming session are exceptionally bright and as the college is run on an absolutely professional basis without the possibility of any spirit of commercialism, it earnestly asks the support of the profession. Its aim is to become the Johns Hopkins of osteopathy [16].

Although students were enrolling in encouraging volume [17], the administration was forced to apply certain disciplinary measures to check the aggressiveness of some of the young learners. A few upper classmen became so eager to enjoy the emoluments that accompanied successful osteopathic medical practice that they collected fees from patients even before they had received their diplomas. The trustees put a stop to this by requiring each student to sign a pact when he matriculated, agreeing not to practice for compensation before he had graduated and passed the State Board examinations. Each student was asked to sign the following pledge:

I, _____, hereby agree that while I am a student in the Chicago College of Osteopathy, I will not care for nor will I treat patients, neither will I make professional calls, until I have been duly graduated by the Chicago College of Osteopathy and have been licensed by the examining board of the State in which I intend to practice, except under the supervision of the Clinical Staff of the Chicago College of Osteopathy, and

I further agree not to attend any other school or college while I am a student in the Chicago College of Osteopathy, except by permission of the Board of Trustees of the said Chicago College of Osteopathy, and

I further agree to comply with all the Rules and Regulations of the Chicago College of Osteopathy while I am a student therein [18].

The Board of Trustees also found it prudent to expel a few students who had been guilty of violating regulations. One was dismissed because of "indifferent work, copying examination and non-attendance of classes," while another was charged with "appropriating property not belonging to himself [19]."

Of far greater significance than the occasional misdemeanors of CCO students, however, was the formation of the Chicago Women's Osteopathic Club by women osteopathic physicians and their friends "to work along the lines of social hygiene, child hygiene, and sanitation." The Club intended to work closely with the Women's Bureau of Public Health Education of the AOA and the Federated Women's Clubs.

Dr. J. Furman Smith was named president; Dr. Agnes V. Landes, first vice president; Dr. Blanche M. Elfrink, second vice president; Dr. Nettie M. Hurd, recording secretary; Dr. Jessie A. Wakeham, corresponding secretary; and Dr. Grace L. Smith, treasurer [20]. Several of the officers were CCO faculty members.

A matter of great satisfaction was recorded by the College in 1916 when the State of New York, one of the most desirable areas for an osteopathic physician to practice in at that time, designated CCO as an institution whose graduates would be admitted to the examination for license to practice in that state.

New York State had always demanded the highest educational standards for its osteopathic practitioners. Many schools were unable to comply with the state's strict teaching requirements. Even the Chicago College expressed some concern when, early in the year, the Board of Regents of the State of New York announced that, in addition to having completed a high school education, all matriculants must have completed one year of college.

The new New York State requirement was not looked upon favorably by the entire CCO Board of Trustees. Many of its members felt that the College would be pinched financially if it offered a year of college work before accepting candidates for its four-year program. They also felt that the school would suffer a decrease in the number of students applying for admission and that the entire plan would result in a reduction in the number of osteopathic physicians at a time when they were badly needed by the public [21]. Nevertheless, the CCO trustees, after long discussion, agreed to accept the additional requirements demanded by the State of New York and also to add to the school's curriculum the subjects of ophthalmology, ear, nose and throat, roentgenology, and anaesthesia.

The resultant approval of CCO by New York's state Board of Regents was greeted with great satisfaction by the College, which noted:

> This is a distinct recognition of which both the College and the profession may be proud. Not all medical colleges, by any means, are recognized by the New York Board of Regents. It is considered the highest educational board in this country and its recognition of this college at once places our educational system on a basis which cannot be gainsaid or spoken of contemptuously [22].

Contrary to the fears of some of the trustees, the raising of entrance requirements and the adoption of a mandatory four-year program did not lessen the number of students seeking to enroll in the College, but actually *increased* the number of inquiries. The Board's secretary, Dr. Edgar S. Comstock, reported to *The Osteopathic Physician:*

> Even with going on an absolute four-year basis and an entrance requirement of a four-year high school diploma, there was a very substantial increase of matriculants over last year, the increase of students being about 30 percent over last year. During the past year the college has absolutely qualified with the requirements of the New York State Board of Regents and the college was registered in New York, giving the college the highest standard of any osteopathic college [23, 24].

The exhilarating effect of New York State's accreditation of CCO was also reported by Dr. W. Burr Allen, Dean of the Faculty, who wrote *The Osteopathic Physician:*

> It is the aim of the Chicago College of Osteopathy to prepare its graduates so that they are scientific men and women who are able to correlate every new development in science with the principles and the application of osteopathy. It cannot be expected that they will apply these

principles, under the newer conditions, as they are applied by the earlier graduates [25]. Those who say the newer graduates have not learned osteopathy are not abreast of the times. They are still living in the nineteenth century.

The students who have been inclined to go to the medical college after taking the osteopathic course or who have spent a few years in practice have not done so because their therapeutics were weak, but because their knowledge of diagnosis or surgery was weak. The Chicago College of Osteopathy aims to stop this once and for all. The graduate is expected to be both a physical and laboratory diagnostician, with no apologies to make to any physician of any school that he may meet in the field of practice.

\*\*\*\*\*\*\*\*\*\*

The regents of the University of New York have made an unprejudiced examination of the Chicago College of Osteopathy and have declared it worthy to be registered in New York state. That means that every student in the college has at least an accredited high school diploma or a full equivalent and will graduate with a four-year diploma in osteopathy. The New York law requires seven months in each year. The Chicago College of Osteopathy gives nine months.

Now we appeal to all osteopathic physicians in the field to help us carry out this ideal program. Send us student with proper preliminary education and who have the osteopathic ideal and who want to be physicians in every sense of the word. Do not allow them to enter an inferior institution and lose time and proper training. We cannot thereafter accept full credits from any college not registered with the New York board of regents.

Dr. Allen carefully explained CCO's policy of accrediting transfer students. He wrote:

Those who have had one year's work in such an institution [one considered inferior] will be given no credit. Those having done two years work will receive one year's credit. Three years only two years' credit; four years, three years' credit. Let the educational institutions stand on their merits and receive support accordingly. The profession of Chicago, which is made up of men and women of ability from all the osteopathic colleges, are now behind the Chicago College of Osteopathy. They know what the osteopathic institutions are and what they should be. If the profession as a whole will stand with them they will make the Chicago College of Osteopathy come up to the dreams of all who look for higher educational standards. No doubt the time is now at hand when all the osteopathic colleges will be rated as first class educational institutions. In fact, it must be so, but while the Chicago College of Osteopathy is blazing the way it looks for the cooperation from the profession [26].

The entry of the United States into World War I forced the nation's schools to re-evaluate their structure and programs. CCO was no exception.

[ 55 ]

Its leaders spoke out strongly to support what they believed the College must do, and one of its prominent faculty members, Dr. Ernest R. Proctor, unhappy over some of the school's policies, even resigned. Dr. Proctor had served three terms as President of the CCO Board of Trustees (1914–1917), was disappointed in what he felt to be serious shortcomings of CCO and thought it best to withdraw from the College in 1917. He wrote detailed explanations of his action to various osteopathic publications, and perhaps the one which appeared in the *Journal of the AOA* for June, 1917, summed up his feelings as well as any. He wrote:

It seems best at this time to make a statement to the profession so that my principal reasons for resigning from the Chicago College of Osteopathy as official and instructor may be known.

When I first came to Chicago, I took an interest in the school here and began to work to bring about a more friendly feeling among the profession. After several years of patient work, we were fairly well united, and that seemed the proper time to reorganize the school under the control of the profession [1913]. The college buildings and equipment, also the hospital and equipment, were owned and controlled by individuals. An inventory was made of the equipment and value of the property (which was far in excess) and the rental based upon that. This rental was later reduced, but still took practically the entire income except what had to be spent for running expenses and new equipment which was moderate. There seemed no chance to develop the school under this plan. The work was wearing, not only upon myself but upon others, without accomplishing anything in the way of an ideal osteopathic center as long as individuals received and controlled the income.

The osteopathic profession must get business men interested so as to have their business experience and financial support. Then back of this an endowment. It is time for the A.O.A. to start a move to endow one or two schools. I am not afraid of osteopathy; it will live in some form the same as religion. But we must endow schools if we wish the scientific teaching of osteopathy to take its proper place among the healing arts. There are plenty of men and women who would be glad to give a goodly portion of their time to such colleges.

The United States is at war and a war that will likely last for several years, which means that our young men must go and fight instead of studying their chosen profession. Can our schools live? Not unless the A.O.A. and the profession get behind some well thought-out move, with the cooperation of their patients and their patients' friends.

We need business men, money and better cooperation with less thought of personal praise and individual gain. The call to the front to fight for the Science of Osteopathy is to everyone in the profession, and it came years ago from our beloved founder, Dr. A. T. Still, and it is ever before us. Awake and join the regulars and be a fighter for the just cause of osteopathy in the front ranks [27, 28].

Dr. George H. Carpenter, who in 1917 began a ten-year tenure as CCO president, believed that "The greatest stimulus is having the regular practitioner go to the school and relate his experiences [29]." Dr. H. H. Fryette, strongly opposing a suggestion that the number of osteopathic colleges be reduced, said: "I am opposed to cutting down our good schools. It is better to keep the schools separate and get new business. We have not enough osteopathic schools in the country; Chicago can support two schools. The more schools and the better schools we have the easier it will be for the good schools we now have [30]."

Dr. Carl P. McConnell said:

> Mutual cooperation is demanded. We should discuss the subject of teaching osteopathy. Perhaps our schools are not teaching osteopathy as they should. What have the schools to do relative to teaching osteopathy? Is it advisable to have a declaration of principles? [31].

Dr. Edgar Comstock declared that the colleges must have the endorsement of the profession at large, that they must be supported with endowments and divorced completely from any profit motive. He proposed a plan for dividing the United States into eight districts with an endowed college in each, a plan he believed would result in greater rapport between the colleges and the profession. Dr. Frank Farmer urged more uniformity in the teaching of osteopathic principles in the colleges.

In the meantime, the war was having its effect upon the operations of CCO. Shortly after the United States entered the conflict, committees from the Chicago Osteopathic Association and the Illinois Osteopathic Association, along with members of the CCO faculty and student body, organized the Illinois Osteopathic Unit. It was an admirable attempt to band the osteopathic physicians of the state into a single unit and offer the unit to the nation or state to serve "in time of war or other public calamity [32]." Its organizers planned also to form an active field unit and offer its services to the American Red Cross. Military drill was begun on the campus with classes scheduled on Tuesday and Friday nights from 6:45 to 9 o'clock in military drill and first aid. Physicians, students, nurses—all were invited to join the wartime program.

Realizing the increased demand for osteopathic physicians in a wartime economy, the Chicago Osteopathic Association launched a drive for funds and pledged $15,000 to help endow an osteopathic hospital. The goal was $250,000, and served as an early example of the fund-raising drives to come in later years as the College sought to expand and extend its work in the community [33].

Other events taking place as the College went on a wartime footing were the appointment of Myron W. Bowen as Business Manager and Dr. L. C. Hanavan as Superintendent of the College's affiliated Chicago Osteopathic Hospital [34]. Some fifty faculty and staff members signed up to attend lectures on psychology and pedagogy given by Dr. George D. Bivin of the University of Chicago [35]. In the spring forty seniors received their D.O. diplomas at the school's commencement exercises.

These were interesting events, some of them highly significant, but they were merely a prelude to the important developments that were to come in 1918 as the nation geared itself to a wartime footing and the Chicago College of Osteopathy set a course that would permanently establish its prestige and influence.

## REFERENCES

1. *Journal AOA,* April, 1913, p. 446. (Vol. 12, No. 8).
2. From the *Minutes of the Board of Trustees* Meeting for March 8, 1913.
3. *Ibid.*
4. From the Report of the Committee on Education at the AOA Convention in Kirksville, August, 1914. Published in the *Journal AOA,* August, 1913 (a year earlier), p. 747. (Vol. 12, No. 12)
5. *The Osteopathic Physician,* April, 1913, p. 1. (Vol. 23, No. 4)
6. *The Osteopathic Physician,* May, 1913, p. 4. (Vol. 23, No. 5)
7. He no doubt had in mind the dissension among the various osteopathic groups. He felt, and rightly so, that CCO would be a great unifying force.
8. *The Osteopathic Physician,* April, 1913, p. 2. (Vol. 23, No. 4)
8a. Dr. Grace E. Clunis, CCOM '29, recalls Drs. Fannie Carpenter and Blanche Elfrink as outstanding osteopathic physicians and teachers. "Dr. Fannie," she says, "was a 'beautiful woman' in every respect and an excellent osteopathic practitioner who stressed the value of manipulation. 'Dr. Blanche' was an obstetrician whose word in the delivery room was absolute law. No interne dared make a move until she felt all preparations were in order. She was meticulous in every phase of her work." Other outstanding women included Myrtle Fryette, wife of Dr. Harrison Fryette, and Mrs. Harry Riley, wife of the Board chairman during the days of the merger with the Colorado Osteopathic Foundation. Mrs. Riley, Dr. Clunis recalls, personally attended to many of the day-to-day operating details of the Hospital, making sure that room decor and facilities were attractive and appealing.
9. *1913–1914 CCO Catalogue.*
10. *Journal AOA,* March, 1913, p. 407 (Vol. 12, No. 7)
11. *Ibid.,* May, 1913, p. 557. (Vol. 12, No. 9)
12. *Journal AOA,* May, 1913, p. 557. (Vol. 12, No. 9)
13. *Ibid.,* September, 1913, p. 47. (Vol. 13, No. 1)
14. Dr. O'Connell became so active in the work of the Institute that he resigned from his position as President of CCO in 1914. He was succeeded by Ernest R. Proctor, Dean of the Faculty, who, in explaining the reasons for accepting Dr. McConnell's resignation, wrote that "it was due to the belief that he would be of greater service to the profession as Dean of the P.G. Department than as head of the Chicago College of Osteopathy, and

it is for the reason that the Chicago College wishes to do whatever seems to be for the best interests of the profession as a whole that we consented to spare Dr. McConnell as the head of our College." (*Journal AOA,* March, 1914, pp. 405–406; Vol. 13, No. 7). Dr. Proctor was succeeded as Dean of the Faculty by Dr. W. Burr Allen.

15. The Research Institute hoped to obtain substantial funds from the osteopathic profession at large, and the AOA suggested that its members contribute at least $1.00 a month to help carry on the Institute's work.

16. *Journal AOA,* July, 1914, p. 672. (Vol. 13, No. 11)

17. In the fall of 1914 there were 1,475 student enrolled in the seven accredited U.S. osteopathic colleges. One had a total of 675 students, another, 375, two with more than 100, and three with 75 each. (*Journal AOA,* December, 1914, p. 192 (Vol. 14, No. 4).

18. From the Minutes of the Board of Trustees Meeting, Aug. 19, 1914.

19. From the Minutes of the Board of Trustees Meeting, Nov. 7, 1914. The trustees brooked no nonsense from their own members, either. At their meeting on April 14, 1914, they decreed that the Board of Directors would start meetings promptly at 6:30 p.m. at a place designated by the President and "each member will see to it that he or she has had dinner before that time and is ready for the business meeting at the time specified."

20. *The Osteopathic Physician,* October, 1914, p. 12. (Vol. 26, No. 4)

21. Minutes of Meeting of CCO Board of Trustees, Feb. 8, 1916.

22. *Journal AOA*, November, 1915, p. 155. (Vol. 15, No. 3). New York not only prescribed the completion of a one-year college program for applicants to osteopathic colleges, but insisted that only a four-year course in osteopathic colleges would be acceptable. This latter requirement presented no problem for CCO, since the College had been offering four-year programs since 1914. As late as 1922, only two schools had been approved by New York State: Chicago and Philadelphia.

23. *The Osteopathic Physician,* March, 1916, p. 9. (Vol. 29, No. 3)

24. The day-to-day operations of the school were from time to time accented with strictly non-curricular annoyances. Dean Allen reported to the trustees that some of the bones making up the skeleton used in the College had disappeared, and Dr. J. B. Littlejohn was assigned to seek a much-needed replacement. The Board also found it necessary to post a notice "in a conspicuous place in the college building, forbidding the playing of cards, dice, and like games in the college building." (From the Minutes of the Meeting of the Board of Trustees, Jan. 22 and April 1, 1916).

25. He was no doubt referring to the increasing use of drugs by the osteopathic profession in order to keep its practitioners on an equal footing with the M.D.'s by using the most modern means available for treating man's illnesses.

26. *The Osteopathic Physician,* February, 1916, p. 12. (Vol. 29, No. 2).

27. *Journal AOA,* June, 1917, pp. 1224–1225. (Vol. 16, No. 10). Although Dr. Proctor resigned from CCO at this time, he later returned to the school and served on its faculty until 1932. He organized the CCO Children's Clinic in 1918, established a student loan fund, and took charge of the AOA Children's Clinic at the Chicago Osteopathic Hospital in 1921. He died in 1942 after many years of outstanding service to the College and the Community.

28. Minutes of meetings held by the Board of Trustees from Feb. 24, 1917, to March 6, 1920, have apparently been lost, and news of activities at CCO during these years must be sought in the osteopathic publications issued during this interval.

29. *Journal AOA,* September, 1917, pp. 48–49. (Vol. 17, No. 1)

30. *Ibid.,* p. 49.

31. *Journal AOA,* September, 1917, p. 49. (Vol. 17, No. 1)

32. *The Osteopathic Physician,* June, 1917, pp. 6–7. (Vol. 21, No. 6).

33. *Ibid.,* February, 1917, p. 25. (Vol. 31, No. 2)

34. *Ibid.*, July, 1917, p. 27–30. (Vol. 32, No. 1). Bowen was a graduate of the University of Wisconsin and an expert on business management. Dr. Hanavan, COH's first superintendent, was called "one of the best loved men of the profession." He was graduated from the Littlejohn College in 1917, and after a year of post-graduate work in obstetrics and surgery, joined the CCO staff. He remained at CCO until his untimely death of a coronary thrombosis in 1938. He delivered nearly 2,000 babies during his years as head of the hospital's obstetrical services. He was a native of Stratford, Ontario, Canada.
35. *Ibid.*

# Department of State.

## JAMES A. ROSE, Secretary of State.

---

**To All to Whom These Presents Shall Come—Greeting:**

*WHEREAS, a* **CERTIFICATE,** *duly signed and acknowledged, having been filed in the office*
*of the Secretary of State on the* ___21st___ *day of* ___May___ *A. D. 1900*

*for the organization of the*

*The American College of Osteopathic Medicine and Surgery.*

*under and in accordance with the provisions of* "*AN ACT CONCERNING CORPORATIONS,*"
*approved April 18, 1872, and in force July 1, 1872, a copy of which certificate is hereto attached.*

*Now Therefore, I, JAMES A. ROSE, Secretary of State of the State of Illinois, by virtue of*
*the powers and duties vested in me by law, do hereby certify that the said*

*The American College of Osteopathic Medicine and Surgery.*

*is a legally organized Corporation under the laws of this State.*

*In Testimony Whereof, I hereto set my hand and cause to be*
*affixed the Great Seal of State.*

*Done at the City of Springfield, this* ___21st___
*day of* ___May___ *in the year of our*
*Lord one thousand ~~eight hundred and ninety~~ 900*
*and of the independence of the United States the one hun-*
*dred and* ___24th___

Seal

*James A. Rose*
Secretary of State.

(006)

Original charter for the American College of Osteopathic Medicine and Surgery (predecessor of CCOM),
was dated May 21, 1900. It authorized the College to operate "not for profit" and "to discover, formulate and teach the improved methods of surgery, obstetrics and treatment of disease in general so as to
systematize and place on a scientific basis the osteopathic methods of healing and treating disease. . . ."

**STATE OF ILLINOIS,** } SS.

_____COOK_____ County,

To JAMES A. ROSE, Secretary of State:

We, the undersigned, *J. Martin Littlejohn, James B. Littlejohn and Edith M. Williams*

citizens of the United States, propose to form a corporation under an Act of the General Assembly of the State of Illinois, entitled "An Act concerning Corporations," approved April 18, 1872, and all acts amendatory thereof; and for the purpose of such organization we hereby state as follows, to-wit:

1. The name of such corporation is _____

THE AMERICAN COLLEGE OF OSTEOPATHIC MEDICINE AND SURGERY.

3. The management of the aforesaid COLLEGE shall be vested in a Board of FOUR Directors, who are to be elected ANNUALLY

4. The following persons are hereby selected as the Directors to control and manage said Corporation for the first year of its corporate existence, viz:

*J. Martin Littlejohn, James B. Littlejohn, David Littlejohn and Elizabeth W. Littlejohn*

5. The location is in CHICAGO in the County of COOK State of Illinois.

SIGNED:

*J. Martin Littlejohn*
*James B. Littlejohn*
*Edith M. Williams*

Final page of the 1900 charter showing the signatures of the three individuals who applied for the important document: J. Martin Littlejohn, James B. Littlejohn, and Edith M. Williams (Mrs. James B. Littlejohn). David Littlejohn was named a Director, along with the three charter applicants. The document empowered the College to confer degrees and diplomas.

The American College of Osteopathic Medicine and Surgery remained in its original quarters at 405 West Washington Street, Chicago, for only one year. In 1901 it was located in this building at 334 West Monroe Street. The three-story structure, with basement, accommodated 24 students during the 1901–1902 term, and Dr. J. M. Littlejohn reported that the institution was enjoying "a pleasant prosperity."

Dr. James B. Littlejohn, second of the three brothers who founded the College. He was a skilled surgeon and an outstanding teacher and administrator.

Dr. David Littlejohn, youngest of the founding brothers. He remained with the College only a few years, later became a nationally-known public health administrator.

Littlejohn Sanitarium. Although founded and operated as a private institution, its facilities were available to the College for teaching and observation purposes. It was located in the "Windsor Park" area at 76th Street and Saginaw Avenue, Chicago.

This was the Littlejohn Hospital in 1906. It was located at 1408 West Monroe Street, not far from the College and was a vital part of the College's teaching program.

The Littlejohn College Building as it appeared in 1900 in the 1400 block on West Monroe Street. The College occupied the building until moving to Chicago's south side in 1918.

*Dr. J. Martin Littlejohn, left, seated next to Andrew Taylor Still, the founder of osteopathy, in Kirksville, Missouri, around 1900. Dr. Littlejohn was then on the staff of the American School of Osteopathy which Dr. Still established in Kirksville in 1892. Photo belonged to the private collection of Dr. Arthur H. Paul, Bridgeport, Conn.*

*This 1904 advertisement indicated that the College was now located at 495 West Monroe Street, its third location since its founding in 1900. The College took great pride in being able to offer students the resources of the huge Cook County Hospital, a facility few other osteopathic medical schools could match.*

Dr. W. John Deason, Director of the short-lived A. T. Still Research Institute in Chicago. He was a CCO faculty member, an eye, ear and throat specialist, and a dedicated researcher.

Dr. Fred Bischoff, an outstanding figure during CCO's early years. He spent his entire professional career with the College, served many years as either Treasurer or Secretary of the Board.

Dr. Harrison H. Fryette, one of the early nationally prominent CCO faculty members. His studies on the construction and movements of the human spine were major contributions to osteopathic medicine.

Dr. Edgar S. Comstock was Secretary of CCO for more than a decade (1913–1924) and frequently served as the College's spokesman. He was Dean during 1918–1919.

*The A. T. Still Research Institute, 122 South Ashland Avenue, was a gift from the Chicago and Illinois osteopathic associations. The Institute opened in 1913 but was forced to close in 1918 because of financial woes. The apartment building shown here was purchased to augment the original building, cost only $20,000.*

*CCO building in 1913. Although the Littlejohn College and Hospital became known as the Chicago College of Osteopathy in 1913, the College continued to use the Littlejohn buildings until 1918.*

*Original building of the Chicago-based A. T. Still Research Institute. It had been the home of a prominent Chicago citizen, but was offered for sale because of industrial intrusion into the area.*

Older CCO graduates will remember the intersection of Lake Park Avenue and 55th Street—before the neighborhood became a center for urban development and change. Many well-known city sites disappeared as urban renewal programs gained momentum and brought into existence new buildings. shopping centers and malls.

Dr. Joseph H. Sullivan was one of the first to practice osteopathic medicine in Chicago. He was a close friend of CCO (and lecturer) for many years, and a relentless fighter for the recognition of osteopathic medicine.

Dr. Blanche Mayes Elfrink, wife of Dr. Walter E. Elfrink of the CCO faculty, was for many years a member of CCO's Department of Gynecology and Obstetrics. She was one of the city's best-known obstetricians.

# 5

# THE MOVE TO HYDE PARK
## (1918)

ALTHOUGH shrinking enrollments brought about by manpower demands of World War I created serious survival problems for most of the osteopathic colleges, the Chicago College of Osteopathy, foreseeing increased demands upon its facilities because of wartime needs, accepted the hour as a propitious one for acting boldly and dramatically. The physical facilities of the school were becoming increasingly inadequate and the College trustees and administrators believed that the time had come to move so strikingly as to leave no doubt in the public's mind that the profession of osteopathic medicine was truly coming of age.

The trustees and school's leaders were as one in believing that a larger school and hospital would draw more of the area's osteopathic physicians into the CCO orbit by providing them with attractive accommodations. Then, too, such facilities would do much to raise the standing of the profession in the public's esteem and would, in the long run, prove more economical of operation than the crowded quarters on Monroe Street.

Undaunted by the ferocity of a savage influenza epidemic that was taking a fearsome toll in human life not only in Chicago but across the entire nation, the Chicago College of Osteopathy transferred its base of operations from Monroe Street to an attractive building on Ellis Avenue between 52nd and 53d Streets on Chicago's south side [1]. The four-story structure was dignified and decorous, and believed to be capable of meeting the needs of both the college and the hospital. On the first floor of the main section, which housed the College, were located osteopathic treating rooms and business offices; on the second were lecture rooms, an eye, ear, nose and throat operating room, X-ray laboratory and diagnosing room; on the third floor were additional lecture rooms and laboratories. The fourth floor was devoted to laboratory equipment.

The hospital section, although limited by today's standards, was complete and adaptable. The operating room could be converted into an amphitheater where clinics in surgical, gynecological and obstetrical work were held. On the first floor were offices, operating room and wards; the second was devoted to private rooms.

The move to Hyde Park was advantageous for a number of reasons. Its location near the University of Chicago permitted CCO students to attend courses at the University which were not offered at CCO. Outstanding members of the U. of C. faculty ("some of the best scientific men in the country") were available to teach classes at the Chicago College. The school was located near public transportation which made access to the campus much easier and convenient. This was especially so for south side patients who accounted for 40% of the clinic's clientele [2].

The half-block of property on which the building stood had a frontage of 461 feet, and a depth of 158 feet. A 261-foot section of the property was used as "an outdoor gymnasium" and provided room for additional building purposes when the need arose. Total cost of the property was $130,000, but CCO trustees considered this a bargain, for the ground alone was valued at more than $60,000 and the cost of duplicating the building was estimated at between $200,000 and $225,000. Amortization was to be distributed over a seven-year period.

The College had optimistic plans for paying off the debt. It established the sum of $200,000 as the amount necessary to "swing the deal" and looked to future endowment funds as the principal means for removing the indebtedness. Dr. Comstock, CCO secretary, announced that a $100,000 endowment was already in hand which would provide an income of $5,000 a year. He and the College had high hopes that enough osteopathic physicians—at least 200—would agree to invest $1,000 in bonds, paying for them either in a lump sum or in fixed installments.

Bonds were issued in denominations of $1,000, $500 and $100 and offered as attractive investment opportunities. The $1,000 bonds could be purchased either in their entirety or in ten yearly payments of $100 each; $500 bonds were payable either as lump sums or in five yearly payments of $100 each; $100 bonds were payable in cash.

The pledges by osteopaths would not be considered as gifts but as loans bearing 5% interest. M. W. Bowen, the business manager, explained that "The corporation is not asking for one cent from the osteopaths themselves. All they desire is the use of their savings for a period of ten years, giving in return five per cent on their money and an institution of which they can well afford to be proud [3]."

Chicago alone, it was pointed out, had 150 practicing osteopaths, and the State of Illinois some 300. In the neighboring states there were 60 in Wisconsin, 105 in Michigan, and 75 in Indiana, all of whom would be directly benefited by the new osteopathic center and who should be willing to pledge financial support. Soon Dr. Comstock was able to announce with great pride that over $30,000 had been subscribed and that first and second mortgage payments of $5,000 each had been made.

The College appealed to the public at large for help, too. It offered membership certificates in denominations of $10 and $25, the smaller one entitling its purchaser to a 10 percent reduction on all hospital bills for a period of five years from date of issue, and the larger certificate the same reduction to all members of the buyer's immediate family.

Having acquired a new building early in 1918, both the College and the Hospital prepared for September openings. The Chicago Osteopathic Hospital was incorporated on February 5 and a charter issued by the Illinois Secretary of State. In the fall, some three hundred guests attended the hospital's formal opening under the auspices of the Women's Board [4]. College and hospital officals greeted the visitors as they were guided through the building with its 50-bed capacity and the facilities for a total enrollment of 200 students and nurses.

At the annual meeting of the Corporation in March, Dr. George H. Carpenter was elected President of the College; Dr. James B. Littlejohn, Vice President; Edgar S. Comstock, Secretary (he was also Dean of the College); and Fred Bischoff, Treasurer. The Board of Trustees increased its membership from seven to eleven, and organized itself into three working committees: (1) Finance; (2) Educational matters; and (3) Hospital.

The trustees also determined the qualifications of Corporation members, ruling that active members were those "actively engaged in the work of the college." Those who contributed $500 to the College would be considered "Life Members"; other interested individuals could become "Associate Members" of the Corporation by paying $100 to the College. Active members had the right to vote, while associate members did not.

The opening of the expanded Chicago College of Osteopathy and its affiliated Chicago Osteopathic Hospital (COH) came as exhilarating news to the entire osteopathic profession. But there was bad news along with the good. The A. T. Still Research Institute was in serious financial trouble and would soon suspend its operations in the building on South Ashland Boulevard. The death of the Institute's business manager, Dr. C. M. T. Hulett in January, and the resignation of Dr. Frank Farmer as Chairman of the Institute's Board of Trustees, seemed to signal increasing misfortunes for the research center that had begun so hopefully five years earlier and whose nearby presence was welcomed so warmly by the Chicago College of Osteopathy.

At a meeting in March, the Institute's Administrative Council sharply reduced expenses for the year by readjusting contracts and transferring the research work to the Pacific branch of the Institute at Los Angles where Dr. Louisa Burns carried on her outstanding work for many years.

The Institute had suffered financial woes from the very outset. Although a fund-raising drive in 1913 resulted in pledges amounting to $90,952 for endowment, only $41,829 was ever paid into the fund. This amount yielded an income far below that needed for carrying on the projects of the Institute. A drive for financial help from the public also failed to produce satisfactory results. Many of the pledge redemptions were slow in being fulfilled or were ignored altogether.

With the outcome clearly discernible, the administrators and trustees agreed that to continue operations in the face of mounting deficits would be foolhardy and acted to dispose of the property as best they could. The Chicago property was sold at a $4,000 profit and all salaried workers, with the exception of Dr. Burns and a bookkeeper, were dismissed.

While the Research Institute seldom achieved the results which had been anticipated, it was not difficult to rationalize and present reasons why the death of the research center was inevitable. Those close to the Institute admitted privately that the "property was not at all well adapted to research purposes." Further, that the heavy-stone construction "with handsome dark hallways, staircases, ponderous chimneypieces, dingy parlors, dining rooms, bed chambers and bathrooms" represented "about the least adapted and least adaptable place on earth for research laboratories."

*The Osteopathic Physician* witnessed the Institute's demise with considerable satisfaction and was happy that the property had been sold at a profit. *The Osteopathic Physician* commented:

> We have only lost a little time and may have learned the lesson by experience, which is a good teacher. Let us start right next time. A satisfactory laboratory for research workers would be a small inexpensive building or a second story loft with good light, air, space enough for various laboratories, good ventilation to carry off poisonous gases, plenty of ground to keep the animals on and bury carcasses and used up material in, with no danger of being voted a nuisance by close neighbors, or stopped from burning offal or becoming subjected to search and seizure by the Society F.T.P.O.C. to A. Such quarters with heat and janitor service could easily be secured for from $1,200 to $2,400 a year in any suitable locality selected and even $600 per annum might do for a beginning as long as qualified workers were few.

We congratulate the research trustees on getting rid of their fancy house and grounds and upon being able to unload their investment at a profit of $4,000. It might have been a whole lot worse [5].

And with this obituary, the work of the A. T. Still Research Institute in Chicago had come to a disappointing end!

## REFERENCES

1. The four-story building was originally known as the "Home for Jewish Friendless and Working Girls." Its purchase by the Chicago College of Osteopathy was first considered at a Board of Trustees meeting on January 16, 1918. Its actual purchase (for $130,000) was authorized by the Trustees at a meeting on February 2, 1918.
2. The remaining 60 percent of the cases represented patients who had attended clinics throughout the city for help and, not obtaining relief, were hoping the Chicago Osteopathic Hospital would succeed where others had failed.
3. *Journal AOA,* April, 1918, pp. 462–463. (Vol. 17, No. 8).
4. *The Osteopathic Physician,* October 1918, p. 9 (Vol. 34, No. 4).
5. *The Osteopathic Physician,* April, 1919, pp. 2–3. (Vol. 35, No. 4).

# 6

# POST-WAR YEARS
# (1918–1920)

Less than a year after the College began its new career on Chicago's south side, it was evident that even the enlarged quarters were inadequate for the growing school and that expansion must be considered for its teaching and hospital facilities. Most obvious of all was the desperate need for a separate hospital building to accommodate the steadily-growing clientele. This meant, of course, the launching of aggressive fund-raising measures to provide the needed finances.

In January, 1919, Dr. George H. Carpenter, college president, and Dr. Edgar S. Comstock, secretary, signed a contract with the Ward Systems Company of New York and Chicago, authorizing that firm to launch a $50,000 fund-raising drive. Under the terms of the contract, Ward would assign two men to conduct the campaign which was scheduled to begin on January 27 and run for a period of not less than eight weeks. There was an option to extend the campaign for an additional ten weeks if the $50,000 goal was not reached during the original time period.

The College agreed to pay Ward Systems $350 a week for its services, and it was agreed that the total cost of the preliminary campaign would not exceed $4,000. A second period, if needed, would be limited to an expenditure of $9,500.

The College agreed to "furnish a necessary and adequate headquarters and banquet hall, with all necessary assistants, office furniture, including desks, typewriters, telephones, etc., banners, clock dials or cash registers, or other devices with proper electric attachments and connections, bulletin boards and services of painter, stationery, newspaper and other advertising, printing, postage, and such suppers and banquets as may be necessary."

In the meantime, the College went full throttle on its own. It ran full-page advertisements in osteopathic publications featuring a photograph of the

College and listing the names of 107 Chicago area osteopathic physicians who were supporting the school and hospital professionally and financially. The advertisements informed the readers that the Chicago College of Osteopathy had "the best possible foundation, a wonderful building which we are now using for both College and Hospital. We will erect another big building on the north side of this lot to be exclusively a Hospital, the present building to be entirely devoted to College purposes."

News bulletins from the College reported that "the Chicago College of Osteopathy is overflowing with students and the hospital is turning away patients because of its inability to furnish rooms." It should be noted that this situation came about after the College had occupied its Ellis Avenue building for only a short time, a building which had been depended on "to care for our needs for at least four or five years [1]."

To raise the needed revenue for expansion, the College Corporation authorized the issuance of $400,000 in bonds "for the purpose of taking up the mortgages on the present property and converting them into a first and redemption mortgage, securing the entire bond issue for remodeling the present building for college use only and for building and equipping an A. T. Still Memorial Amphitheatre for clinical purposes in surgical and anatomical demonstration for post-graduate courses, conventions, etc., and to build and equip a new hospital building as a necessary part of college equipment."

The College proudly pointed to its physical assets, affirming that its properties had been conservatively appraised at a value of $180,000 and that experts estimated the property to be worth at least from $225,000 to $250,000 at current market value. The College Corporation at this time had an equity of more than $70,000 in the property "as it stands" and the trustees reported that total assets of the school were approximately $230,000 "for which only $150,000 in bonds is being floated at the present time." The remaining $250,000 of the $400,000 goal "will be secured by the new hospital building and the new A. T. Still Memorial Amphitheatre when these buildings are erected."

The College hoped to be in a position to set aside $21,620 each year for "the purpose of improvement, equipment and retiring of the bonds." It was also anticipated that this amount would be doubled to some $42,000 a year when the new hospital was completed, so that in a fifteen-year period a total of $600,000 will have been collected for the purpose of retiring the bonds. As an added precaution, the trustees promised to set aside the money raised through bond purchases and to spend none of it until at least $150,000 had been subscribed.

Encouraging impetus was given to the fund-raising effort in April when J. Ogden Armour, wealthy meat packing magnate, made a $10,000 gift to the

Corporation. A few weeks later, a group of twenty individuals pledged to contribute $2,000 each and to pay off the pledges by April, 1920. A tag day netted more than $6,000 for the Chicago Osteopathic Hospital and in June the world-famous coloratura soprano, Mme. Galli-Curci, a staunch friend of osteopathic medicine, raised $8,000 for the College by giving a benefit concert in the Chicago Auditorium. On all fronts the drive for financial support was producing heartening results.

While the financial drives were off to a good start, some dissension developed in the College's administrative circle. On July 7, 1919, Dr. Edgar Comstock, the college's secretary, wrote a letter to Dr. George H. Carpenter, the college's president who was vacationing at Clear Lake, Iowa, notifying him of what had transpired at a meeting of the Board of Trustees. At this meeting, Dr. Comstock wrote, Dr. James B. Littlejohn, the vice president, had urged a number of reforms. They included the following:

1. Immediate raising of funds to provide separate buildings for the College and Hospital. The money would be raised either by bonds, stock, or subscription.
2. Appointment of a competent superintendent of the hospital with full authority for its operation.
3. Dismissal of student employees and replacing them with internes and helpers from the outside.
4. Reorganization of the College teaching staff under the supervision of a Dean who would be responsible for the entire educational section of the College and report directly to the College administrative committee and the Board of Trustees.
5. The organization of a private clinic "on the order of the Mayo clinic" in the College hospital, all revenues to accrue to the Hospital.

Dr. Comstock, who was serving as both Secretary and Dean, was not a little miffed at the suggestion that the College reorganize its teaching staff and appoint a Dean who would be responsible for the entire educational section of the College. He no doubt interpreted this as a reflection on his own handling of the position. Moreover, he felt that Dr. Littlejohn was looking for a man "especially prepared in educational matters, but not a member of the profession." He believed this to be a hint that he resign so as to permit the appointment of a new Dean. He recalled, too, that many of the suggestions made by Dr. Littlejohn had been offered in the past by various administrators, but that no action had been taken. He wrote spiritedly to Dr. Carpenter:

> It strikes me as rather peculiar that many of the things which I have recommended and worked for consistently during the entire year, and to which there has been little or no attention paid, are now practically em-

bodied entirely in the communication of Dr. Littlejohn of July 4 [2] and stated as an ultimatum that either they be adopted, or his resignation goes into effect. It would then appear on the minutes that they are all the suggestions of himself and no suggestions have been made in the past from the college department, relative to the same situations. The attitude of some members of the Board, towards the college and Dean has been such that we feel that conditions are getting somewhat unbearable, and therefore probably greater progress could be made without my presence in that Position.

You will probably recall that in the past I have several times kept out of the position that was awarded me so that someone else could hold that position, which would appear to better advantage of the institution, and also many times have I stepped into a breach which was left by the resignation of someone or the withdrawal of someone, to carry on the work until permanent arrangements could be made. Apparently this has received little or no appreciation from many on the Board and we feel we have been utilized something as a "George" to do any little job that comes along, and when the job is done, to receive the criticism for its not having been done better, and a kick in the shins instead of a pat on the back for having done the best we could under the circumstances existing.

I don't write this in a spirit of faultfinding or in a spirit of pique, but I cannot help but feel that there are some on the Board who would like me to be displaced by someone else for some reason or other.

I am sorry to bring this matter to your attention while you are away on your vacation, and I trust you will not allow them to worry you, as things must come out alright. I would like your advice in the matter because I do know that you appreciate the situation.

Most sincerely and fraternally yours,<br>Edgar S. Comstock

Happily, Dr. Comstock was later mollified, for he remained at his post as college secretary and continued his excellent work until ill health forced him to retire in the mid 1920's [3].

Keeping pace with the school's financial campaigns were noteworthy professional and academic events. Dr. W. J. Deason, former director of the A. T. Still Research Institute, organized a "second to none" ear, nose and throat clinic at the College, with much of its equipment being paid for by Dr. Deason personally. Drs. J. B. Littlejohn and Earl R. Hoskins, a pioneer in X-ray work, opened an osteopathic X-ray laboratory. Such a facility had been badly needed since the Research Institute shuttered its doors.

Dr. James A. Fraser, a member of the CCO Board of Trustees, made newspaper headlines in 1919 by restoring to health a 13-year-old girl, Lydia Gray, who for forty days had been in a coma caused by "sleeping sickness [4]." [Dr. Fraser was a graduate of ASO, practiced in Evanston, Ill., and had as one of his distinguished patients French Field Marshal Ferdinand Foch at one time.]

Aiding the return to normalcy after the hectic war days, the College took a number of steps to expedite the transition from war to peace. A special mid-year class was offered for war veterans so they could qualify for admittance as full-time students in the fall term [5]. Concurrently, the College announced a post-graduate course to be offered just prior to the opening of the national AOA Convention in Chicago in late summer.

To provide for an ever-increasing number of patients, the Chicago Osteopathic Hospital remodeled the third floor of its quarters in the main building to make available two surgical operating rooms and eleven additional private rooms for surgical cases.

Perhaps one of the most important events in the immediate post-war period was the appointment of the College's first full-time dean. The naming of Dr. Jerome Hall Raymond to succeed Dr. Edgar S. Comstock not only brought to fulfillment the fears which Dr. Comstock had expressed in his letter to Dr. Carpenter in July, but marked the first time that an individual from outside the osteopathic profession had been hired to serve as Dean.

The increasing enrollment at the College precluded any course other than having a full-time Dean. The time had come when the multiplying duties of the position required the services of a full-time executive. Dr. Raymond was highly qualified. He had received his Ph.D. degree from the University of Chicago, had been President of both the University of West Virginia and of the Toledo University and Medical School, and was well known as a teacher, lecturer, and educator. His tenure as Dean brought new vitality to the College, and under his leadership the institution made highly important contributions to osteopathic education and practice. Dr. Raymond introduced badly needed new educational theories and techniques to the College. Since it was normal for medical schools to require a second year of pre-medical studies prior to enrollment, Dr. Raymond established a Junior College on the CCO campus to provide these two years of pre-medical training.

### REFERENCES

1. *Journal AOA,* November, 1919, p. 110. (Vol. 19)
2. Evidently a letter written by Dr. J. B. Littlejohn and read to the Trustees at their meeting. As was indicated in an earlier footnote, many records of the Board meetings from February 24, 1917, to March 6, 1920, have disappeared and are therefore no longer available as source materials.
3. *The Osteopathic Physician* echoed the sentiments of the entire College when it said of Dr. Comstock: "He has sacrificed himself in every possible way to make the school a success,

and succeeded notably in bringing it through the war period in a highly satisfactory manner." (November, 1919, p. 30, Vol. 36, No. 5)

4. The young teen-ager, daughter of Mr. and Mrs. Herbert L. Gray of Evanston, had been treated by many physicians and specialists, none of whom succeeded in arousing the unconscious girl. Her malady had been brought about by Spanish influenza, and her case had puzzled the country's finest medical authorities, many of whom pronounced the case as hopeless. Less than two months after Dr. Fraser was called into the case, the girl was on her way to full recovery. (*The Osteopathic Physician,* May, 1919, pp. 1–2, Vol. 35, No. 5)

5. Forty-nine CCO students served in the U.S. armed forces during World War I, and the College happily announced that none of them were killed or even seriously wounded.

# 7

# GROWING PAINS: THE THIRD DECADE
## (1920–1930)

As THE Chicago College of Osteopathy entered its third decade, it had a student enrollment of 162 and a faculty that included some of the most distinguished osteopathic physicians, scientists and teachers in the country. For a sampling of the College's prestigious faculty at this time, consider the following:

Dr. James B. Littlejohn, one of the original founders, Chairman of the Department of Surgery, President of the Associated Colleges of Osteopathy, writer, lecturer, Vice President of CCO.

Dr. Carl P. McConnell, expert on the osteopathic lesion, President of the AOA (1904), President of the CCO Board of Trustees, editor of the *Journal AOA,* co-author (with Dr. Charles C. Teall) of a widely-used textbook on osteopathy *(The Practice of Osteopathy),* researcher, scientist, lecturer.

Dr. George H. Carpenter, heart specialist, President of CCO, Vice President of the Illinois Osteopathic Association, lecturer and teacher and for forty years a member of the faculty, seventeen as President of the CCO Board of Trustees, and one of the best known osteopathic physicians in the Chicago area.

Dr. Harrison H. Fryette, designer of the articulated spine, member of the AOA Board of Trustees, President of the AOA (1919–1920), chairman of the legislative committee of the AOA, recipient of the distinguished service award by the AOA, an expert on osteopathic technique and whose greatest contribution to osteopathy, according to many, was his understanding and teaching of the physiological movements of the spine.

Dr. Wilborn J. Deason, Director of the one-time Chicago-based A. T. Still Research Institute, Professor of Osteopathic Physiology, textbook author, researcher, Chairman of the Eye, Nose and Throat Department.

Dr. Samuel V. Robuck, Chairman of the Department of the Practice of

Osteopathy, Professor of Diagnosis, prolific writer of articles for professional publications, President of the AOA, master of osteopathic technique.

Dr. Earl R. Hoskins, pioneer X-ray scientist, Chairman of the Department of X-ray whose untimely death in 1934 deprived the profession of one of its foremost technicians.

Dr. Andrew A. Gour, Chairman of the Department of Corrective Gymnastics, specialist in spinal deformities, newspaper and magazine columnist, contributor to osteopathic journals, courageous fighter for osteopathy in its battle to win equal rights in the practice of medicine.

Drs. Blanche Elfrink and Jessie O'Connor of the Department of Obstetrics and Gynecology, two women osteopathic practitioners known throughout the Chicago area and beyond for their professional talents. To these should be added the names of Dr. Myrtle Fryette, wife of Dr. H. H. Fryette; Dr. Edith Littlejohn, wife of Dr. James B. Littlejohn; Drs. Nettie M. Hurd (orificial surgery) and Grace L. Smith, both prominent in their fields and ardent workers for the progress of the College they served.

Dr. Ernest R. Proctor, President of the CCO Board of Trustees (1914–1917), pediatrist, authority on children's diseases and the beloved founder and director of the free children's clinic [1].

Dr. Fred Bischoff, for eleven years Treasurer of the CCO Corporation, fervid advocate of the importance of osteopathic research, winner of the AOA Distinguished Service Award (1932) and recipient of the honorary degree of Doctor of Science in Osteopathy from CCO (1941).

Dr. Harry L. Collins, surgeon, Chairman of the Department of Gynecology, President of the CCO Board of Trustees for more than a decade, and for thirty years a member of the faculty.

There were others, like Dr. James M. Fraser, prominent Evanston osteopathic physician, Treasurer of the A. T. Still Research Institute and for three years a member of the AOA Board of Trustees; Drs. Oliver C. Foreman, Chester H. Morris (osteopathic technique), E. J. Drinkall, John C. Groenewoud, Walter Elfrink, W. Burr Allen, Fred W. Gage, Edgar S. Comstock (acute and infectious diseases), long-time Secretary of CCO, Wilbur J. Downing, Jr. (osteopathic principles and practice), and many others. Some of these were older men, their reputations well-established; others were younger teachers, but whose work was already attracting the attention of the osteopathic profession [2].

Although superbly staffed, the College nevertheless had its problems on other fronts during the 1920–1930 decade. Early in 1920 it became apparent that the school could no longer afford to pay 6% interest on the bonds it had authorized just a year earlier and the finance committee of the Board of Trustees recommended that their sale be discontinued. Inflation, resulting in much higher costs for material and labor than had been originally estimated for the proposed new hospital, prompted the finance committee to offer three options to bond purchasers: (1) donate all or part of the money outright to the College; (2) lend the amount already committed for a six-month period only, with the promised rate of interest to be paid from tuition receipts; and (3) apply for full refund. To atone for the shortcomings of the bond sales, the committee urged that renewed efforts be made to sell $500 life memberships in the Corporation [3].

During the early years of the decade at least two developments indicated the increasing influence and stature of the College and Hospital: the increasing popularity of the clinic, and the nurses' training school. Directed by Dr. W. A. Schwab, the Clinic was gaining patronage month after month. Patients who could afford modest payments were offered as many as eight treatments for $5.00; those who could afford nothing at all were treated free of charge. The hospital stated "no case is ever turned away and fully half the cases cared for are free of charge [4]."

Along with the successful Clinic operations was the opening of an outpatient department for patients who were too ill to come to the hospital and thus needed home care. The College announced that the outpatient department would "take care of patients confined to their beds or homes at a nominal fee. Care will not be refused to anyone because of financial stress [5]." Through these developments the College and Hospital were steadily increasing their services to the community.

The Chicago Osteopathic Hospital's Nursing School, too, was gaining in stature and prestige. Although limited in the number of women it could accept for training, the Hospital was attracting more and more women for the three-year training course. Inducements offered by the Hospital included free tuition, room, board, and laundry [6]. In 1922 the Nurses Training School received full accreditation from the Illinois Department of Registration and Education, and all women who completed their training were permitted to take the state board examinations for the R.N. diploma.

Of more than passing interest at the time were a series of events which led to the founding of a Junior College at CCO, a development looked upon with considerable satisfaction and one which must be credited in large part to Dean Jerome H. Raymond. The Chicago College of Osteopathy had quickly adopted the requirement issued in 1920 by the New York Board of Regents that the College offer a year of pre-Freshman work in physics, chemistry, and biology, and followed this up with a two-year pre-Freshman program in 1923, thus offering the equivalent of a Junior College curriculum for pre-medical students. In 1924 Dean Raymond announced with great pride that the Junior College was now a reality and had its own faculty and operating budget. A year or two later it was a full-fledged member of the American Association of Junior Colleges and of the North Central Association of Colleges and Secondary Schools [7]. Unfortunately, the career of the Junior College was a short one, for by 1930 it was no longer listed in the school catalogue. It may well have begun its decline with the death of Dean Raymond in 1928.

CCO students believed their education to be the best obtainable in their field. Sixty graduating seniors in 1923 were so eager "to express our gratitude and appreciation to the Dean, Faculty, and Board of Trustees of the Chicago College of Osteopathy" and "to show our approval of the ever increasing standards and to do our part in keeping our Alma Mater the leading Osteopathic College of the world" that they promised, in a signed document, to send at least one qualified student annually to study osteopathy at the Chicago College, to pay $25 annually for ten successive years, beginning May 31, 1924, on the anniversary of their graduation, and "to purchase life membership certificates to the Chicago Osteopathic Hospital as soon as they could financially do so." This was acknowledgment, indeed, of the training they had received.

The names of two young men who were to have a profound effect upon the character of the College first appeared in the school's official records during this decade. One was that of a 1921 CCO graduate who only a year later was appointed house physician for the Chicago Osteopathic Hospital: Dr. Floyd F. Peckham, later to serve as Chairman of the Board of Trustees, President of the AOA (1951–1952) and whose personal contributions during stormy years did much to keep the school from suffering the fate so many other osteopathic colleges had suffered [8]. The other was that of a senior student who in 1924 was selected, with four others, to become an intern at the Chicago Osteopathic Hospital. He was Richard Norman MacBain, who for thirty years was to serve as CCO president and direct the College in its educational program and expansion that would rank it among the great osteopathic centers of the world [9].

Although osteopathic medicine is now generally accorded full recognition by the medical profession, it was not always so. One of the most publicized confrontations between osteopathic practice and medical science occurred in 1924 when Dr. Morris Fishbein, eminent physician and at that time associate editor of the *Journal of the American Medical Association,* wrote an article for H. L. Menken's *American Mercury* magazine denouncing osteopathy and classifying its practitioners as "non-descript healers." Dr. Fishbein pulled no punches in his attack, alleging that osteopathy had wandered from the original concepts of Dr. A. T. Still and, by approving the use of drugs, was now attempting to "enter the practice of medicine by the back door."

The attack was vigorously answered by Dr. Andrew A. Gour, Professor of Corrective Gymnastics at the Chicago College of Osteopathy, in an article, "The Sinister Trail of the Medical Trust" published in *Pearson's Magazine* in June, 1924. Dr. Gour accused Dr. Fishbein of "donning the full regalia of a pope" and of "uttering the awful curse of ex-communication against all methods of healing that have not yet received the apostolic blessing, but chiefly against that arch heresy—osteopathy." Their controversy is remembered today only as a footnote in the history of the healing arts in the United States, but it was typical of the vehement personal vendettas that were common in earlier periods.

The question of whether osteopathy should or should not approve the use of drugs and whether the Chicago College should teach *materia medica* ignited a heated brouhaha. In 1924 the Senior Class presented a petition to the Board of Trustees requesting that *materia medica* be taught as part of the curriculum. The *Journal AOA* in its issue for January, 1925, reported the event and stated that the Board had acceded to the request and had recommended that *materia medica* be taught during the final two quarters of the senior year. In the February issue, Dr. Edgar Comstock, CCO Secretary, presented a lengthy denial, saying that the Board's action as announced in the *Journal* came "as a complete surprise to the members of the Board of Trustees," pointing out that the AOA would automatically rule against such a policy, and that teaching *materia medica* would be of little comfort to the young D.O. graduate unsuccessfully seeking to work in the general hospitals of his community.

Dr. Comstock revealed that the College did offer a course in "Comparative Therapeutics" so that CCO students "will be sufficiently informed as to the action of various drugs, their untoward effects as well as their therapeutic results, and their comparison with the distinctly osteopathic therapeutic measures." He added that the Board of Trustees also made a concession to the point of permitting interested students to use one of the College classrooms for the teaching of *materia medica* but that the students would be obliged to "stand the expense of fee to the instructor whom they may secure [10]." Officially, therefore, the College pursued a hands-off policy.

The College won much good will throughout the state when, in March, 1925, after a vicious tornado swept through southern Illinois and Indiana, it dispatched a number of its physicians and senior students to Carbondale, Illinois, to administer medical aid to tornado victims. Dr. W. C. MacGregor, surgeon and diagnostician from the College faculty, was appointed to direct the work of the emergency hospital, and the medical aid rendered by him and his staff saved many lives. The tornado itself was a disaster of unprecedented proportions. Two days after the tornado struck, the death toll was announced at 848; nearly 3,000 were injured. Damages were estimated to range from $10 to $12 million. Relief trains from Chicago and other cities rolled into the stricken areas for several days as southern Illinois and Indiana buried its dead, treated the injured and sought to restore normal operations. Cash contributions to quickly-established relief funds poured into Carbondale, Murphysboro and other communities as news of the disaster spread.

The financial pinch which had begun in 1920 with the suspension of bond interest payments grew steadily worse. In 1926, Dr. Oliver C. Foreman of the Board of Trustees noted with alarm that the College's enrollment had shrunk from 235 to 120 with corresponding losses in tuition revenue. Perhaps, he ventured, the school should abandon its five-year plan and return to its former four-year program, thereby attracting many potential matriculants who were shying away from the five-year program and enrolling in other schools where standards were lower. Dr. Foreman, however, received little support for this suggestion; the College refused to return to its former four-year plan.

Nevertheless, the College's financial plight was serious and at the Board meeting in September the trustees were told that the College had sustained an operating loss of $8,600 for the 1925–1926 year, that the indebtedness had reached a formidable $116,000, and that enrollments were dropping off sharply. So desperate was the College for money that Dean Jerome Raymond wrote sadly, "I hardly know how we will manage to get through this period of stress and strain [11]."

When Harry L. Collins took over as President of the Board of Trustees early in 1927, he felt it timely to remind the trustees that "the chief assets of the institution are the courage and altruism of the individuals who obligated themselves morally and financially to make this institution possible [12]." He added that while the College had an indebtedness of more than $100,000, the College's property evaluation was more than twice that amount, and he attempted to reassure the trustees that "The ones in whose hands now rests the destiny of this institution have its welfare at heart, and all parties pertaining thereto [13]."

In 1928 conditions in the College were in ferment. In sharp contrast to the student contentment that prevailed in the early 1920's, there was now open student dissent along with mounting financial problems. The president of the Senior Class organized a student revolt against Dean Raymond, who not long afterward became seriously ill. Some faculty members also joined the movement to remove Dean Raymond from office, thereby increasing the forces seeking the Dean's removal. So upsetting was the situation that the Board of Trustees launched a full-scale investigation and at its meeting on February 19, issued a statement reviewing the reasons for the student unhappiness and proposing remedies. The Board stated that "The feeling of dissatisfaction, we believe, has its roots in the following conditions existing at the present time:"

1. During the last five years, the college, while consolidating its position financially, has been steadily losing ground in volume of student enrollment. This has given the impression to the student body that they are connected with an institution that is retrogressing, rather than progressing. The psychology operating here may be compared to that which makes a defeated army mutiny. . . . During the years 1920–1921 when there was a sophomore class of 60 and a freshman class of over 50 with a total enrollment of 215, the constant undercurrent of discontent was not so evident and it was possible to take disciplinary measures and to adjust student difficulties without creating a general dissatisfaction over comparatively minor incidents.

2. The Dean, by his position, bears the chief responsibility for the dwindling student body. . . . The criticisms of the Dean, apart from his responsibility for student enrollment, are largely based on the fact that the constantly recurring student difficulties are dealt with in an inconsistent manner. By so doing, the Dean has laid himself open in the minds of the students to charges of favoritism and partiality. At times almost phenomenal forbearance is manifest and again a comparatively minor incident will be treated as a personal affront and be met with a burst of anger. The students feel that they do not have a sympathetic and impartial ear to which to carry their difficulties. The loyal and whole-hearted service of the Dean to the welfare of the institution is fully recognized. At the same time we must face the fact that there is a clash of personalities which cannot in the minds of the committee be adjusted.

3. The Board of Trustees is the highest tribunal to which students can appeal. Their criticisms against this body rest on the following:

(a) Lack of familiarity of most of that body with the more frequent irritating and trivial things connected with the college. The students feel that in a difference between students and Dean, the Dean has the ear of the Board while the students do not. This difficulty applies largely to minor matters which of themselves do not justify a direct appeal to the board but which accumulating over some time, result in open demonstration of dissatisfaction.

(b) The tendency which develops in the Board of Trustees with their more complete knowledge, mature minds and greater debating skill to overwhelm a student or group of students appearing before them. The students are out-pointed in debate but not convinced in their encounters with this body.

(c) The Board of Trustees has, on several occasions, taken the students into their confidence and laid their situation frankly before them. The students have been asked to cooperate, to be patient, and to trust in the plans and good intentions of the Board and their ability to deal with the situation. Up to the present the good offices of the Board have not resulted in the removal of either of the two main causes of discontent dealt with above.

The student body is steadily but surely diminishing in number while that of all other osteopathic colleges is growing.

The breach between the Dean and students is steadily widening.

We would like to draw to the attention of the Board the fact that the success of the college rests on the numbers and quality of the students graduated. An economically conducted college without students to teach serves no purpose. The students are customers, clients, patients, and we have something to sell them and through them to others. They are young, emotional and impressionable and can be assets or liabilities according to the way in which they are handled. A policy of humoring their demands would be disastrous; a policy of steady resistance to consistent, oft-repeated, deep-rooted objections will be equally dangerous.

The trustees favored student protests reaching them through the Student Council, but realized that many of the student demands were "neither wise nor practical" and that "any attempt on the part of the students to dictate the policy of the institution cannot be too strongly condemned, that such dictation would speedily mean the end of the institution."

Student protest, the Board summarized after interviewing many of the students, was based on a number of grievances: (1) they felt that CCO was losing ground because of dwindling enrollments and that the Dean was personally responsible for student depletion; (2) that the Dean "had many personal peculiarities obnoxious to some students;" (3) that in small matters he was becoming irascible; (4) that he showed partiality to some favored students in arranging of classes; and (5) that "he took a consistent stand against any effort to carry out athletic or social activities." The students admitted that Raymond was a good educator, but felt that this was not enough, and they expressed open admiration for Dr. W. J. Deason who had sided with them in their controversy with the administration.

The Board censured Dr. Deason for being a disruptive influence and for "unethical conduct" in defying the warnings of the Board of Trustees, and on February 22 voted to suspend him [14].

B. F. Wells, Board secretary, reported that arrangements had been made by an outside source for transferring one-third of the entire student body to other schools (presumably those who had been involved in the protest movement) and that a rival institution had, by means of attractive offers, attempted to induce a wholesale desertion of the students from the CCO campus. Perhaps at no time in the College's history was there as serious a student crisis as during these months in 1928 [15].

The Board did not absolve the faculty, either. It believed that certain groups and individuals were using the student body to "further their own plans and interests" and of "fanning the fires of discontent into flames." The trustees concluded that the faculty had been guilty of making "unwarranted and unprovoked attacks on the Dean in regular class hours, followed by meetings of faculty members with certain student groups [16]."

The early months of 1928 had indeed generated "a difficult situation" as Dr. Wells told the Board in September. He was referring primarily to the student dissension, but the financial situation was growing steadily worse. Dr. Floyd F. Peckham, acting business manager, revealed with considerable uneasiness that the College had issued $1,200 worth of checks with only $59.42 in the bank (but which he hoped would be covered by forthcoming tuition receipts!). The College was leading a hand-to-mouth financial existence, issuing checks periodically with insufficient cash on hand but which it hoped would be provided by anticipated student tuition fees. The situation had shown no improvement in late summer, and Dr. Peckham sadly informed the Board that the College and Hospital had sustained a loss of $1,182.41, that the business of the Hospital had fallen off and that "more patients are needed [17]." The small graduation class of nineteen (five of whom were women) at the June commencement was also a matter of concern.

There were some bright spots. The College spent nearly $1,000 for advertising and promotion to attract students, a bold measure put into effect in spite of the severe financial pinch. A small dental clinic was opened, and twelve different "special clinics" were offered "so that we can care for practically any kind of disease." Some new equipment was added. The first athletic director was appointed—Dr. Morris Berk. The College and Hospital, formerly managed as a single operation, were separated, and the Dean of the College was informed he could carry on the duties of his office "subject only to the exigencies of the exchequer". The by-laws were revised so that ten of the Board's eleven members would be active or life members of the Corporation; the remaining member was to be elected by the Illinois Osteopathic Association. The postgraduate courses offered each year during the holiday season were becoming highly popular and registration for the 1928–1929 session was larger than ever. It seemed obvious that the recent internal disturbances at the College had not adversely affected the professional work of the school.

Yet try as it might, the College could not get its financial house in order. The fiscal worries continued—and grew worse. The situation became so

alarming that serious consideration was given to a number of merger proposals. One of these, coming out of a Board of Trustees session, suggested a
possible merger with the University of Chicago. In such an event, the College would turn over its properties to the University of Chicago with the
provision that the College itself remain intact and be operated as an osteopathic teaching institution. There was talk that such a merger would
result in a student body of 1,000, and there were optimistic predictions that
affiliation with the Midway institution would not only give CCO "university
standing" but bring about "the removal of all financial worries." So attractive
was this merger possibility that Drs. S. D. Zaph, Fred Bischoff, and E. R.
Hoskins were appointed a committee of three to confer with University of
Chicago officials as to the feasibility of such a union [18].

There were other merger suggestions, all indicating that the Chicago College was financially shaky and thus receptive to any proposal that promised
fiscal relief. There was even talk by outsiders that Bernarr MacFadden,
nationally-known health faddist and magazine publisher, had purchased a
controlling interest in the Chicago College and would use it to demonstrate
and promote his health theories. Dr. Samuel V. Robuck officially denied this
rumor and wrote to the *Journal of the American Osteopathic Association* "that
the Chicago College of Osteopathy would remain strictly an osteopathic
institution [19]."

Happily, relief was on the way! From the Osteopathic Foundation of
Colorado!

The Colorado Foundation came into existence at Boulder, Colorado, in
1927 "for the promotion of osteopathy." Its founding had been made possible by means of a generous grant from "an invalid now restored to health",
and its purpose was "the promotion of Osteopathy." Additional gifts arrived,
and the Foundation began looking about for ways to best carry on its work.
And, its administrators asked, what better way than through an osteopathic
educational institution?

Late in 1928 the Foundation forwarded an inquiry to CCO to ascertain
precisely why the Chicago College had been founded and what it was trying
to do. The trustees answered the inquiry on December 14 and pointed out
that two major objectives motivated the work of the College:

1. Development and teaching from the osteopathic viewpoint of
anatomy, physiology, pathology, diagnosis, therapeutics, etc. (Osteopathic
education).
2. More and more teaching through clinical experience, and the belief
that the effective osteopathic college must be properly equipped both as to
faculty personnel and clinical facilities.

These ideals meshed with those of the Colorado Foundation and, in the summer of 1929, the Foundation offered to extricate the Chicago College of Osteopathy from its financial dilemma by placing in escrow or trust a sum of $105,000 to insure the payment of $55,000 on the First Mortgage due in November, 1930, $25,000 to meet the Second Mortgage bonds due in May, 1930, and $25,000 to pay off current unsecured indebtedness. The Foundation also offered to make all disbursements in the future to properly maintain the College and Hospital.

In return for this financial salvation, the Foundation asked that complete control and management of the Chicago College of Osteopathy Corporation be transferred to the trustees of the Osteopathic Foundation of Colorado. To expedite the shift in control, it was suggested that a limited number of individuals, chosen by the Foundation, replace the current voting membership of the Chicago Corporation, and that those elected would become active members of the Corporation while those replaced would (upon their resignation) become honorary life members without the right to vote or hold office. Such an arrangement thus called for the resignation of all active members of the Corporation so that the new organization could begin with a completely new slate. The Foundation agreed to return control of the Corporation to the Chicago College if the Foundation should cease to exist within the next five years, on condition, however, that the Foundation be reimbursed for mortgage payments advanced in the meantime.

On July 24, 1929, Dr. Harry L. Collins, President of the CCO Board of Trustees, wrote Dr. Harry L. Riley, President of the Colorado Foundation trustees, expressing the Chicago trustees' favorable reception of the Colorado proposal and submitting a draft of resolution confirming the merger. On August 2, Dr. Riley wrote the following letter to Dr. Collins:

> Careful consideration has been given to the draft and resolution prepared by Mr. Caldwell [CCO attorney] and to the suggestions contained in your letter of July 24th, but as indicated in my night letter, it does not seem that the plan proposed by the Chicago College of Osteopathy is entirely in accord with the proposal made on behalf of the Osteopathic Foundation. In order to indicate the scope of activities for which the Foundation was organized, it might be well here to set forth the second paragraph of its certificate of incorporation wherein the objects for which the Association was formed and incorporated are set forth as follows:
>
> (1) To establish, support and maintain a college or colleges or other educational institution wherein the students may be taught the science of osteopathy, in any or all of its branches as now understood or hereafter developed; (2) to educate and train nurses in the care and treatment of sick and disabled persons; (3) to conduct scientific research, of which the object shall be the prevention and treatment of disease and the alleviation of

human suffering through the development and application of the science of osteopathy; (4) to confer degrees or other marks of distinction, as the Board of Trustees may deem proper, on those persons who shall complete, in a satisfactory manner, the course of study established by this association or who may achieve distinction or attain prominence in the development or application of the principles of osteopathy; (5) to establish, support and maintain hospitals, sanitoria or other institutions for the purpose of affording care and treatment to sick or disabled persons of every creed, nationality or color; (6) to fulfill such other objects and purposes, incidental and kindred to those above mentioned, as the Board of Trustees may, from time to time prescribe; and (7) in order to accomplish said purposes, and each or any of them as herein set forth, to acquire, by gift, purchase or otherwise, and to hold, mortgage, convey and otherwise dispose of all kinds of property, both real and personal, either within the State of Colorado or in any other of the States, Territories and Dependencies of the United States; and to do any and all things necessary, suitable and proper for the accomplishment of any of the purposes or for the attainment of any of the objects or for the exercise of any of the powers herein set forth, whether herein specified or not, either alone or in connection with other firms, individuals or corporations, either in this State or throughout the United States, and elsewhere, and to do any other act or acts, thing or things, incidental or pertinent to or connected with the business hereinbefore described or any part or parts thereof, if not inconsistent with the laws under which this corporation is organized."

The letter went on:

For the purpose of carrying out the above objects, or such of them as may be undertaken from time to time in the judgment of the Trustees of the Foundation, considerable sums of money have already been made available, and, subject to unforeseen contingencies, even larger sums are assured for the future, both by way of direct gift as needed, and through testamentary benefactions; but it is the emphatic expression of those parties who have given this financial assurance that, once the aid of the Foundation has been pledged to an established institution or for the construction of a new plant, its efforts shall not be made subject to the control or influence of others whose judgment may not be wholly in accord with that of the Foundation's representatives. In line with this expression, therefore, it is necessary to insist that if the Chicago College of Osteopathy shall desire to accept the aid of the Foundation, the control of its future administration shall be transferred without reservation or restriction. In other words, the proposal of the present resolution to the effect that the transfer shall be burdened with the possibility that the property shall revert to your present corporation at the end of three years cannot be accepted.

We recognize a desire on the part of the parties now in interest that the College shall not be removed from Chicago or its environs, and we are willing to give such assurances to that end as may be desired, provided they are so framed as not to hinder the operation of the institution within the accepted field. At the present time, as we understand your by-laws, the ultimate control of the Chicago College rests with a voting membership which has the power of selecting the active trustee. It is our proposal that this membership, by resignation of the voting right in favor of representatives of the Foundation, shall transfer to such representatives the power of selecting and perpetuating the active management of the College. It is our view, clearly, that this may be through selection and classification of members under the present by-laws or by the amendment of such by-laws. In accordance with existing provisions, so as to establish a new plan or organization.

In return for the absolute transfer of control of the College to representatives of the Foundation, we will provide for the deposit of sufficient funds under escrow or trust instructions which shall provide for their use in the payment of (1) the first mortgage indebtedness of the present Corporation in the principal sum of $55,000 due in November, 1930; (2) the second mortgage indebtedness of $25,000 due in May, 1930; and (3) the present unsecured or open indebtedness of the Corporation in the aggregate principal sum not to exceed $25,000. It should further be understood that the present policies of the College with respect to courses, methods of instruction, etc., are to be continued unless and until changes therein are dictated by research and experience, and that it is now proposed to continue with the present faculty so long as relations are mutually satisfactory.

Your very truly,
H. L. Riley

On August 6, 1929, Dr. Collins replied to Dr. Riley as follows:

Dear Doctor Riley:

After conferring with my associates, I am hastening to answer your letter of August 2nd. As was stated in the draft prepared by Dr. Caldwell, the proposals in it were not to be considered final but to serve as a basis for discussion. You will remember that exactly the same proposals were talked over between you, Dr. Bischoff and myself in Mr. Caldwell's office and that it was your suggestion that they be put in written form.

My associates and I agree that the objections which are pointed out in your letter of August 2nd can be met and we are willing to make the necessary recommendations and take the necessary steps to meet your wishes. We recognize the legitimate desire on the part of the Trustees of the Foundation that the efforts of the Foundation shall not be made subject to the control or influence of others. Consequently we are willing to accept the assurances you give in your letter without asking that they be formally incorporated in any document or otherwise expressed so as to interfere with the control of the College or to raise the possibility of a reversion of the property to the Corporation. We are doing this because we have thorough confidence in the bona fide intentions of the Trustees of the Foundation to continue the College in the best interests of osteopathy and believe that the institution would not be removed from Chicago or its vicinity without a clear necessity for the move in the best interests of the profession.

Consequently we accept your proposal and undertake to recommend that the entire present voting membership surrender its rights and in lieu thereof accept honorary memberships (which have no voting rights or voice in control) under the by-laws. We further undertake to recommend that, simultaneously with the foregoing, such persons as are named by the Foundation be elected to active membership so that the complete control of the Corporation will be in the hands of the Foundation. The foregoing seems the most expeditious and effective way of meeting your wishes, since it does not involve any amendment to the by-laws and accomplishes an immediate and unrestricted transfer of control. If, however, some better method of accomplishing the same end occurs to you, we shall be glad to give it our careful consideration.

There is one contingency, however, involved in the foregoing which perhaps should be provided for. It is possible that out of our present membership some one or two might refuse to make the necessary surrender. We do not know of any such person but must, of course, take precautions against all contingencies. If this happens, we should be willing immediately to recommend that instead of transferring complete control of the Corporation to you, complete title to the property and complete control of the institution be transferred by the Corporation to such persons or to such corporation as you name for the purpose. This, according to our attorneys, can probably be done without unanimous vote.

It is our understanding from your letter that, if and when abolute transfer of control of the College to the Foundation is effected, the Foundation will provide for the deposit of sufficient funds under escrow or trust instructions which shall provide for their use in the payment of the various items of indebtedness specified in the last paragraph of your letter.

If the proposals indicated by this letter are satisfactory to the Foundation, we shall, of course, immediately take all steps indicated as necessary. We appreciate the spirit in which the negotiations are being conducted and hope that this letter may prove a satisfactory response to the proposal of the Foundation.

Yours very truly,
Harry L. Collins
President of the Board of Trustees

On August 7, Dr. Collins received the following telegram from Dr. Riley approving the terms:

PROGRAM OUTLINED IN YOUR LETTER AUGUST SIXTH ACCEPTABLE ON TRANSFER OF ENTIRE VOTING RIGHTS TO REPRESENTATIVES OF FOUNDATION STOP HAVE NO OBJECTION TO UNDERSTANDING THAT IN EVENT OF OUR RETIREMENT WITHIN FIVE YEARS PROPERTY WOULD BE RETRANSFERRED ON EQUITABLE BASIS SUBJECT ONLY TO OUR PRESENT MORTGAGE ADVANCEMENT.

HARRY L. RILEY

At a special meeting on August 8, the Chicago College of Osteopathy Corporation trustees voted to recommend to the Corporation membership "the transfer of the management control or properties of the Corporation, the College and Hospital" to the Osteopathic Foundation of Colorado. They looked upon the Colorado offer as "an opportunity for advancement and growth such as it has not had before and is not likely to receive again." They were convinced that "the Foundation intends to maintain the College on a high plane and in the interests of the Osteopathic profession; that it intends steadily to improve the College in personnel, equipment and efficiency; and that it will be to the advantage of the osteopathic profession that the proposal be accepted."

Later in the month, to fulfill the terms of the agreement, letters were sent to all active members of the Corporation asking for their resignations and enclosing proxy forms with the request that they be promptly returned. To further fulfill the agreement, the trustees elected as active members of the Corporation three men from the Colorado Osteopathic Foundation: Dr. Harry L. Riley [20], Merritt H. Perkins, and William J. Foster. They also empowered Dr. Riley "to deposit funds, sign checks, borrow funds or in any other way conduct the business of the Chicago College of Osteopathy," and the transfer of assets and control was so complete that the trustees even authorized Dr. Riley to have access to the safety deposit box in the vaults of the first National Bank which was held in the name of the Chicago College of Osteopathy Corporation.

On September 10, 1929, three men held a special meeting at the College. They were Dr. Harry L. Riley, Merritt H. Perkins, and William J. Foster, all of the Colorado Foundation. Dr. Riley served as chairman and Mr. Perkins as secretary. Chairman Riley announced that the resignations of all active members of the Chicago College of Osteopathy Corporation had been received and that "the three members present at this meeting constitute the only active members of the corporation." He added that all members of the former Board of Trustees had also submitted their resignations, as requested, and that all former active members of the Corporation had been awarded honorary memberships.

The three men constituting the new ruling body announced that the Articles of Incorporation of the reorganized corporation would call for a board of seven trustees, and that the corporation's post office address would be No. 34, The Hampden, 3853 Langley Avenue, Chicago. To confirm their status, the three men passed a resolution stating that:

> The management of the aforesaid Chicago College of Osteopathy shall be vested in a Board of three Trustees, who are to be elected in accordance with the By-Laws of this corporation.

Near the conclusion of the session, the chairman announced that it was now in order formally to elect a Board of Trustees to fill the vacancies caused by the resignation of the former Board members, and accordingly, Messrs. Riley, Perkins, and Foster were nominated as Trustees until the next annual meeting and until their successors were elected and qualified.

The first "annual meeting" was held at Boulder, Colorado, on September 26, 1929. Attending were the three new trustees as well as Dr. Harry L. Collins, President of CCO and Dr. Richard N. MacBain, Dean of the Faculty. The chief purpose of the meeting was to appoint Drs. Collins and MacBain as the chief administrative officers of the College and to prepare the College to resume its normal operations. For the next seven years, the Chicago College of Osteopathy was, in a sense, under the control of "outsiders," yet few would deny that this interregnum meant the deliverance of the College from an intolerable financial crisis and the ultimate emergence of an institution that was stronger and better capable of meeting the problems that lay ahead [21].

## REFERENCES

1. By 1930, some 500 children ranging in age from infancy to 14, were being accepted and treated annually—without charge.
2. Faculty salaries were, of course, shockingly low when compared with those prevailing today. Full professors' salaries ranged from $1,200 to $3,000, with the average around $1,200. Instructors received $900 a year. Also reflecting the low costs at that time were the tuition fees, which were $60 per quarter ($30 for half-time students). Post-graduate tuition was $25 per month. The College's entire income for the 1919–1920 school year was only $54,350. Operating budget for the Chicago Osteopathic Hospital was $50,444 for the 1920–1921 year and room rates were increased to $5 and $6 per day!
3. Dean Jerome Raymond remonstrated to the Trustees in a report in March, 1923: "Many of our people do not seem to know what a budget is and consequently pay no attention to it. . . . If we are to avoid financial disaster it is necessary for us to live within our income. . . . Some demand that an elevator be installed . . . others urge an ambulance entrance . . . some insist that the walls and ceilings must be calcimined more frequently . . . others wish additional nurses employed . . . some regard the janitor service insufficient . . . others demand more instruments for the Operating Room . . . some wish the fire escapes painted . . . others demand that a new sidewalk be constructed around the building . . . some wish the iron fence around the vacant lot painted . . . others insist that we shall at once construct an addition to the building . . . some insist that we are too crowded with students, others that we have not enough students. . . . Our critics forget that we have almost no money, and that we have imperative demands for all the money we have. . . . I think we should have a two-year moratorium of money-spending suggestions."
4. *Journal AOA,* October, 1922, p. 102. In 1921 a total of 16,407 treatments were given in the dispensary.
5. *Ibid.,* March, 1923, p. 428. (Vol. 22)
6. Nurse trainees, after passing a three-month probationary period, were paid $20 per month during the first year, $25 per month in the second year.
7. 1925 *CCO Catalogue.*

8. The Basic Science Building completed in 1968 was named in Dr. Peckham's honor. In 1952 he was awarded an honorary Doctor of Science degree by CCO. He was born in 1895, died in 1970 after spending a full half century with the College in one capacity or another.

9. The six-story MacBain pavilion of the Chicago Osteopathic Hospital is named in his honor. Dr. MacBain was affiliated with the College and Hospital for 43 years, guided the institution through some of its most perilous times.

10. *Journal AOA,* February, 1925, p. 460. (Vol. 25)

11. In a letter to Mrs. S. V. Robuck, dated October 20, 1927. Mrs. Robuck was President of the Board of Directors of the Chicago Osteopathic Free Children's Clinic.

12. From the Minutes of the Board meeting, April 20, 1927.

13. *Ibid.*

14. He was later reinstated with full faculty privileges. (Board of Trustees Meeting, March 4, 1928)

15. Dean Raymond, object of the revolt, died on February 22, 1928, of pneumonia and Dr. B. F. Wells was named Acting Dean. Whatever may have been Dean Raymond's shortcomings, he was an outstanding educator and administrator. When he became Dean in 1919 the College was heavily in debt, but he met this crisis head-on and succeeded in obtaining much needed additional equipment and facilities. The *Journal AOA* stated: "Dean Raymond's work at the Chicago College did much to raise the standard of osteopathic education." (March, 1928, p. 566; Vol. 27)

16. Minutes of the Meeting of the Board of Trustees held February 19, 1928. (This was a special Sunday meeting called to discuss the critical situation.)

17. Minutes of the Meeting of the Board of Trustees, July 12, 1928.

18. Minutes of the Meeting of the Board of Trustees, Sept. 10, 1929.

19. *Journal AOA,* October, 1928, p. 122. (Vol. 28)

20. Dr. Riley made frequent trips to the CCO campus, was a regular lecturer at the College and became one of the most respected and admired members of the faculty. He served for eight years as President of the CCO Board of Trustees (while the College was under the control of the Colorado Foundation). Dr. W. Fraser Strachan, recently retired CCOM faculty member, recalls Dr. Riley as one of the most gifted osteopathic manipulators of his day who often demonstrated his skills to CCO classes.

21. In an annual report issued many years later (1966–1967), Dr. MacBain stated that the support of the Colorado Foundation provided "new strength and purpose for the College" by assuming financial responsibility for its operation and relieving the college of a debt that had become impossible to carry. He paid high tribute to the leadership that the foundation provided, stating that through the work of Dr. H. L. Riley the curriculum was reoriented and new emphasis given to the possibilities of manipulative therapy and its teaching.

# 8

# CCO IN THE 1930'S: A MERGER AND DISSOLUTION

ANNOUNCEMENT that the College was now under the control of the Osteopathic Foundation of Colorado appeared in the 1930–1931 school catalogue. An opening paragraph read:

> In the summer of 1929, the Trustees of the Osteopathic Foundation, a Colorado corporation, made a very thorough investigation into the work of the Chicago College of Osteopathy and determined that the college was qualified to receive the support of the Foundation in its effort to promote the development and application of the science of osteopathy. This support has now been extended to the College and has served to establish more firmly the institution in achieving the purposes of its organization [1].

The transition was made smoothly. Many would detect little difference, if any, in either the policies or administration. Dr. Harry L. Collins as President and Dr. Richard N. MacBain as Dean spearheaded a faculty that was as outstanding as ever. It included Earl R. Hoskins, Professor of Comparative Therapeutics and Secretary of the College; Benjamin F. Wells, anatomy; Russel Rice Peckham, anatomy; Samuel V. Robuck, diagnosis; Ernest R. Proctor, comparative therapeutics; James B. Littlejohn, surgery, assisted by S. D. Zaph, H. L. Collins, and Earl Hoskins; Floyd F. Peckham, clinic director; Wilbur J. Downing, Sr., and others whose names were well known throughout the college, state and national professional circles.

The paralyzing economic depression of the 1930's was felt by the College as it was by other institutions and organizations. In December, 1931, the Trustees were forced to borrow $20,000 to run the College and secured the loan "by a trust deed on the property of the institution." Student hardships were common. Dr. George H. Carpenter, writing in *The Forum of Osteopathy,* described what some of the students were doing to remain in school:

[ 99 ]

We have had many students at the Chicago College of Osteopathy who have been obliged to work during their entire course. Some of them have had jobs in newspaper offices, wrapping and loading papers for morning distribution or going on the trucks for the same purpose. Some have worked in the central post office, handling parcel post packages all night, others have been employed in the night force to open mail in some of our big wholesale dry goods houses ... many instances of hard work and sacrifice could be found among the girls in our college, too [2, 3].

During the 1930's the College lost a number of outstanding faculty members through death or retirement. Death claimed Dr. Russel R. Peckham, Professor of Anatomy and Technique (at the age of 36); Dr. Earl R. Hoskins, nationally-known X-ray pioneer; Dr. Joseph H. Sullivan, dean of all Illinois osteopathic physicians and a long-time teacher and friend of the College; Dr. Carl P. McConnell, one of the pioneers who had done so much in the earlier years to set the course the school was to follow; and Dr. Louis C. Hanavan, noted gynecologist and obstetrician who had delivered scores of babies in the Chicago Osteopathic Hospital.

A number received "emeritus" status as they entered retirement following years of service. These included Drs. H. H. Fryette, W. J. Deason, George H. Carpenter, Ernest R. Proctor, Chester H. Morris, and Charles A. Fink. The latter was one of the small group that helped to reorganize the school in 1913.

The College also lost the services of Dr. James B. Littlejohn who in 1931 asked to be relieved of his teaching duties (but who remained in close touch with the College until his death in 1947), and Dr. J. S. Denslow, Professor of Osteopathic Manipulative Technique who transferred to the Kirksville College of Osteopathy and Surgery in 1938.

By far the most critical event in the career of the College in the 1930's was the dissolution of the merger with the Colorado Osteopathic Foundation, for this meant that once again the College was strictly on its own. On December 22, 1936, a special meeting of the Board of Trustees was held at Boulder, Colorado, "to discuss the retirement from active participation in the management of the Chicago College of Osteopathy of officers and members of the Osteopathic Foundation of Colorado; and, in the event of such retirement, to complete the necessary formalities for transferring such management into other hands."

The shift in management was effected quickly. At the meeting, applications for active membership in the Chicago College of Osteopathy were presented by Drs. H. L. Collins, Richard N. MacBain, and Fred Bischoff; the applications were promptly approved. This done, Dr. Merritt H. Perkins resigned as Secretary of the Board of Trustees and was succeeded by Dr. Fred Bischoff; Mrs. Minnie Foster Riley resigned as Vice President of the Board of Trustees and was replaced by Dr. MacBain; Dr. Harry L. Riley resigned as President and was succeeded by Dr. Harry L. Collins [4].

Thus the seven-year association with the Colorado Foundation came to an end, and those who had been present at the consummation of the merger were present at its dissolution—and stood ready to carry on.

When the Chicago College of Osteopathy resumed its activities, totally independent of the Colorado Foundation which had sustained it for seven years, its Board of Trustees included Drs. Fred Bischoff, Thomas J. Houston, Floyd F. Peckham, R. N. MacBain, and H. L. Collins. In June, 1937, Dr. Peckham was named Treasurer of the Corporation, an assignment which perhaps only someone with his outlook and qualities could have long tolerated.

The financial ills which had plagued the College in earlier years were quick to return. In 1937 Dr. Peckham was instructed to borrow $5,000 to help meet current expenses. A year later, Dr. Peckham glumly reported that, in spite of a total income of $132,000 the College was losing approximately $3,000 a month. "Our whole fault, if it is a fault," Dr. Peckham explained, "lies in the fact that our policy of continually giving better service in the hospital and doing a better teaching job in the college seems to keep ahead of our income [5]."

Other statistics corroborated his disturbing disclosures. In June he had to borrow $2,000 to "meet coming expenses." On September 7 he told the Trustees that the College had a credit of only $665 in the bank with which to meet an accumulation of unpaid bills totaling approximately $6,400! The school year had ended with a deficit of nearly $5,000. This was not surprising in view of the continuing monthly deficits. Yet Dr. Peckham never seemed to lose his spirit of optimism. In spite of the financial troubles, he predicted that "we will come through in some manner," while at the same time admitting that "the picture for the coming year is not encouraging or pleasant."

In mid 1938 came an administrative change which was to influence the College for the next thirty years. On June 12, 1938, Dr. MacBain tendered his resignation as Dean of the College and accepted the college presidency as Dr. Collins felt it time to relinquish the chief executive post. Succeeding Dr. MacBain as Dean was Dr. L. B. Whetten who had joined the staff in 1936 as assistant dean to help with recruiting and business operations [6].

In the same year another significant event occurred—quite unexpectedly. In March, the Illinois Secretary of State notified the College that the

Chicago Osteopathic Hospital, its affiliate, was considered "dissolved" inasmuch as no annual report had been filed by the hospital. The Board of Trustees replied that it had received no word whatever indicating that dissolution proceedings were even in progress, but took action immediately.

On March 1 the trustees elected a Board of Directors to control and manage the Hospital, appointing Drs. Collins, Bischoff, Peckham, MacBain and Houston as directors, and naming Dr. Collins, President; Dr. Bischoff, Secretary; and Dr. Peckham, Treasurer. An application for a new charter for the Hospital was filed on March 17, and not long afterward a revised charter attesting that "The Chicago Osteopathic Hospital is a legally organized Corporation under the laws of the State of Illinois" was received.

The purpose of the Chicago Osteopathic Hospital was outlined in the application for the new charter as follows:

> To operate a general hospital and to provide facilities for the care and treatment of human ailments; to operate and conduct a general clinic, outpatient department, and school, and to provide facilities for the care and treatment of private, semi-charity, and charity patients; and for the education and training of students, nurses and internes, as well as for post graduate study; and to have all the rights and privileges accorded by the laws of the State of Illinois, to corporations organized for educational and charitable, or eleemosynary purposes.

So once again the Hospital was in good standing and prepared to carry on its work.

The growing popularity of the radio during these years gave the College an opportunity it had not enjoyed in earlier times: the chance to explain the work of its physicians and teachers to listeners in thousands of American homes. Early in 1938, the Chicago Osteopathic Society, in cooperation with the Committee on Public and Professional Welfare of the American Osteopathic Association, inaugurated a series of thirteen weekly educational interview type broadcasts over radio station WAAF in the Palmer House.

Many of the osteopathic physicians interviewed were, of course, from the Chicago College of Osteopathy. Dr. H. L. Collins participated in a discussion on "Osteopathy's Part in the Public Health"; Dr. Martin Beilke on "Your Everyday Sports and Health"; Dr. Samuel V. Robuck on "Rules of Health"; Dr. Fred Shain on "The Posture Parade"; Dr. Earl J. Drinkall on "Your Feet and Your Health"; Drs. Chester H. Morris and Hal Shain on "Backaches and Injuries"; Drs. Charles A. Fink and Ernest R. Proctor on "What Do You Know About Yourself?" These programs, broadcast on

Wednesday afternoons, did much to bring about a better understanding of osteopathic medicine by the general public.

As the decade drew to an end, the financial troubles persisted. At the meeting of the Board of Trustees on June 21, 1939, Dr. Peckham reported that "The institution has exhausted all possible means of credit" and that "other loans are impossible without the personal signatures of individuals on the Board." The money pinch was so bad that the Board recommended borrowing $1,000 from both Drs. Collins and Peckham "for a period of one year or less at 5% interest," explaining that "this method of obtaining the necessary funds would be better than having the individual members sign for notes at the bank where the institution had been doing its business." Only the income from the Chicago Osteopathic Hospital was making it possible for the College to hang on doggedly to its day-to-day operations.

The College's administrators speculated that an increase in the number of individuals on the Board of Trustees would help alleviate the constantly-recurring financial crises, provided that these additions represented fields of activity outside the osteopathic profession. L. B. Whetten, the Dean, was one of these, and he urged that more lay members be added to the Board, people "who are removed from the institution and who have no vested interests." Such a diverse membership, he believed, would assure an unprej-udiced and efficient administration. Dr. Whetten's proposal was indicative of the growing dependence on influential individuals not involved in osteo-pathic practice but who were nonetheless interested in the work the College was attempting to do.

There were other internal reorganization proposals, such as establishing a board of governors to handle financing and fundraising; an endowment committee to handle the funds donated to the college; a board of governors for the Hospital; an executive faculty committee—all evidence that the col-lege must again take stock and adjust itself to the increasing financial pres-sures by considering ways and means for raising money and to extend its services wherever it could.

In the meantime, Dr. MacBain had his own ideas of what must be done in the field of osteopathic education, particularly as it applied to his own Col-lege. Speaking on "The Modern Trends in Osteopathic Education" before the delegates to the national AOA convention in Dallas, Dr. MacBain said:

> The future of osteopathy, as far as it relates to the college, depends upon our ability to keep our sense of direction in therapy, to guard against orthodoxy in treatment, to place a very special emphasis on osteopathic

principles and practice in the classroom, and to support the whole program with a fully supervised program of clinical teaching and clinical research [7].

Again:

> We are witnessing an evolution or a revolution in the economics, the ethics, and social position and in time-honored prerogatives of the physician. Industrial medicine, insurance medicine, group medical service, hospital insurance programs, governmental health programs, social security plans, agitation for state medicine, are phenomena that portend some fundamental changes in the vital interests of our profession. Our educational institutions must keep themselves adaptable, ready to make the required adjustments in their methods of training that will meet modern needs in the social and economic, as well as in the scientific fields [8].

The address contained a sound analysis of what the times were bringing about and what osteopathic education must do to prepare its students to meet the changes swirling around them. It was a challenging message as the Chicago College of Osteopathy looked to the 1940's.

## REFERENCES

1. On November 26, 1930, William J. Foster, one of the three trustees, died, and at a special meeting held on December 10 in Boulder, Mrs. Minnie Foster Riley was elected to fill the unexpired term. She was reelected at the annual meeting the following year.
2. *The Forum of Osteopathy,* August, 1930, p. 107. (Vol. 4, No. 5)
3. Only 19 CCO students were graduated in June, 1931. A total of only 376 students was graduated in 1931 by the six osteopathic colleges in the U.S. Total enrollment at these schools was 1,849, with 9 percent representing women students. The ratio of M.D.'s to D.O.'s remained heavily in favor of the medical colleges which were graduating approximately 13 M.D.'s for each D.O. turned out by the six osteopathic schools. (*Journal AOA,* October, 1931, pp. 41–45; Vol. 31)
4. Dr. Collins was a charter member of the American College of Osteopathic Surgeons and an outstanding leader in osteopathic education. His students at CCO described him as "a real instructor who knows his material and how to put it out."
5. In a report to the Trustees, September, 1938.
6. One of Dr. Whetten's first moves was to send personal letters to the personnel departments of the nation's fifty largest colleges asking them to inform their students of the opportunities offered by the osteopathic profession. Unfortunately, the response was negligible. Dr. Whetten arrived at CCO by way of the University of Chicago's Graduate School of Education. He was well qualified and popular with the students.
7. *Journal AOA,* February, 1940, pp. 299–303. (Vol. 39)
8. *Ibid.*

# 9

# TURBULENT YEARS: THE 1940'S

THE Chicago College of Osteopathy had been on precarious financial footing for some time and it became even more so during the pressures of World War II.

During the two or three years preceding the war itself there was little indication of the severity of the months that lay ahead. In November, 1940, Dean Lester B. Whetten presented to the trustees a plan for expansion which appears to be the first full-scale proposal for increasing the school's physical plant. Dr. Whetten submitted a plan for adding a three-story addition to the four-story building into which the school had moved back in 1918 and which, with other improvements, would cost in the neighborhood of $875,000. The $60' \times 27'$ building addition would provide an additional class room; a new administrative office; six to eight new clinic examination rooms; a new men's lounge and washroom; additional storage space for both the College and the Hospital; a morgue for post mortem examinations; a new and modern surgery area with amphitheatre; seven additional private hospital rooms and a ward for hospital patients.

While expansion talk was in the air, administrative changes were also in the making. During the early 1940's the school administration recommended that a "Board of Governors" be established to assist the Trustees in directing the affairs of the College. Dr. MacBain, who proposed the plan, said:

> It is imperative that the direction of the College be placed on a wider basis and that our alumni, the profession at large, and the public be represented. . . . The Board of Governors will have direction of the public relations of the College, student recruiting, finance, executive personnel and matters of general policy.

He went on:

> The establishment of the Board of Governors represents a transitional stage in the evolution of the college control. The powers now held by the Board of Trustees will be delegated to the Board of Governors during the next few years. The Board of Trustees will act as a consultative and advi-

sory body to the Board of Governors until such time as it seems advisable and expedient to merge the two bodies into one Board.

On Sunday, November 24, 1940, the Board of Governors held its first meeting and was attended by Drs. R. C. McCaughan, Charles A. Fink, George H. Carpenter, H. L. Samblanet, L. B. Harned, Walter P. Bruer, and W. S. Fuller. During this session several additional members were nominated for board membership. These included Dr. Albert W. Bailey of Schenectady, New York, John C. Tully of LaGrange, Illinois and Frank W. Anderson of Chicago.

Early in 1941 still other individuals were nominated when it was proposed that the membership of the Board of Governors be increased to fifteen. Named to join the group were Donald Walsh, circulation manager of the *Chicago Daily News;* John Dale Russell of the Division of Social Sciences at the University of Chicago; Theodore S. Chapman, of Chapman & Cutler law firm; and Willard Henry, official of a well-known paper company [1]. The diversity of management control which had been considered for some time was now coming to pass.

What appears to have been the first honorary degree conferred by the Chicago College of Osteopathy was the Doctor of Science in Osteopathy degree awarded at the 1941 Commencement Exercises to Dr. M. L. Axelrod of the Detroit Osteopathic Hospital. On November 4, 1940, Dr. Harry L. Collins, CCO president, wrote to Dr. Axelrod as follows:

Dear Dr. Axelrod:

It is a pleasure for us to inform you that the Board of Trustees of the Chicago College of Osteopathy, in its regular meeting on September 18th, 1940, voted unanimously to confer on you the honorary degree, Doctor of Science in Osteopathy.

The trustees, officers, and faculty of the College have known of your splendid work in anesthesia for some time and have observed with approval the development of this work in one of our leading osteopathic institutions. It is in recognition of your success in your chosen field, and of the service that you have rendered thereby to your profession, that this degree is awarded.

We would be pleased to have you attend our Commencement exercises in June, 1941, for the formal presentation of the diploma.

Very sincerely yours,
H.L. Collins
President—Board of Trustees

Fred Bischoff
Secretary—Board of Trustees [2]

On November 7, 1940, Dr. Axelrod, accepting the honor, wrote to Dr. Collins as follows:

> Dear Dr. Collins:
>
> It is with sincerest thoughts that I extend to you and the other members of your Board of Trustees my deepest appreciation for the honor you have bestowed on me.
>
> The credit for accomplishments is not entirely one-sided. The Osteopathic Profession in general is also entitled to their share of credit in being able to enthusiastically receive what little information I have put forth.
>
> It will be a pleasure to attend your Commencement exercises in June in order to receive the formal presentation.
>
> With kindest regards, I am,
>
> Very sincerely yours,<br>M. L. Axelrod [3]

The fast-approaching wartime economy and the preparation of the nation's manpower for whatever national emergency might arise again threatened the normal operations of the College—as had been the case on a former occasion when war requirements brought about reductions in income and enrollments. As early as May 21, 1941, the Trustees learned that the College was again experiencing increasing difficulties in obtaining bank loans, and that even the bank which had been receiving most of the College's business was limiting borrowing to a loan of $5,000 only.

In October, President MacBain wrote Frank H. Anderson of the Canteen Corporation that the College would "undertake a drive to raise sufficient funds to take care of the present deficit (which was running from $1,500 to $2,000 a month) for the current school year and try to secure a sufficient reserve to insure operations for the School year following (1941–1942). We will be guided in our decisions as to the future of the College by the size of our enrollment at the beginning of the 1942–1943 school year." Dr. MacBain explained that if the drive for financial support failed and the hoped-for financial reserve to cover operations for 1942–1943 also failed to materialize, a final decision would be necessitated in June or early summer "so that students who are depending on our College would be able to make other arrangements for the completion of their education."

There was again talk of mergers, this time with one or more of the three midwestern osteopathic schools located in Des Moines, Kansas City, and Kirksville. Two of the schools, Dr. MacBain conjectured, would suspend operations only if their assets were exhausted completely, and the third was "relatively wealthy" and with assets primarily in the form of buildings and real estate which "would have little value for purposes other than those to which they are now being put." Dr. MacBain concluded: "I doubt if a merger would be practical or possible in the near future."

On October 16, 1941, Mr. Anderson wrote Dr. MacBain suggesting that a group of the school's most active supporters meet "to face the issues bluntly." These men would include Drs. MacBain, Collins, Lindberg [4], and Peckham, and Messrs. Henry, Farrell, and Anderson. As a leader in this group Mr. Anderson believed the College had one of three options: (1) merge with another school; (2) attract more students within a specific length of time; or (3) discontinue the school. Obvious to all was that a substantial amount of money must be raised if the school were to survive.

In December, 1941, Dr. MacBain wrote Mr. Anderson again—to report that requests for funds had been sent out and that $12,545.25 had been received in contributions by the College, plus pledges for an additional $3,061.50. The cash received would permit the college to reduce its operating deficit and, with the help of winter quarter tuition fees payable on January 1, 1942, pay off all current obligations outstanding prior to December 1 as well as covering the January 1st payroll. It was, however, another stop-gap measure [5].

With the entry of the United States into World War II, the College was forced to tighten its belt as never before. In January, 1942, Dr. MacBain reported in a letter to alumni that the monthly salary payroll of $3,175 had been slashed to $2,185—a cut of $990 and one which the faculty itself had voted to accept. The number of full-time employees was reduced from 10 to 25 percent, and salaries pared by 50 percent. Commenting on the economy measures, Dr. MacBain said:

> This reduction does not quite meet our needs, but it brings us much closer to operating within our budget. We trust that at the end of this school year in June, we will be able to pick up the extra amount needed by gifts. We are at least approximating a balanced budget.

In a letter to the faculty, Dr. MacBain presented further details regarding the College's critical situation. He stated that while the faculty and staff organization had been based on a student enrollment of 150 to 170 students, the actual enrollment had dropped to an alarming 93. The combined operations of the College and Hospital were incurring a monthly deficit of $1,500 to $2,000, most of it by the College. Gifts had declined sharply since the outbreak of the war and the erasure of deficits by such income could no longer be counted on. The order was to cut, cut, cut!

Dr. MacBain wrote: "It has become necessary for us to institute every possible economy that each and all of us can devise in the next six months.

We must get along on a minimum of equipment; a minimum of new purchases and saving of every minor item that we can think of."

Many lay members of the Board of Trustees felt that the situation was now so acute that operations in 1942 should be suspended altogether and the faculty assigned to hospital duty and thus be available when the national emergency was over and the institute could resume normal operations. Dr. MacBain opposed this proposal strongly, however, contending that to pursue such a measure "would be a grave decision and one which would mean the loss of practically all the ground we have gained." If worst came to worst, Dr. MacBain protested, "we would attempt to operate some kind of a school for those who are able to attend and go through the motions of giving an education, depending largely on volunteer instructors."

As part of the war-dictated strategy, the College went on an accelerated teaching program at the beginning of the 1942 spring quarter, compressing its normal four-year program into three calendar years by omitting vacations and requiring students to study through the summer months [6].

The serious financial plight of the College did not go unnoticed by the osteopathic profession, for the ills which plagued the Chicago institution were shared in many respects by the other osteopathic colleges. Under the sponsorship of the American Osteopathic Association, a united fund-raising campaign was launched in 1943 to save the osteopathic colleges from complete disaster. Designated as the "Osteopathic Progress Fund," a nationwide drive to raise nearly $1 million was begun [7]. The drive was directed at both the profession and to those outside the profession for the purpose of "increasing greatly the [colleges'] facilities for wartime and postwar teaching and public service." The Chicago College of Osteopathy, one of the four colleges involved, was asked to raise $200,000 for new or improved buildings and equipment, laboratories and teaching personnel.

Quotas were assigned to the other colleges as well: the College of Osteopathic Physicians and Surgeons of Los Angeles, $250,000; the Kansas City College of Osteopathy and Surgery, $125,000; and the Philadelphia College of Osteopathy, $250,000. The campaign was publicized as "one of the most important osteopathic forward movements in unison since the founding of the first Osteopathic college some fifty years ago [8]."

The drive began in June, 1943, and was to end in August of that year. In preparation for conducting its full share of the campaign, the College signed a contract on May 7, 1943, with the American City Bureau, a professional fund-raising organization located in New York City, for conducting the drive to raise $200,000. Under the terms of the contract, the American City Bureau would assign three men to direct the campaign: a campaign manager who would serve for 14 weeks; an assistant campaign manager who would serve for 12 weeks; and a publicity director who would work a total of two weeks. In return for the firm's services, the College would pay the American City Bureau a fee of $9,150, with $4,150 payable at the end of the seventh week of the campaign, and the balance at the termination of the 14-week campaign. The CCO drive was to begin on May 17.

The College prepared for the campaign with thoroughness. It appointed Purcell L. Smith, president of the Middle West Service Company, as general chairman and organized three separate divisions for the active solicitations: (1) the Chicago District Division, which included Cook, Lake, and Du Page counties; (2) the Campus Division, which consisted of the College and Hospital faculty, employees and students; and (3) the College Area Division, which embraced the nearby states of Michigan, Ohio, Indiana and Wisconsin. Twenty-five alumni leaders were appointed to handle the campaign in the surrounding states, with Dr. Samuel V. Robuck acting as chairman of this wing of the fund-raising campaign.

To explain and publicize the drive, the College issued a folder captioned "Wartime Responsibilities" and under the heading "A Challenge to Osteopathic Physicians" informed the reader:

> Due to ever-increasing public obligations placed on osteopathy, it is now urgent that immediate steps be taken for the expansion of the physical facilities and faculties of approved osteopathic colleges in order that osteopathic education, training and research may take its rightful place in the science of healing. The study and practice of osteopathy have been certified by the War Manpower Commission as critical occupations in which there exist a serious need for additional persons to perform services necessary to the health, safety and welfare of the nation.
>
> War demands have made it necessary for the colleges to accelerate their courses, strengthen their work in osteopathic concept, public health, tropical medicine, in war services generally. They must operate on a 52-week basis. Up to this point, the colleges have been able to take the developments in their stride. These greater demands and recognitions are a mandate to the osteopathic profession to increase its values and services, within an emergency limit of time.

The Chicago College of Osteopathy knew exactly where the $200,000 would be spent. The breakdown was as follows: $50,000 for faculty, to maintain professorships and fellowships; $10,000 for research, to finance sustained investigations and provide for personnel and equipment; $100,000 for enlarging the College-Hospital Building facilities, teaching beds, and maintenance; $6,335 for purchasing books and equipment for the library; $24,665 for departmental and laboratory equipment; $9,000 for administrative purposes, including a full-time president.

Leaders of the Chicago phase of the national campaign worked hard to make the drive a success. In August, leaders in the Campus Division announced that their quota of $10,000 had already been over-subscribed. Dr. Robuck, who directed the metropolitan Chicago district solicitation, announced that more than 3,000 friends of osteopathy had been contacted and a special booklet, "New Osteopathic Horizons" had been prepared to help the fund-raising. Harry Bliss, director of the Chicago District Division, happily announced that Dr. H. L. Samblanet had accepted the task of organizing a "500 Club" for the purpose of persuading at least fifty contributors to become members by subscribing $500 each. The "500 Club" was limited to members of the profession, and in August Dr. Samblanet reported that the largest single contribution up to that time had been received—a pledge of $2,500! [9]."

The drive continued briskly on all fronts. On August 27, the College reported that it had raised $66,193 of its $200,000 quota (national receipts amounted to $373,000). Dr. Floyd Peckham, CCO treasurer, announced that building plans were proceeding on the assumption that the drive would succeed. "The first thing," he declared, "that will be done is to erect a new building to increase the number of teaching beds." He added: "The great immediate need is for every doctor in the profession to make his or her gift to the college of his or her choice. Delay is the most dangerous thing we have to face [10]."

Although both the College and the AOA had high hopes for the campaign's success, it was evident that the full quota would not be reached within the time period originally scheduled. The College trustees accordingly voted to continue the campaign "over a considerable period", and while the number of contributions and pledges was slowly increasing from month to month, the AOA and the American Association of Osteopathic Colleges drew up a five-year plan early in 1946 to continue the solicitation on a national scale until December 31, 1950, and set a goal of $7,500,000 [11].

In 1943, Willard J. Henry, vice president of the Southern Advance Bag & Paper Company, succeeded Dr. Harry L. Collins as President of the Board of Trustees. Before leaving office, Dr. Collins informed the Board of Trustees that the College was in constant readiness for Federal inspection to prove that its teaching and hospital facilities met government standards and the "changing status of medical and osteopathic education accompanying the social and economic conditions." He admitted with some sadness, however, that "the college and hospital have not been able to take many positive steps toward extensive improvements in the academic and physical spheres. It is hoped that the successful outcome of the Fund Raising Campaign will make some major improvements possible [12]."

The College boosted its tuition fees from $80 per quarter to $100 [13] as wartime costs shot upward and the college's enrollment shrivelled to 92. Dr. Collins told the trustees that library facilities were grossly inadequate and the trustees agreed to hire the librarian from nearby George Williams College on a part-time basis for $75 per month. The trustees went even further by authorizing the expenditure of $500 for library needs but with the hope that the Student Council would contribute half this amount from student activity fees. The library staff offered its help by soliciting gifts in the form of textbooks, subscriptions to periodicals and other necessary materials with the hope that such gifts might help wipe out a budget deficit of $2,300.

The College was having trouble with the draft boards. These manpower agencies remained unconvinced of the sincerity of many students seeking deferments in order to study osteopathic medicine and who were accordingly refused deferment from the armed forces. The draft boards also viewed with suspicion many older students who had been studying in other fields but who now decided to transfer their interests to osteopathic medicine. Yet in spite of such skirmishes, the College continued to maintain its No. 1 ranking among the osteopathic colleges in the results scored by its graduates in state board licensing examinations [14]. Achievements of this kind helped in some measure to soften the impact of financial setbacks such as the loss of $10,897 in operating expense for the 1943–1944 school year!

As the war continued, conditions at CCO gave no indications of improvement. In April, 1945, at the annual meeting of the Corporation (held in Room 1717 of the 25 East Washington Street office building) President MacBain detailed some of the problems confronting the college and hospital. They appeared serious, indeed.

Since July 1, 1944, he reported, no new students had been deferred to enter professional training. "The only ones who have matriculated," he said, "have been men physically disqualified for military service, veterans discharged from the Armed Forces, and women. In the past year, only eight students have matriculated in the College. Our enrollment has dropped from 129 in 1940 to 56 at the present time. A further decrease will probably take place during the summer when two classes numbering 18 and 19, respectively, are to be graduated. New matriculations, while expected to be larger than during the past year, will hardly compensate for this decrease."

The College would, Dr. MacBain promised, concentrate its recruiting among the discharged veterans and was contacting the Veterans Administration and government vocational guidance agencies acting on behalf of service men, to acquaint them with the opportunities offered by osteopathic medicine. The College also lost some of its faculty members to the armed forces and was bracing itself for further losses in personnel.

In the face of all its problems and difficulties, however, the College still had $115,000 on hand from the Osteopathic Progress Fund and several thousand dollars more in "very good pledges." It had land, buildings, and equipment valued conservatively at $250,000. Floyd Peckham expressed the hope that the profession would continue "a program of annual giving" and that "large sums may eventually come from interested lay people who are financially able to contribute."

Aware of such reassuring facts, the Board of Trustees, at a special meeting on August 29, 1945, voted to borrow $125,000 from Cooper, Kanaley and Company for erecting a new three-story addition to the main college building. The new structure would utilize the ground floor for hospital and administrative offices, and the second and third floors for 50 additional beds for hospital patients [15]. On November 28, more than 200 persons attended groundbreaking ceremonies for the hospital addition which would, with its fifty additional beds, increase the Hospital's total bed capacity to 105 and make possible five more internships. Perhaps no one in the crowd was happier than Dr. George H. Carpenter who had been president of the College for so many years and who from 1916 to 1927 had served as President of the Hospital's Board of Trustees as well.

In 1946, the war now ended, the College began modifying its wartime schedules. The June class of 1946 was the last one to be accepted for the 36-month accelerated program. The classes entering in the fall of 1946 and the spring of 1947 would complete their programs in 39 months, while matriculants in September, 1947, would be on the regular four-year program. In October, 1946, Dr. Walter C. Eldreth was appointed full-time Dean and at the annual meeting in the fall the trustees learned that, in spite of increasing hospital admissions and revenues, the corporation was still losing money. It had, in fact, sustained a deficit of $1,352 for the 1945–1946 year. This was, happily, a smaller one than in many previous years, but it was nevertheless a matter that needed correction at the earliest possible moment.

As the decade began drawing to a close, the College stirred with new life. Enrollment reached a total of 215 for the 1949–1950 year, with 74 percent represented by veterans. Applications for admissions were showing healthy increases and all facilities, Dr. MacBain reported, were being "stretched to the limit." The faculty now numbered 61, with twenty-seven of the teaching staff ranked as full professors, nineteen as associate professors, and fifteen as assistant professors, plus eight instructors and thirteen laboratory assistants. The outpatient clinic was handling an average of 175 people daily, and the Hospital's nursing staff consisted of 29 registered nurses, two graduate nurses, three undergraduate nurses, and nine aides. It was a well-trained, efficient staff.

An event of tremendous importance to the development of the Chicago College—perhaps one of the most rewarding during the school's first half century—was the working arrangement effected, in 1949–1950, with the Detroit Osteopathic Hospital located at 12523 Third Avenue, and the Art Centre Hospital at 5435 Woodward Avenue, also in Detroit. These two institutions, one with a bed capacity of 172, and the other with 75, in one swift stroke increased the Chicago school's bed capacity to 340 teaching beds. By virtue of this arrangement, an exchange of faculty members became possible with a net increase of twenty to the Chicago College's actual teaching corps.

The liaison meant much to the students' professional training as well. Seniors were now assigned to spend three months in residence at the Detroit hospitals thereby gaining valuable clinical experience in both the Chicago and Detroit osteopathic centers. The senior class was divided into sections with each assigned to Detroit at a different time of the year so that, at any given time, a contingent of CCO seniors was in residence there. The initial arrangement was made with the Detroit Osteopathic Hospital in late 1949, the one with the Art Centre Hospital in June, 1950. The association was a happy one in every respect, and the arrangement with DOH remains in effect today.

In 1947 the College lost two of its respected and admired founders: James B. Littlejohn, who died in Chicago on May 21, and his older brother, J. Martin Littlejohn, who died in England on December 8. These men were indeed two individuals who cast "long shadows" among the small group which established the college in 1900 and directed its early progress.

Before the end of the decade Dr. Harry L. Collins resigned as President of the Board of Trustees, after serving in that position during various periods for a total of twelve years, so that he could devote full time to his hospital staff duties and his work as Chairman of the Department of Surgery. At the Board meeting on September 9, 1948, Dr. Floyd F. Peckham was elected to succeed him and thus begin his eighteen years of distinguished service as President of the Board of Trustees.


The Chicago College of Osteopathy could look back on its first fifty years with pride and satisfaction. Its student body had grown from a total of four and a faculty of five in 1900 to an enrollment of 241 and a faculty of 71. It had two large, well-equipped buildings with a 105-bed capacity on the Hyde Park campus with classrooms, laboratories, and clinics. Its annual budget had grown from $5,000 in 1900 to $723,512, and applications for admission were coming in so heavily (600 for the 1949 fall term!) that Dean Walter Eldrett remarked that "it would require an extreme amount of screening to obtain the desired ones to be admitted." Tuition was set at a flat $500 for the school year but with the cheerful explanation that this figure was still below that charged at some of the other osteopathic hospitals and substantially lower than that which prevailed at most medical schools. Hospital facilities were being taxed to the utmost, the number of patient visits increasing from 21,223 to 27,615 in a single year (1949–1950). The Hospital desperately needed additional nursing help and offered a 10 percent bonus to those completing a full year of service.

Additional space was also sorely needed in the College. Dr. MacBain urged the Trustees to give thought to a new anatomy laboratory so that the one then in use could be converted into classrooms. A new classroom seating 75 students was a "must," Dr. MacBain proclaimed, and any new addition should be in terms of at least two stories and costing between $40,000 and $50,000.

Deficits were still appearing with monotonous regularity, and the CCO president announced a loss of $27,516 for the 1949–1950 year, but this was reduced by income from other funds to a net loss of $1,105. Gift income, however, was beginning to take on substantial proportions. The $42,713 received during 1949–1950 was looked upon as an omen of what might be anticipated in the years ahead.

While the achievements during the College's first half century could be noted with considerable gratification, there remained in the background a familiar refrain. It was expressed succinctly by President MacBain in his report for 1949–1950: "The college and hospital have now outgrown the new plant facilities constructed since 1945. We lack adequate classrooms for our larger student body. Our clinic volume is limited by lack of space. Our anatomy laboratory is crowded, and the growing hospital occupancy will soon require consideration of additional bed and service rooms. We recommend that plans to secure all possible financial support be studied."

### REFERENCES

1. Minutes of the Meeting of the Board of Governors, November 24, 1940.
2. Minutes of the Board of Trustees Meeting, November 4, 1940.
3. From the Minutes of the Meeting of the Board of Trustees, November, 4, 1940.

4. Dr. Ralph F. Lindberg was superintendent of the Chicago Osteopathic Hospital at this time and a member of the CCO faculty.

5. The assets of the College corporation were considered to be sound. The College had 461 feet of frontal property on Ellis Avenue, a 50-bed, fully equipped hospital, a college capable of handling 200 students with the necessary laboratories, classrooms and teaching equipment. The College was also actively recruiting, and a three-reel promotional film, "The Training of an Osteopathic Physician" was being well received by P.T.A. groups, senior classes in high schools, pre-medic clubs and other organizations from which matriculants might be expected.

6. The year 1942 brought other significant events, too. In June, Lester B. Whetten resigned as Dean to join the staff of the University of Colorado and was replaced by Dr. Seaver A. Tarulis. Two of the school's most prominent faculty members died: Dr. Fred Bischoff, who had served for many years as either Secretary or Treasurer in addition to carrying on his other duties as Board member, physician and teacher; and Dr. Ernest R. Proctor, organizer of the free children's clinic and another long-time member of the faculty and Board of Trustees.

7. *Journal AOA,* June, 1943, pp. 449–451. (Vol. 42). The full title of the campaign was "The Osteopathic Progress Fund for the Advancement of Professional Education and the Public Health and Welfare."

8. *Ibid.*

9. *Journal AOA,* August, 1943, pp. 572–573. (Vol. 42)

10. *Ibid.,* September, 1943, p. 24. (Vol. 43)

11. The Chicago College, however, announced with great satisfaction that its quota of $200,000 was reached in July, 1946, and that a new clinical teaching hospital was nearing completion and would be ready for occupancy in the fall of 1946.

12. *The President's Report,* August 11, 1943.

13. This increase prevailed until 1946 when the tuition was raised to $135 per quarter.

14. *The President's Report,* August 11, 1943.

15. By the fall of 1946 the cost of the new building had risen to an estimated $294,000! When the hospital wing was dedicated on February 8, 1947, the cost had reached approximately $300,000.

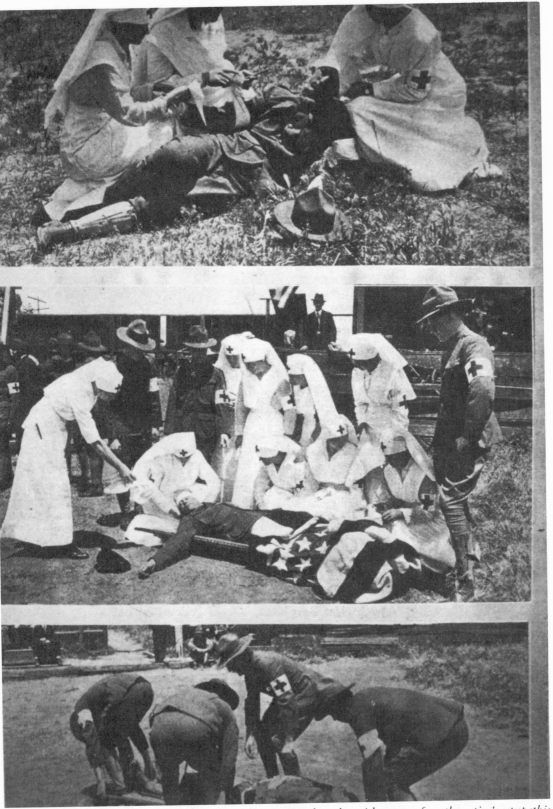

U.S. declaration of war against Germany and her allies in 1917 brought quick response from the nation's osteopathic colleges. At CCO, military drill was instituted, along with classes in first aid. Physicians, teachers, nurses, students and others signed up for these activities. Photo shows typical wartime activities on the campuses of the osteopathic colleges.

*Treatment of war casualties is demonstrated by nurses and medics. CCO students, faculty and staff members quickly volunteered for wartime service, and in collaboration with the AOA and Chicago Osteopathic Association, formed a field unit trained and equipped for war duty. Dr. W. Burr Allen was chairman of CCO's mobilization effort.*

*In the summer of 1918, during a savage influenza epidemic, the College moved from its quarters on West Monroe Street to this building on Chicago's south side. Built originally as an orphanage, the structure for many years housed both the College and the Hospital. Sections of it are still in use today. Remodelling was made from time to time as the need arose.*

*This is the south wing of the CCO building on Ellis Avenue. For many years the entrance to the Clinic was located in this wing. Patients from throughout the city sought medical help as the College offered its services to all. Clinic patients paid if they could, were given free treatment if they could not. No one was turned away.*

*Rapidly expanding needs as CCO moved into its new quarters in Chicago's Hyde Park section prompted fund-raising campaigns to obtain money for new buildings, equipment, staff additions. This 1919 advertisement offered 6 percent real estate bonds and emphasized the College's physical assets to back up its financial soundness.*

*Student recruiting was a "must" for all osteopathic colleges. This 1918 advertisement urged osteopathic physicians everywhere to send students to CCO. Often letters were sent to colleges and universities pointing out the career opportunities which osteopathic medicine offered men and women. Field recruiting was also conducted.*

*The Chicago Osteopathic Hospital took great pride in its nurses' training program. This 1919 advertisement announced that 25 pupil nurses could be accepted for training immediately. In addition to the rewards listed, there were also financial inducements: a salary of $20 per month during the first year, and $25 per month during the second!*

Dr. Fred W. Gage of CCO was one of the College's early courtroom fighters. He won an important legal victory for Illinois osteopathic physicians in 1917. He was also a CCO trustee.

Dr. Samuel V. Robuck retired from CCO in 1965 after 51 years with the College as physician and teacher. He was nationally known for his work as lecturer and writter. His career with CCO began in 1914.

Dr. James A. Fraser, CCO faculty member, won national acclaim in 1919 when he helped restore to health a 13-year-old Evanston girl who had been in a coma for 40 days. Other physicians had called her case hopeless.

Dr. Jessie O'Connor was Chairman of the Department of Gynecology in the early 1920's and for many years Vice President of the Board of Trustees. She was one of a number of outstanding women D.O.'s at the College.

A search for the most perfect human spine was widely publicized in 1921. Here Drs. Oliver C. Foreman and Chester H. Morris of CCO examine the backs of chorus girls appearing in a Chicago theater with the famous Eddie Cantor. Prize for the person adjudged to have the most perfect spine was $1,000.

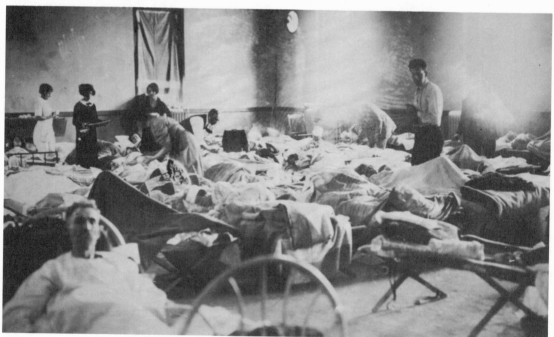

This hurriedly set up medical depot was typical of the first aid stations in Carbondale and other southern Illinois communities in March, 1925, after a vicious tornado killed 848 people and injured nearly 3,000 others. CCO sent Dr. W. C. McGregor and a number of senior students to administer aid. Many relief trains rushed supplies to the area.

*Perhaps no single individual was more dedicated to the welfare of the College than Dr. Floyd F. Peckham, after whom the Basic Science Building is named. He was outstanding as Treasurer, Board secretary, administrator, teacher. He served CCO for many decades.*

*Dr. W. Don Craske was an M.D. as well as a D.O. He graduated from CCO, later became Chairman of the Department of Surgery. He was another of those who fought relentlessly to obtain equal rights for osteopathic medicine and CCO accreditation.*

*Jerome H. Raymond, Ph.D., was CCO's first full-time Dean and the first chosen from outside the profession. He did much to raise the standard of osteopathic medicine and education. He was dean from 1919 to 1928.*

*Dr. Martin V. Beilke's career with the College spanned more than four decades. He graduated from CCO in 1928, knew personally many of the College's early teachers and administrators.*

*A CCO football clinic in the 1930's. Directed by* **Dr. James A. Stinson,** *the clinic treated many football players in Chicago's south side area. In one year alone (1931) more than 113 players were treated at this clinic and more than 500 treatments given; sixteen teams in the south end area took advantage of the clinic's services.*

*Dr. Earl R. Hoskins was an X-ray specialist and one of the College's brilliant professional pioneers. His technique of photographing the spine represented an important advance in osteopathic X-ray work.*

*Dr. James A. Stinson of the CCO faculty was a specialist in treating athletic injuries. Here he is shown with Ed Linke of the Washington Senators baseball team in 1935.*

The Detroit Osteopathic Hospital, Detroit, Mich. In 1949, CCO effected a working arrangement with the Michigan hospital for exchanging students and faculty members. The 172 beds of the Detroit hospital substantially increased the number of teaching beds available to CCO, and provided valuable additional facilities for CCO intern training.

Art Centre Hospital, Detroit, Mich. This hospital entered into a working agreement with CCO at the same time the pact with the larger Detroit Osteopathic Hospital was signed. Although smaller than DOH, its 75 beds, when added to those at DOH, gave the Chicago College of Osteopathy a total of 340 teaching beds.

One of the last available photographs of Dr. J. Martin Littlejohn is this one taken in 1938 in London. He was guest of honor at the opening of a bazaar in Livingston Hall, Westminster, a gala event sponsored by the Ladies Osteopathic League to raise funds for the British School of Osteopathy. In the photo, left to right: Lady Dorothy D'Oyle Carte, President of the Ladies Osteopathic League; Mrs. Clark, Chairman of the League; Dr. Littlejohn; Dr. Dorothy Wood and Mrs. Mitchell Fox, Vice Presidents.

# 10

# THE PACE QUICKENS: THE 1950'S

AFTER the achievements of the school's first fifty years had been duly noted and celebrated [1], the College Corporation felt that an appropriate manner in which to begin the next half century would be to increase the number of trustees serving on the Board and to broaden the number of fields from which they were selected. In October, 1951, the by-laws were therefore revised to hike the Board's membership to fifteen and to spell out the qualifications of the Trustees.

The Board ruled that one of the fifteen must come from the osteopathic profession at large; three from the CCO Alumni Association; six from business, industry, and finance; one from the field of education; one from the legal profession; one from organized labor; one from philanthropy; and the fifteenth would be the President of the Illinois Osteopathic Association (IOA) whose term on the Board would coincide with his term of office as IOA president.

An accompanying important change as the College began its second fifty years was the decision to make the school's presidency a full-time, rather than a part-time, position. In August, 1951, the Board invited Dr. Richard N. MacBain to continue his duties as President, but as a full-time administrator, and to "assume the responsibilities of Chief Executive Officer of the Corporation [who shall] become responsible for the activities of the Chicago College of Osteopathy and the Chicago Osteopathic Hospital, including the faculty, staff, and all other employees of the institution." The President would be responsible to the Board of Trustees and "report to them from time to time as practical [2]."

The 1950's witnessed expansion plans for the College that would have delighted the school's founders—together with an ever-widening sphere of activity and influence. In the 1952–1953 school year the College's budget for the first time passed the million dollar mark, reaching a figure of $1,006,496. The Hospital and Clinic were providing nearly $100,000 worth of free and low-cost medical service to low-income patients. A Mid-Century Fund drive was begun to raise $150,000 for building purposes.

Providing tremendous impetus to the College's growing recognition and prestige was the ruling of the Illinois Supreme Court in 1955 ordering the Illinois Department of Registration and Education to approve the Chicago College of Osteopathy as a school "whose graduates are eligible to take the examination for a license to practice medicine in all its branches." This momentous decision culminated more than thirty years of struggle by the College and the osteopathic profession in Illinois to win the right of CCO graduates to take the examinations qualifying them to practice medicine in all its branches and to offer the services which they had been trained to provide. [The story of the College's long fight to win full accreditation and for its graduates the privileges accorded other members of the medical profession, is narrated in the chapter "Road to Victory" in the Appendix.]

A 94-page report by an outside committee which had investigated the College gave the institution a highly favorable rating while at the same time recommending specific changes. The report read, in part:

> The Chicago College of Osteopathy is a credit to the profession. When one considers the hardships and the difficult legal stituation which exists in the state of Illinois, it is hard to conceive how an institution such as this has done so well with the funds which are available to it. The administration, faculty and student body seemed equal if not superior to that found in other medical institutions of learning. The frankness and willingness to share the problems and evaluate their weaknesses was a particularly commendable spirit. The addition of the new hospital unit in recent years has increased the efficiency of the entire teaching plant.

The report further recommended that a distinct separation be made between the College and the Chicago Osteopathic Hospital and urged that the educational activities be directed by a Dean of the College and the Hospital operations by an over-all superintendent. Both men were to report to the president of the college. It seemed like a logical distinction.

In the mid '50's, the College launched a 10-year expansion program that was the most ambitious yet attempted. As a start, the College purchased additional property adjoining the campus. This acquisition included 15,000 square feet of property on the northwest corner of 53rd Street and University Avenue and the one-story building which stood on the land. There were other parcels, too, so that a total of 40,000 square feet of land were purchased, including buildings (a two-story school, two large mansions, and a coach house) at a cost of $168,500. The buildings were quickly converted to college use. Into the two-story school building were transferred classes in anatomy, physiology and pharmacology, chemistry, microscopic anatomy and pathology laboratories, and the bacteriology department. One of the mansions was remodeled to provide space for administrative offices, admissions, records, President, Dean, a library, faculty meeting room and other purposes. The second mansion was remodeled for use as a student center, with locker rooms, coffee shop, lounge, recreation rooms, student apartments and dormitories.

These acquisitions were but temporary improvements providing only temporary relief. Much larger facilities were needed. At the Board of Trustees meeting on October 24, 1956, Dr. MacBain recommended that a new basic science building be erected at 53rd Street and University Avenue; that the hospital be expanded; and that a new outpatient clinic be constructed. The cost of these three major improvements, he estimated, would be between $175,000 and $190,000. The College had on hand, he added, $106,000 which had been provided by the Progress Fund and special gifts—enough to get started on the basic science building which was the most pressing need at this time. On December 4, 1956, ground was broken for the new basic science facility at 1122 East 53rd Street.

While the Chicago College was now thinking in terms far more ambitious than those of the past, an admonition received from the Kirksville osteopathic college pleaded that the true purpose of osteopathy should never be forgotten by any of the colleges dedicated to the education and training of osteopathic physicians. In a long letter to Dr. Floyd Peckham, Prof. Irvin M. Korr of the Kirksville school's physiology department warned:

> Too large a portion of the physicians in the profession fail to demonstrate in their practices a comprehension of the basic principles of osteopathy, the osteopathic concept, and of the fundamental difference between osteopathy and allopathy—differences which are basically so great as to have made necessary the establishment of a separate profession. . . .
>
> The growth of the profession—and its survival as a separate and distinct school of practice—require that those differences be sharp and clear in practice, that its distinctive features and the advantages of those features, be unmistakably demonstrated in its practice by every practitioner. Every "non-osteopathic" D.O. misleads a segment of the public as to what is and is not osteopathy. . . .
>
> The D.O. becomes distinguishable from the M.D. only by the inclusion of an additional technique (manipulation). . . .
>
> The winning of a place for osteopathy as a distinct, indispensable, superior (not equal) complete system of healing or prevention will not be achieved in courts, in legislative bodies, in attorneys' offices or in public relations campaigns. It will be won in the educational system, in the field

and in the laboratory. The winning of this victory will bring a new kind of security (and opportunity) to the profession—since no law, no court, no act of Congress or A.M.A. can destroy a scientific fact [3].

The plea from Kirksville was one that Dr. MacBain had stressed time and again during his years as CCO president. In one of his annual reports he stated: "Our justification for existence, our ability to survive and grow, our whole purpose revolves around our ability to use and to incorporate into our teaching the specific and unique contributions which osteopathy makes to medicine. Our success will be directly determined by the degree in which this basic philosophy can be applied [4]."

In 1956 the College began to consider the adoption of a retirement plan for its faculty and staff members, a benefit now enjoyed by teachers and workers throughout the United States. The Trustees believed that such a plan could be financed either through a trust fund administered by a bank or through an "old-line insurance company." It was not until 1962, however, that a workable and acceptable plan went into effect [5].

While faculty pension plans were being studied by the Board members, their attention was drawn to another situation reminiscent of the late 1920's—a student protest. Fifty-five members of the senior class refused to take the final examinations scheduled for February 28, 1956, and were quickly asked to send their representatives to appear before the seven-member Committee on Education of which Dr. Paul van B. Allen was chairman. The senior class spokesman protested to the committee that the College had no set policy for the handling of student problems regarding scholastic failures; that the grading of examination papers was not done until after the announced deadlines; that lines of authority were not well established and recognized; that student orientation was inconsistent at "all levels of school experience," and that they were not given adequate audiences with the Faculty. The students asked that a liaison committee be organized to function between the students and the faculty; that they be permitted to submit an annual report to the Board of Trustees; and that "the various levels of authority and responsibility be clearly established for everyone's information."

The Trustees, after reviewing the student grievances, concluded that the attitude of the students was not a malicious one but informed the students that refusing to take final examinations was a hardly a proper way to express their grievances. The Board determined also that the Senior Class had been subjected to influences not friendly to the College; that the class had been ill-advised; and to help settle the matter, re-scheduled the examinations for March 5. The Trustees expressed their complete confidence in the faculty and officers "whom they considered competent to deal with any suggestions the students cared to make on an individual basis."

President MacBain, replying to an inquiry from a Chicago newspaper which carried news of the students' refusal to take final examinations, explained that such examinations had been given for 26 years and helped to prepare students for the state examinations. Actually, Dr. MacBain declared, the trouble was caused by "senioritis complicated by pre-exam fright [6]."

Meanwhile, building construction moved forward. On September 19, 1957, the new three-story Floyd F. Peckham Basic Science Building at 1122 East 53rd Street was dedicated. More than 500 people attended the ceremonies and banquet which followed in the evening. The building which was to have cost $175,000, now had a price tag of nearly $258,000, not including equipment or furnishings. Yet more than $207,000 had already been raised toward defraying its cost and there was an optimistic feeling that the balance of nearly $51,000 would somehow be paid off as loan installments fell due.

To continue its expansion, the College was eager to acquire more land in the neighborhood so its campus could be increased and beautified. Fortunately, such acquisitions became possible as the result of the city's urban renewal program and the College could realistically anticipate a campus of four and one half acres rather than one of less than two [7].

In August, 1958, Dr. Walter C. Eldrett, who had served as Dean for twelve years, retired to North Carolina and was succeeded by Dr. Robert A. Kistner, a graduate of the College in 1941 and of the Loyola University Stritch School of Medicine in 1953. Several years earlier, Dr. Samuel V. Robuck, a teacher and practitioner who had served for more than forty years as a member of the faculty, retired from active duty and was succeeded as Chairman of the Department of Osteopathic Medicine by Dr. K. R. M. Thompson, a faculty member since 1932 [8].

In the fall of 1958, Dr. MacBain told the Trustees that the time had come to consider the new hospital, a facility that had been badly needed for years. He reported that two parcels of land would soon become available—through urban renewal—as the site for the new building and at a cost of $100,000. The hospital itself, he conjectured, would cost in the neighborhood of $650,000, and he envisioned a four-story building with surgical operating rooms, obstetrical delivery rooms, pediatrics and X-ray departments. The new hospital would raise total bed capacity to 134 and provide twenty additional bassinettes. Dr. MacBain recommended that the project be initially financed by means of a mortgage loan and gifts. After reviewing the possible sources of a loan, the Trustees glumly concluded "it would not be an easy matter to negotiate," and once again considered hiring a fund-raising agency to procure the needed funds. In the wake of such expansion proposals, tuition was again increased—from $750 a year to $800.

Indicative of the manner in which the College was keeping abreast of the times was the establishment in 1959 of a Department of Nuclear Medicine, with Dr. George T. Caleel in charge. Aided by Federal funds, a course in radioisotope procedures as applied to life science was established. Commenting on this development, Dr. Caleel said: "Use of radioactive tracers and medications in diagnosis and therapy is proving very effective in avoiding major surgery and in hastening the recovery from illnesses for many patients [9]."

No individuals worked with greater devotion and dedication for the success of the Chicago College of Osteopathy and the Chicago Osteopathic Hospital than did the women associated with these two institutions. Throughout the years, by means of their volunteer work, tag day solicitations, bazaars, benefits, charity balls and many other fund-raising projects, the faculty and staff wives and other women interested in osteopathic medicine worked tirelessly to advance the work of the Chicago Osteopathic Center.

The activities of the women's groups were particularly prominent during the 1950's, but the contributions of the various women's organizations, though perhaps less publicized, have been vital to the school's growth almost since its founding.

The earliest organized woman's group was the "Woman's Board of the Chicago Osteopathic Hospital" which in 1918 became known as the "Woman's Auxiliary to the Chicago Osteopathic Hospital" when the institution moved from its west side location to Hyde Park. The founders of this group believe that their auxiliary was the first of its kind in the osteopathic profession and that it was the forerunner of the prominent women's national osteopathic association in existence today.

In any event, the members of the woman's auxiliary won the gratitude of all when in, 1918, before the building at 53rd Street and Ellis Avenue could be used for any purpose at all, they appeared with water buckets, soap and scrub brushes and pitched in to do the hard, physical clean-up work necessary for making the hospital wing habitable for patients [10]. Once the hospital began to function, members of the woman's auxiliaries spent many hours making tray favors for patients, wrapping bandages, sewing for the children's ward and hospital, making articles to be sold in the gift shop, entertaining patients, and raising funds for the purchase of new equipment. In one year alone (1954) the women's guilds contributed $7,000 in equipment and cash to the Hospital.

By the mid 1950's, a number of organized women's groups were active in the life of the college and hospital. These included the "Woman's Auxiliary to the Chicago Osteopathic Hospital," the work of which was conducted through six guilds [11]: the Beverly-Hyde Park, North Side, Roseland, South Side Service, Westwood, and West Suburban groups. There was a Woman's Junior Auxiliary to the Chicago Osteopathic Hospital, an organization which initiated the Babies Alumni program at the hospital [12]. Another organization was the Student Wives' Guild. There were still others working at local, state and national levels, but all with a common goal—the advancement of osteopathic medicine.

By 1960 there were nine active women's groups: (1) the *Beverly-Hyde Park Guild,* whose members lived in these two communities, held an annual dinner dance to raise funds, and made gifts to be sold in the hospital's gift shop; (2) the *Children's Service Guild,* whose members concentrated on pediatric services and purchased oxygen equipment, quartz lamps, hyf-recators, and other facilities used in treating children; (3) the *OB Service Guild,* which in 1958 took over the sponsorship of the Babies Alumni Association and whose members worked with the Obstetrical Department staff in any way they could; (4) the *Roseland Guild,* whose members lived on Chicago's far south side and prepared obstetrical aids at their meetings; (5) the *South Side Service Guild,* whose members did volunteer work in the hospital, such as managing and staffing the gift shop, operating a "traveling cart" which visited the bedsides of hospitalized patients, and raising funds through bakery sales and other projects; (6) the *Towne and Country Guild,* formed in 1959, whose members lived in Oak Lawn, Palos Hills and adjacent communities, and helped with tag day solicitations, the sale of Christmas cards and seals, and making tray favors for hospital patients; (7) the *Westwood Guild,* whose members lived in the western suburbs and sewed for the hospital, made articles for the annual bazaar and helped in any way they could with the various activities sponsored by the auxiliary and the sister guilds; (8) the *COH Volunteers,* whose members served as nurses' aides and provided companionship to patients undergoing treatment; (9) the *Student Wives' Auxiliary,* whose members raised funds and prepared themselves to live and serve as future wives of osteopathic physicians.

Some of these women's organizations have disappeared; others have been reorganized and now function under different names. But the work of the women's groups remains an essential part of both the College and the Hospital, and will be counted upon even more heavily as the osteopathic center expands its physical plant and its role in the community.

As the 1950's drew to a close, the Chicago College of Osteopathy had an enrollment of 250, a faculty of 122, and assets of $1 million. Patient visits in the Clinic now numbered nearly 65,000 a year, and a staff of four full-time physicians, twenty-four part-time physicians, eleven full-time clerks, five part-time clerks, and a student physician staff of 120 ministered to the needs of the sick. It was a far cry from the modest roster the Hospital had been able to muster in earlier years.

## REFERENCES

1. The College officially observed its 50th birthday with a banquet at the Del Prado Hotel on September 21, 1950. On this festive occasion, the College honored eight of its faculty members for having served 25 years on the teaching staff. The eight men were H. L. Collins, W. D. Craske, W. J. Downing, S. A. Herzfeld, R. N. MacBain, G. W. Mac-Gregor, F. F. Peckham, and S. V. Robuck.

2. In 1956, Dr. MacBain's contract was renewed for a five-year period, and his agreement with the Trustees was renewed periodically until his retirement in 1967 after nearly fifty years' association with the College.

3. Letter to Dr. Floyd Peckham by Prof. Irvin M. Korr, dated February 8, 1952.

4. From the *President's Report for 1956–1957.*

5. At the Board meeting on May 16, 1962, Dean R. A. Kistner reported that the retirement plan would be handled by the Teachers Insurance Annuity Association (T.I.A.A.). He presented a letter of appreciation, signed by 24 faculty members, stating that the action of the Trustees "indicates a faith in the future of the college and an interest in maintaining a stable faculty."

6. *Chicago Tribune,* February 29, 1956.

7. The South East Chicago Commission which was supervising the south side urban renewal was eager for the college to develop a 25-year plan and promised to make additional land available. The Commission believed that the prosperity of the college would be beneficial to the entire community, and the success of the urban renewal program would mean new employment opportunities and the means for attracting more people to the area.

8. Dr. Ward Perrin was appointed Vice Chairman of the Department of Medicine and at the same time was asked to continue as coordinator of the cancer teaching program. Dr. Perrin was also named Medical Director of the Hospital Staff and assigned to assist Dr. W. Don Craske, chief of staff.

9. *Forum of Osteopathy,* November, 1959, p. 26.

10. The building was originally constructed for use as an orphanage and had been standing vacant for some years when the Chicago College of Osteopathy and the Chicago Osteopathic Hospital moved into it in 1918 during the height of the influenza epidemic.

11. The Woman's Board of the Auxiliary, which supervised and coordinated the work of the guilds, was composed of one representative from each guild.

12. The Babies Alumni Association was comprised of individuals who had been born in the Chicago Osteopathic Hospital. Regular reunions of these "baby alumni" were held, and the group helped raise money for the obstetrical department. The Babies Alumni Association was formed in 1958.

# 11

# FULL SPEED AHEAD: THE 1960'S

THE OBSERVANCE of the College's sixtieth anniversary was accompanied by a disturbing development in California where a number of osteopathic physicians renounced their profession in order to be absorbed into the ranks of the allopathic practitioners, thus sacrificing their identity as osteopathic physicians. This meant the end of the College of Osteopathic Physicians and Surgeons at Los Angeles which had for years been one of the profession's strong teaching institutions.

The renunciation of osteopathy in the west coast state, however, also served to strengthen the determination of the remaining five osteopathic colleges to stand firm in their common cause and to demonstrate their unwavering allegiance to the profession. The trustees of the Chicago College of Osteopathy voted to join with the colleges in Des Moines, Kansas City, Kirksville, and Philadelphia (and with renewed support from the AOA) in making a firm commitment to maintain the osteopathic profession as a separate and distinct school of practice [1]. The schools were united in their conviction that osteopathy had much to offer; that it had an enormous potential; and that it should resist any attempt to have it absorbed into general medicine.

Dr. MacBain was deeply disappointed that the California osteopaths "had surrendered completely to the medical people, renounced osteopathy and said it had no further contribution to make." "This," Dr. MacBain asserted, "we can never accept." In a letter to Dr. Louis A. Astell of Champaign, Illinois, dated September 19, 1961, Dr. MacBain detailed his views in no uncertain terms. He wrote:

> Should the time ever come when Dr. Still's goal and Dr. Littlejohn's goal of adding knowledge to the medical profession is achieved through the incorporation of osteopathy with genuine acceptance in medicine, then there can be no need for two professions. . . .
> You and I and others who think as we do believe that osteopathy has a

definite contribution to make to the science of medicine. We also believe that the contribution has not yet been recognized by medicine for two reasons. First, the closed mind of the medical profession and second, our inability to adequately present our concept to the medical world at large. This inability stems from failure of communication and from lack of clinical and laboratory research, particularly clinical research. We all know the reasons why we have not been able to carry out the type of a research program that we would like and we make no apology for our failure. At the same time, we have not demonstrated to the satisfaction of the "unbelievers" the true value of osteopathic therapy and treatment.

I think the goal of each and every devoted osteopathic physician is to have the benefits of osteopathic treatment made available to the public at large through its acceptance by and incorporation into general medicine. We are a long way from this goal.

He concluded by predicting sadly that the uniting of medicine and osteopathy was "far, far away," a millennium "much beyond your lifetime and mine."

To provide added administrative support for the increased role the institution appeared destined to play, the Board of Trustees at its annual meeting in 1960 voted to increase the membership from 15 to 21: eighteen members would serve three-year terms while three would serve one-year terms. Expiration dates would be staggered so that each year new trustees would take their seats on the Board.

Indicative of the expansion envisaged for the College in the '60's and '70's was a proposal to build a new osteopathic hospital somewhere in the southwest suburban area of Chicago. In March, 1960, Dr. Floyd F. Peckham, Chairman of the Board of Trustees, received a letter signed by five members of the Board [2] asking that a special meeting be held with President MacBain to discuss a new 100-bed hospital. Attached to the letter was a three-and-one-half page prospectus detailing what such a hospital would mean for osteopathic teaching facilities in Illinois and the influence such a hospital would exert in rekindling the zeal of osteopathic physicians toward their profession.

In reviewing the potential benefits of such a new medical facility, the five trustees predicted that: (1) the hospital would stimulate the erection of other osteopathic hospitals; (2) allow doctors to retain patients who were now being lost to other suburban hospitals; (3) give doctors more time for teaching, practicing and serving the profession (because of unified management); (4) serve to unite staff members in fund-raising efforts directed to foundations, industrial and social groups and individuals; (5) supply added revenue for the furtherance of the Chicago Osteopathic College and teaching hospital; (6) make possible sorely needed additional obstetrical beds in suburban areas; (7) attract new osteopathic physicians to the Chicago area; and (8) stimulate the activation of women's guilds, many of which had ceased to function.

The group proposed that the new hospital be administered by the CCO trustees, administration, and active professional staff; that it be maintained for private patients with teaching privileges for interns, residents, and CCO students; and that any profits be used to expand and increase the service of the institution. The proposal, however, did not receive full support, and the Board therefore did not authorize the project. Disappointed, a number of the staff physicians left the institution.

The year 1960 brought other developments indicating the trends that could be expected during the decade. Tuition was raised from $830 to $900 a year, a practice that had been reluctantly pursued almost from the college's founding and which would continue to plague it as spiralling costs seemed to become a way of life. Union efforts to organize the hospital workers were reported by Dr. MacBain, and these were just the beginning of a continuous campaign that would end only when unionization was achieved. There was now also evident a need for adopting some kind of pension plan for college faculty and hospital employees. The point was emphasized when Dr. Mac-Bain cited the case of a CCO instructor who had retired in 1958 at the age of 71 after ten years of service, yet who was completely without pension benefits and whose income of $1200 one year as a visiting lecturer and $600 in another year, even coupled with social security, "was not enough to live on." Dr. MacBain said, "we would like to see these problems minimized in the future." Happily, they were.

Some face-lifting of the physical plant also occurred. A $50,000 expenditure authorization removed the ungainly steps leading into the outpatient clinic and replaced them with an attractive ground-level entrance. At the same time, the appropriation permitted a new waiting room, emergency and first aid room, a new arrangement for the reception and discharge of patients, and a new waiting room for the X-ray department. The Hospital announced these alterations and improvements to be "the first step in a five-year development program."

In the Hyde Park area where CCO was now rooted, the urban renewal program, which would make valuable property available for campus expansion from time to time, was proceeding vigorously. By the end of January, 1961, 315 properties had been purchased out of a total of 652; 90 of 886 buildings had been demolished; 700 families had been relocated and 700 more scheduled for relocation out of a total of 4,000.

Of particular significance to the College were the properties on Ellis Avenue and other neighborhood streets which had become available and which were eyed with more than passing interest by the administration and the trustees.

In the fall of 1961, tuition was again raised, this time from $900 a year to an even $1,000. At the same time the trustees felt it again advisable to engage the services of a fund-raising agency. A firm was accordingly retained at a $15,000 a year fee. The campaign brought scanty results and a few months later the Board voted to terminate it. Adopted in its place was a more modest fund-raising effort costing but $500 a month.

The following year was significant for the College. Early in 1962 the trustees approved an addition to the Chicago Osteopathic Hospital to be built at an estimated cost of $1,542,000. The project would be largely financed through a 15-year loan of $1,200,000 carrying a 5¾ percent interest charge. A mortgage of $1,347,000 was authorized by the trustees at their meeting on March 1 and the College pledged practically all its corporate assets as collateral. Monthly payments would amount to $11,195, including principal and interest.

On April 2, ground was broken for the new addition which would provide 75 additional beds; a new surgical floor with operating suites; a complete new maternity floor with a delivery room wing; a pediatrics department; new X-ray and outpatient laboratories; a central sterilizing plant and a large parking facility [3]. By this time total costs rose to an estimated $1,912,825, including construction, architect's fees, equipment and furnishings, and the purchase and preparation of land for parking facilities. Yet so well had the expenditure been planned that a balance of only $195,183 remained to be raised. The addition of this facility would on all counts represent a major improvement for the Chicago Osteopathic Hospital and one which would add substantially to the services the institution could provide the community.

In keeping with the sweeping social changes occurring throughout the country and the growing recognition of full rights for minority groups, the trustees of the Chicago Osteopathic Hospital issued an important 7-point declaration of policy for its operation. The provisions read as follows:

1. The determination of whether to admit a person in need of hospitalization will be made by the medical staff without regard to race, creed, color or national origin.
2. Admitting personnel will not ask the race, creed, color or national origin of patients before admission.

3. Room assignments for patients will be made without regard to race, creed, color or national origin. Admissions personnel will not maintain records indicating room assignments by race, creed, color or national origin.
4. The quality of medical care and treatment made available by the hospital will be the same for all, regardless of race, creed, color or national origin.
5. All hospital facilities and services will be made available to patients without regard to race, creed, color or national origin.
6. Race, creed, color or national origin will not be a factor in the recruitment, hiring, job assignment, training, or promotion of employees or trainees.
7. Physicians will be appointed to the staff of the hospital on the basis of merit and without regard to their race, creed, color or national origin.

This 7-point manifesto was forwarded to the Chicago Commission on Human Relations and subsequently distributed by that organization. It was solid evidence of the Hospital's intent to serve the community and city without any limitations as to race, color, creed, or nationality.

To reaffirm the purpose of the College, the Articles of Incorporation were again examined to make sure they made clear that the purpose of the Corporation was "To establish and maintain an educational institution in Illinois as a college to investigate, teach, and advance the science of osteopathic medicine." Moreover, "This corporation shall be conducted not for profit but solely as an educational institution with power to establish and maintain general hospitals, clinics, training schools for nurses, laboratories for research and original investigation, and such other establishments in connection therewith as may become necessary [4]."

As if in endorsement of the reaffirmed purpose of the College and Hospital, a $200,000 bequest from the Ode D. Jennings estate arrived. This was the largest single gift the Hospital had ever received from a private benefactor [5].

The acquisition of property adjoining the CCO campus, made possible by the urban renewal program, continued briskly. In addition to the parking facilities acquired in 1962, other land parcels, some of them former sites of private dwellings, were added to the school's holdings in 1963.

In the fall of 1963, the Board approved the purchase of the Gorham property at 5220 University Avenue for $175,000. Later on, the homes at 5206 University Avenue and 5233 Ingleside Avenue were purchased [6]. The Gorham property consisted of a 22-apartment, three-story walk-up building, plus the land, but was not actually taken over by the College until 1965 when the property transfer was finalized.

In October, 1963, Dean Robert A. Kistner presented the trustees with plans for a new college building, a project he indicated could be realized with the help of government matching grants. He projected plans also for additions to the basic science building and the outpatient clinic to cost in the neighborhood of $1.5 million, but with the College committed to raise only a third of this amount because of matching grant provisions. The expansion fever grew more intense.

In 1964, Dr. MacBain outlined one of the most ambitious building proposals the college administration had ever presented to its Board of Trustees. At its annual meeting on October 21, Dr. MacBain proposed a two-step program: Phase I involved a basic science building costing $750,000; a new clinic building costing another $750,000; and an addition of a 5th floor to the Hospital to cost $250,000. The total cost of Phase I was estimated at $2,000,000, with half this amount hopefully to be supplied through government funds.

Phase II was equally ambitious. It envisioned the addition of a 6th floor to the Hospital which could be used as an interim facility while the north wing of the old clinic building would be demolished and replaced by a 6- or 8-story structure providing additional beds, long-term care units, psychiatric units, and other facilities. The total cost would amount to another $2,000,000. So attractive were these prospects that Dr. Peckham, Board chairman, urged immediate application for government grants so the work could get under way [7].

By the mid 1960's the College was releasing statistics that would have stunned its founders. The Hospital had a staff of 471, a 167-bed capacity, 76 physicians, 8 interns, 171 nurses. It was admitting more than 6,000 patients annually, and the number of patient days in 1965 alone totaled 43,340. Patient visits in the same year totaled more than 56,000, and the Hospital's clinic was offering its services to all: to those who could afford private physicians but preferred to take advantage of the clinic; those of limited income who could pay something, but who could not afford a private physician; those on welfare; those of low income but who wanted to pay something rather than accept free services elsewhere; and to hundreds of young mothers who felt that the pediatric clinic would give them guidance and continuing care for their children.

By all odds the Chicago College of Osteopathy was now big business. Its operating income totaled $3,668,000. The amount paid out in salaries and wages accounted for more than $2,200,000 of the total yearly outlay of $3,498,000. The fixed assets of the institution were now nearly $4,000,000!

Like its neighbor, the University of Chicago, the Chicago College of Osteopathy could look back to an important decision it had made just a decade earlier: whether to remain in Hyde Park or move elsewhere. College officials noted:

> Like its giant neighbor, the University of Chicago, the Chicago College of Osteopathy faced critical decisions ten years ago. It had been an established Hyde Park institution for nearly forty years; it had performed an important health service to two generations of Chicago's south side indigent residents; its staff had established private practices in South Shore, South Suburban, and Southwest suburbs—yet the blight, crime, decay, and panic in the area threatened the institution's future. Trustees and staff, after a period of self-study, decided the Hospital, Clinic, and College should remain at its historic site, and cast its lot with the future of Hyde Park.
>
> Once this decision was made the growth period began—new vitality came into the Center; dreams of expansion were converted to blueprints; new equipment and new services were installed. As a result, all departments of the Hospital and Clinic have shown a 100 percent increase in patient services in the ten-year period.
>
> . . . Staff physicians and civic leaders who serve on the Board are confident that this 65-year-old health center is on the threshold of a new day, and its greatest years of service and training are in the future. . . ."

The College was indeed prospering as its staff, student body, and employees totaled more than 800. The salaries and wages paid staff personnel accounted for more than $2 million, a sizable portion of which was being poured into the economy of the community.

Along with such cheerful statistics came a change in the make-up of the boards of trustees at the various osteopathic colleges. The American Osteopathic Association at this time stated its opposition to any faculty or administrative member of a given college serving on the Board of Trustees of that college. The AOA, through its Committee on Colleges of the Bureau of Professional Education, urged that the colleges in the future bar anyone from their boards of trustees who was serving as a teacher or administrator, thus preventing "anyone who might, by virtue of their association, be considered as being placed in a position of conflict of interest by virtue of election to the Board."

On October 30, 1963, the CCO Trustees voted to accept the AOA recommendation but at the same time declared that "no act of the Board of Trustees shall be declared illegal by reason of the fact that a Trustee, or Trustees, may have been elected, or may continue, to hold office in violation of such policy."

The Chicago College of Osteopathy had enjoyed a splendid working relationship with the Detroit Osteopathic Hospital since 1949. In 1965, Dr. MacBain urged an even closer teaching association with its Michigan affiliate. Moreover, he told the trustees, the arrangement would be quite necessary, for only if the College could show that it had six teaching beds for every entering student could the College and Hospital expect to obtain the financial support it sought from time to time. He recommended that the medical director of the Detroit Hospital become an associate dean of the Chicago College and that three associate deans be appointed: Dr. Jerry Polsinelli of Detroit; and Drs. Ward Perrin and George Caleel of Chicago.

On July 1, 1964, a new agreement was adopted by the two institutions, signed by J. Paul Leonard, Chairman of the DOH Board of Trustees, and Dr. Floyd F. Peckham, Chairman of the CCO Board. Designated as an official "Affiliation Agreement," the document read as follows:

### AFFILIATION AGREEMENT

This Agreement, made and entered into as of July 1, 1965, by and between Detroit Osteopathic Hospital, a Michigan not-for-profit corporation (hereinafter called the hospital) and Chicago College of Osteopathy, an Illinois not-for-profit corporation (hereinafter called the college).

### WITNESSETH

WHEREAS the college desires to secure for its students, as part of their curriculum in in-hospital student training, and

WHEREAS the hospital wishes to conduct a program of in-hospital student training in its Detroit Osteopathic Hospital in order, among other reasons, to provide in said hospital, teaching opportunities for the members of its staff, and

WHEREAS, it is the desire of the hospital and the college to affiliate for the attainment of such purposes, it is hereby agreed by and between the hospital and college, as follows:

1. The hospital agrees to accept from the college and the college agrees to certify to the hospital, the students of the college for in-hospital student training, at times to be selected by the college.

2. The hospital agrees to provide for students so certified in-hospital training programs of instruction in its Detroit Osteopathic Hospital all in accordance with the directions and subject to the approval of the dean of the college.

3. The hospital shall appoint members of its staff, subject to the prior approval of the dean of the college to conduct the instruction programs aforesaid. Such teaching staff appointments shall be for terms of one school year subject to renewal upon recommendation of said dean.

4. The teaching staff of the hospital shall report to the college the progress of each student who shall be graded in accordance with the standards to be designated by the dean of the college.

5. There hereby is established an Advisory Committee which shall be known as "The Joint Advisory Committee of Chicago College of Osteopathy and Detroit Osteopathic Hospital" (hereinafter referred to as the committee). This committee shall be composed of the chairmen of the governing boards of the hospital and the college or the designates of such chairmen; the executive director of the hospital; the dean of the college; and the medical director of the hospital. The president of the college and the executive director of the hospital shall serve alternately as chairman on an annual basis.

The committee shall have the following purposes:

a. To initiate, review and correlate joint action of the two institutions toward attaining the highest standards of teaching and research including academic and attending staff appointments affecting the two institutions.

b. To consider such other matters which, from time to time, arise and which are of common concern to the two institutions with respect to the subject matter of this Agreement.

6. This Agreement shall be effective July 1, 1965 and shall continue in effect indefinitely with respect to the parties signatured hereto except that withdrawal from this agreement may be made by either party, given twelve months notice, in writing, of its intention to withdraw from this agreement. Withdrawal shall be effective at the expiration of the notice period of twelve months.

> (*Signed*)  J. Paul Leonard, D.O.
> Detroit Osteopathic Hospital
> Chairman, Board of Trustees
>
> (*Signed*)  Floyd F. Peckham, D.O.
> Chicago College of Osteopathy
> Chairman, Board of Trustees

Until such time as the Chicago College of Osteopathy could increase its teaching facilities to cope with its constantly-growing operations, the Agreement with DOH would fulfill a major need.

The College began its 66th year with the realization that an era was ending and a new one about to begin. Dr. MacBain, who for thirty years as president had guided the institution through good times and bad, was scheduled for retirement in 1967. A committee was chosen to search for his successor. Mr. Donald F. Moore headed a committee composed of Drs. James H.

McCormick, John T. Baker, and Mr. Conrad Orloff to look for a new president.

At a Board meeting a year earlier, on October 27, 1965, Dr. Floyd F. Peckham, for 39 years a member of the Board and for seventeen of them its President, notified the trustees that he wished to retire at the annual meeting in 1966. The retirement of these two administrators would mark the close of an epoch in the history of the College, for these two men had given many decades of their lives to the furtherance of the work of the institution.

On October 16, 1966, Dr. Peckham yielded his gavel as presiding officer of the Board of Trustees to Arthur E. Hjerpe, his successor. In accepting his new post, Mr. Hjerpe said:

> I deeply respect your confidence in me. I accept this responsibility with considerable trepidation—to follow in the footsteps of a gentleman like Dr. Peckham so thoroughly versed in hospital administration and presidential matters.
>
> It has deeply gratified me over the years that we have had excellent cooperation from the personnel of the institution. We have never had a finer meeting than today. I have never seen so much enthusiasm and vigor. We have a great many problems confronting us. We have to get moving into our new construction program. . . . We shall go on with our work.
>
> We pay our deepest respect and thanks to you, Dr. Peckham, for the many years of service to this institution. I say thank you with the greatest and deepest sincerity. I will do the best I can with the help of this board.

To which Dr. Peckham replied:

> I appreciate all the nice things you have said. It has been a privilege to work with you all for many years and an honor to chair this board. I have had quite a lot of board experience and this is, without doubt, the best board I have ever worked with. I know the future of this institution is in good hands. I know Mr. Hjerpe will make a fine chairman.
>
> Once again let me express my deepest appreciation for the kindness of all the board members. It is hard for me to believe it will be 50 years since I came here as a student. For more than 40 of that time, I have held some kind of active position. Again, I thank you all.

Dr. Peckham continued as a member of the Board until December 27, 1967, when he wrote from his retirement spot that the time had come to relinquish this association, too, for the drive to and from the Board meetings was becoming too great a physical strain. On January 24, 1968, the Board accepted his resignation "with deepest regret" and "with recognition of his invaluable service to the osteopathic profession and the community." A subsequent letter represented Dr. Peckham's last official act. He wrote: "It has been a great pleasure and privilege to preside over a group like this for so many years. . . . I bid you all farewell. My best wishes for each one of you individually and CCO in particular. Sincerely, Floyd F. Peckham." His work for the College and Hospital was done.


The times were bringing many changes to the College and Hospital. Dean Robert A. Kistner told the Board of Trustees at its annual meeting in October, 1966, that these changes were having profound effects on medical education. There was now greater emphasis on research than ever before; new ideas were affecting group practice, and curriculum revisions were being made to reflect the latest medical discoveries and trends. The College, said Dean Kistner, was concentrating on the training of general practitioners, on improving its post-graduate education and stressing the need for intensive osteopathic research. He predicted an exciting future for the college, with new buildings, larger faculty and clinical services, a new library, and a student body of 300.

Lending optimism to these hopes was the receipt of another substantial bequest: a gift of $134,179 from the estate of the late Miss Mabel Campbell, a benefactress who had been a friend of the Chicago College of Osteopathy for a number of years. The bequest consisted of blue chip stocks and bonds, and the CCO trustees hoped the interest from the bequest would make possible a "Mabel Campbell Chair of Osteopathic Principles and Practice."

Later in the year, Dr. MacBain announced that the U.S. Government had approved a construction grant of $1.9 million to the Chicago College of Osteopathy, "one of the nation's major sources of osteopathic physicians and surgeons." The grant, forwarded through the Health Manpower Division of the Department of Health, Education and Welfare, made possible a quick start on the school's ten-year expansion program and was to result in a four-story addition to the Hospital at East 52nd Street and Ellis Avenue, and a new Basic Science Building at East 53rd Street and South University Avenue. This was the first construction grant awarded to any osteopathic college by the Department of Health, Education and Welfare.

There was good reason for the Government approval of the construction grant and the commendatory remarks about the Chicago College, for the school now had a student body of 275 and was training 13 percent of the osteopathic physicians and surgeons practicing in the United States. The outpatient clinic was handling 81,000 patient visits yearly [8], yet COH officials regretfully remarked that this volume "still falls far short of meeting the need." The tuition fee now amounted to $1,500 a year, yet it fell woefully short of covering the instructional cost of a student, calculated at $3,835 a year [9].

On June 30, 1967, Dr. Richard N. MacBain retired as CCO president, and the trustees at their June session passed a resolution paying tribute to the man who had for 30 years directed the College: "Resolved, that the Board recognize the excellent and intelligent service Dr. MacBain has rendered the Corporation during his incumbency; that the Corporation has attained its present stature through the earnest efforts and untiring devotion of Dr. MacBain."

As Dr. MacBain appeared before the trustees in his final moments as president, he had a last recommendation to offer: change the name from the "Chicago College of Osteopathy" to the "Chicago College of Osteopathic Medicine." The Chicago College, he pointed out, was the only one still calling itself a "college of osteopathy;" all the others had changed their designations to institutions of "osteopathic medicine." Reluctant though he was to change the CCO name which had endured for so many years, he declared that it was desirable to "fall in line" and give the institution a name more indicative of the real purpose of the College. The new name was officially adopted during the summer of 1970.

Early in 1967, Mr. Donald F. Moore, chairman of the committee assigned to select a new president, announced that more than 70 names had been submitted for the position and that forty of these had been screened for further consideration. On March 1 he reported that the search "has been a long and frustrating job," but that "we have boiled down our original list of 71 potential candidates to 19." On May 10, Mr. Moore reported that the committee had unanimously agreed to the selection of Thaddeus P. Kawalek, Ph.D., as president to succeed Dr. MacBain, and the trustees promptly approved. Dr. Kawalek's term of office would being on July 1, 1967 [10].

Dr. Kawalek soon launched the College on a program of expansion and service such as it had never before experienced. A dynamic administrator who liked to cut red tape and move forward at full speed, he pushed vigorously the completion of the construction program that had been approved before Dr. MacBain's retirement. In August, 1967, ground was broken for the three-story Basic Science Building, the first project in CCO's ten-year, $15 million development program. At the same time, substantial renovating was being done in the clinic, patient and service areas, and in the hospital itself.

The additions to the physical plant were vital. The College was extending its health care delivery throughout the community and city. It was now in constant touch with agencies such as the Cook County Department of Public Aid, Visiting Nurses Association, Schwab Rehabilitation Hospital, Community Referral Service, Alcoholics Anonymous, Chicago Police Department, Illinois Association for the Mentally Retarded, Illinois State Department of Children and Family Services, Social Security Administration and others.

At the close of the 1967–1968 academic year, Dr. Kawalek's first term as chief executive of the College, the school announced that its total income for the year was an impressive $6,407,855. Its total expenses were $6,055,722. Student enrollment was 282, and applications for entrance totalled 1,253, remarkable evidence of the College's growing prestige and influence. Of the 1,253 applications, 316 were processed and 94 were accepted.

Dr. Kawalek looked down the road and saw more. He believed the College should seriously consider admitting only students with at least a bachelor's degree. He hoped that the student body would become more diversified so as to represent a broad cross section of society.

He indicated that the College must now have a full-time, not a part-time, administrative staff, for only with deans, department chairmen and teachers serving full-time could the College realize its true potential.

He asserted that emphasis upon research must be maintained, for "The Chicago College has a serious responsibility to develop the talent, the scholarship, and the scientific interest which will lead to supportive documentation for the osteopathic concept and the osteopathic system of health care." He was keenly aware that space was desperately needed by the College library which had 10,000 volumes on its shelves but should have 60,000 in order to keep pace with the progress in medical education.

He also saw the need for a full-time department of planning and development, a department which had the complete sanction of the Board of Trustees. The department would have more than fund-raising and public relations responsibilities. It would be the medium responsible for developing the expansion and improvement of the institution on all fronts and of initiating a long-range plan for the entire Chicago College of Osteopathy.

Dr. Kawalek and the trustees' committee believed that the department of planning and development should "encourage planning, evaluate programs, establish purposes, assess leadership requirements, recommend public relations programs, enlist alumni support and project a fund-raising plan that will undergird the long range growth of the institution."

It should do even more. It must establish a long-range academic program and a master plan for expansion. It should be a department that would work closely with the college president. The committee decreed that from 1½ to 2 percent of the institution's annual budget might profitably be invested in the planning, public relations, and fund raising phases of the College [11].

Vital though such a department was to the institution, the services of a specialized professional planning agency was also needed to make a study of the school's entire development potential, to conduct surveys and to recommend a course of action consistent with the financial resources that were likely to be available. In short, a long-range master plan was urgent.

After making a nation-wide search, Dr. Kawalek recommended to the trustees in 1968 that two firms be authorized to make such a study: (1) Lawrence Lackey and Associates of San Francisco, a company that had served as consultant for the University of Connecticut Health Center, the University of Miami School of Medicine, the Methodist Hospital of Sacramento, the University of Oklahoma Medical Center, the School of Medicine of Rutgers University, and others; and (2) Lester Gorsline Associates of Tiburon-Belvedere, California, a group specializing in the planning of medical centers and medical education programs. Gorsline Associates had planned the development of the Health Science Center of the State University of New York at Buffalo, the Medical Center of the State University of New York at Stony Brook, the programming and expansion of the Division of Health Sciences at the University of Washington in Seattle, and others. The two firms were obviously well qualified to assist the faculty and staff in planning the future of the college.

The Board of Trustees approved engaging the two firms, and shortly thereafter a planning committee of faculty and staff, with Dr. George T. Caleel as chairman, was appointed by Dr. Kawalek [12]. Four principal goals were set: (1) to identify the planning objectives of the College; (2) to project the needs necessary to satisfy these objectives; (3) to evaluate the adequacy of existing facilities; and (4) to recommend a general concept for long range site use.

To identify development objectives, each department was surveyed and the data collated to analyze alternatives for development. Illustrative projections were made for upgrading the College's resources: (a) while retaining class size at present levels, or (b) while increasing class size.

The latter alternative was chosen as the basis for long range planning, and an annual graduating class of 100 physicians was accepted as a rational measure of future growth.

Accordingly, the objectives of the Development Program and Plan were established for expanding the staff and facilities required by contemporary criteria:

1. To provide teaching for undergraduates, allied health students, student nurses and other degree candidates.
2. To support 175,000 annual outpatient visits; 500 acute, 100 extended and 50 self care patient beds.

3. To sustain the associated institutes and campus amenities characteristic of a full medical center.
4. To adopt site development criteria that are in accord with the renewal objectives of the Hyde Park–Kenwood Plan.
5. To create a center capable of supporting affiliated off-campus health activities.

The Planning Committee, meeting with the representatives of the two consulting firms, drafted an outline of a long-range program consisting of four parts: (1) Phase I—a clear statement of the objectives; (2) Phase II—an assessment of the needs of the college; (3) Phase III—analysis and review of the present facilities and an estimate of space requirements for future needs; (4) Phase IV—analysis of the present site of the College and the preparation of a funding development program.

The four-phase plan represented a master blueprint to guide the College for the next ten to fifteen years and would, in the opinion of the conferees, enable the College to "seek dynamic solutions to the problems inherent in growth and expansion—problems resulting from increased demand for health care services, student-faculty functional relationships, utilization of space, creative public relations, and above all, funding and fund raising essential to realize the objectives of the institution."

One of the most pressing needs, the College observed, was to develop satellite facilities, both to satisfy its academic objectives and to increase its capacity for regional and metropolitan, as well as community, osteopathic care. An extensive dialogue was begun within the College to define the satellite concept and to outline the facility needed. Dr. Kawalek stated that "The College intends to reexamine, as this need is defined, and modify or reaffirm the planning criteria assumed by this program in sizing the onsite patient care and referral capacity of the College. Moreover, the successful establishment of an adequate affiliated institution within the metropolitan area and the consequent development of clerkships, joint or exchange programs may facilitate some reduction in the onsite capacity. Too, the capacity of the affiliated hospital may be developed in addition to that of the College itself. In either case, neither the Program nor the Plan is intended to compromise the satellite facilities concept."

The Board of Trustees ordered the project pushed at full speed.

Notwithstanding the physical long-range planning, it seemed an appropriate time to honor some of the men who had given many years of their lives to the college. At the annual meeting of the trustees on July 1, 1968, seven faculty members, representing a total of 239 years of service to the College, were honored. The seven were: Dr. Martin C. Beilke, 39 years; Dr. K. R. M. Thompson, 35 years, Dr. S. Edward Stanley, 32 years; Dr. Malcolm A. Tangblad, 32 years; Dr. W. Fraser Strachan, 36 years; Dr. Seaver A. Tarulis, 30 years; and Dr. W. Don Craske, 35 years. In his remarks honoring the group, Dr. Kawalek said:

> In this day when every profession is placing emphasis on youth, we dare not and we will not forget the veterans who have carried the burdens, fought the battles and have been responsible for the survival of the profession. Educators are now building and planning for the 21st century. We are building on foundations which pioneers have laid in the mid-20th century. Any society or profession which ignores its veteran statesman denies its heritage and limits its future.

Befitting the growing stature of the College and Hospital, the trustees for the 1968–1969 academic year approved the largest budget in the history of the institution—a thumping $6,600,000! Some 67 percent of this was earmarked for salaries and wages. The greatest share of the budget, $4,700,000, was needed to operate the hospital and outpatient clinic; $894,000 was slated for the college. In just five years, the budget had increased an incredible 82 percent—from $3.6 million to $6.6 million! The student body now numbered 300, yet was still not large enough to prevent another raise in tuition, which increased from $1,500 a year to $1,800.

While campus unrest at this time was making newspaper headlines throughout the country as students defied college authorities, seized buildings and staged sit-ins, there was no hint of such turmoil on the CCO campus. Dr. Kawalek credited the students with vision that extended far beyond the classroom, with having a genuine concern for the healing arts and with the roles they would play when they embarked on their careers as osteopathic physicians. The students were indeed active and on the move, the CCO president admitted, "but they are moving in the right direction, and it is our responsibility as educators to see that the entire student body is inculcated with the philosophy, 'Physician, broaden thy vision.' "

On June 4, 1968, the College announced that its Board of Trustees had established an endowment fund and had set aside $225,000 in cash and securities to establish the "Mabel Campbell Chair of Osteopathic Principles and Practice," an endowed professorship which would serve "to give financial stability and to assure the future of osteopathic education at the college." [13] It was a meaningful way of giving "each generation a link with the past, and to assure donors that gifts designated for specific long-term purposes will be used in accordance with their wishes." The trustees hoped that $1,000,000 might be raised to serve as a permanent endowment fund.

On January 10, 1969, another important step in the College's 10-year expansion program was taken, namely, the groundbreaking for the new 6-story hospital wing to be named the "Richard N. MacBain Pavilion" in honor of the man who had served the institution so long. Among the community and civic leaders attending the ceremonies was George Wells Beadle, president of the University of Chicago, who expressed what so many others attending the event must have felt when he said:

> Our community strength in health care and related research increases every day and your growth is a tremendously important part of it.
>
> This groundbreaking is very special because it is another and very important expansion of confidence in a central city area that over a period of 15 years has achieved national symbolic significance in its successful efforts to renew itself as a stabilized interracial community.

Andrew A. Athens, who had succeeded Arthur J. Hjerpe as Chairman of the Board of Trustees when Mr. Hjerpe retired as vice president of the Portland Cement Company and withdrew from active participation in many of his activities, responded:

> "This is part of Phase I of the 10-year, $10 million expansion program. The 3-story Basic Science Building which is also part of Phase I is under construction and scheduled for completion in the fall.
>
> The second phase of the expansion program scheduled for 1969–1970 is the construction of a modern 6-story $4 million outpatient and diagnostic clinic. The clinic will offer a total health care to low income and medically underprivileged patients on Chicago's south side.
>
> The final phase of the 10-year program will be another addition to the hospital, increasing bed capacity to 375. This addition will make possible 110,000 patient days of health service annually.

As the College launched its 1969–1970 year with an operating budget of nearly $9 million, a warning was given by Dr. Kawalek to the trustees at their annual meeting in October that they must face up to the drastic financial changes that were taking place. He said, "You can no longer operate the institution on the earnings and income from the hospital alone. The costs of the educational program itself are outstripping what revenue we can generate from the hospital. The hospital cannot continue to accept the financial obligations of the educational program. . . . We must carefully begin to develop a program to bring about the kind of financial support necessary for the educational program. It is easy to look upon the institution as strictly a hospital function. It is not; it is educational. It is to provide learning experience to educate qualified physicians. You cannot look upon the hospital as a sole source of revenue. We must seek funds from other sources. . . . It is not enough to look at our immediate needs. We must try to project tomorrow's needs."

It was a thought to temper the heady talk of the 15-year plan and the ever expanding services envisioned for the College.


There were other things to think about. One of them was the difficulty in hiring certified D.O.'s for faculty positions. It was an admittedly formidable task to persuade a physician to give up a lucrative practice to accept a full-time teaching post. The young physician completing his residency usually found himself burdened with a sizable financial debt. He would accept a faculty position for a few years, then strike out on his own to areas where financial rewards were more substantial. As a result, Dean Kistner noted, the College more often than not could hire a physician only for the final ten years or so of his career, at a time when he had achieved security and was financially independent.

To counter this situation, CCO decided to expand its post-doctoral educational program for training specialists by supporting their further training in approved medical institutions. This support encouraged students to return to the Chicago College of Osteopathy and accept teaching posts. It served also to check the wholesale admittance of CCO graduates to regular medical hospitals (under AMA sanction) as interns and residents in order that they might be absorbed into the general field of medicine and thus remove their identity as osteopathic physicians. It was a serious problem, but CCO believed that its policy is helping to stem this annual loss of graduates to the allopathic branches of medicine.


The 1960's ended with gratifying realizations and great prospects. Applications for admissions were arriving in unprecedented volume. During the 1969–1970 year, 1,345 applications were received. This was the highest number ever recorded by the College and from these 84 new students were selected. The student body totaled 307, a figure which only a few years earlier was posted as something to be realized only in the promising future. Student loans amounted to $453,685 as three out of every four students entering the College relied upon some type of loan program for their education. The College received more than $653,000 in grants for general research, cardiovascular training, clinical cancer training, basic and special improvements.

The College and Hospital had 555 employees. Patient and service visits totaled 97,755 to make the clinic one of the busiest for its size in the city of Chicago. Operating revenue totaled $8,300,094, with outlays slightly exceeding income, yet permitting the College to operate without touching its bank reserves. The College received more than $400,000 in gifts during the year, the highest ever received in a single year.

Talk of building a satellite hospital increased. At the annual meeting of the trustees in October, 1969, Dr. Kawalek left no doubt that such a facility was a "must." He said:

> If we are to hold qualified, competent physicians, we are going to have to provide a satellite operation close to our institution, both from the standpoint of providing an adequate number of patients for particular specialties, as well as attracting and holding qualified specialists for teaching.
>
> If we hope to have a chest surgeon or a pediatric cardiologist, the number of patient beds available to use would not currently support that particular physician. He must have sufficient beds available to him for patient care. He needs a broader and more varied population to supply the patients.
>
> We must accept the concept of a satellite hospital for this institution —we must accept and work for it.

It was something to think about as the College concluded another ten-year period and faced the next.

## REFERENCES

1. The CCO trustees passed the following resolution: "Resolved, that the Board of Trustees of the Chicago College of Osteopathy endorses the policy and program of the American Osteopathic Association and the American Association of Osteopathic Colleges in taking whatever steps are necessary to maintain the osteopathic school of medicine as a separate profession fully prepared to make its contribution to the public health and to cooperate with all other agencies and groups that sincerely promote the same objectives. It is the opinion of the board that the goals of the osteopathic profession in making its contribution to medicine as an independent school of practice have not yet been reached and that its separate and distinct status should be continued until they are. The board further resolves that as individual members they will have no further interest in carrying the responsibilities of board membership should the Chicago College of Osteopathy lose its osteopathic identity." The trustees left no doubt as to where they stood!
2. Austin V. Clifford, Paul van B. Allen, Donald F. Moore, Orland R. Murphy, and Paul Grant.
3. This parking area was large enough to accommodate 205 vehicles and was bounded by 52nd and 53rd Streets, Berkeley and Ellis Avenues. It was purchased from the Department of Urban Renewal for $68,892, and was attractively landscaped with walkways, and garden mall. (*Chicago Tribune,* June 21, 1962)
4. From the minutes of the meeting of the Board of Trustees held October 10, 1962.
5. Mr. Jennings, a Chicago industrialist, had been a patient in the Chicago Osteopathic Hospital and of osteopathic physicians from 1927 until his death in 1954. The money was

left in trust until Mrs. Jennings died in 1962. COH was one of several institutions which benefited from Mr. Jennings' generosity.

6. For $36,000 and $27,500, respectively.

7. In keeping with such expansion thinking was the establishment of an Office of Planning and Development for the College. This was done in 1965 with Dr. Leo K. Bishop, formerly vice president of the National Conference of Christians and Jews and Chicago's 1960 Junior Association of Commerce "Man of the Year," as Director.

8. Of this total, 22,068 visits were made by recipients of public aid from the Cook County Department of Public Welfare.

9. For the 1965–1966 school year, tuition receipts totaled $343,752. Receipts from all sources amounted to $939,629.

10. Dr. Kawalek had been Dean of Faculties and Professor of Education Administration at Roosevelt University, and later Vice President and Dean at Columbia College.

11. On July 1, 1969, Earl C. Kubicek, Development Officer with the University of Chicago during the highly successful multi-million dollar "Campaign for Chicago" and previously associated with Dr. Henry Townley Heald in the development of Illinois Institute of Technology, was elected Vice President for Planning and Development to head up the newly created department.

12. Members of the committee included Drs. Richard T. Caleel, W. Don Craske, Jr., Wilbur J. Downing, Jr., Richard L. Jensen, Robert E. Kappler, Harold Katzen, A. F. Kelso, Robert A. Kistner, Norman J. Larson, P. R. Lombardo, George F. Marjan, Donald G. Pelino, Roderick C. Salach, Leo Stein and Seaver A. Tarulus. Others on the committee included David L. Allen, Mrs. Clare Conine, Charles O. Jarasek, John R. MaCauley, George V. Malmgren, Jr., and John Scuderi.

13. In 1968, Dr. Norman J. Larson, Class of 1935, and a long-time member of the faculty, was appointed to this post and became the first to occupy the chair. In accepting his appointment as the "Mabel Campbell Professor of Osteopathic Principles and Practice," Dr. Larson said: "We will seek to maintain a well-balanced approach to therapy, integrating all the knowledge and techniques now known to the healing arts."

# 12

# NEW VISTAS: THE 1970'S

THE OFFICIAL change in name from "The Chicago College of Osteopathy" to "The Chicago College of Osteopathic Medicine" in the summer of 1970 seemed to signal the approach of a series of momentous events for the institution which would celebrate its diamond anniversary in 1975 [1].

On September 18, the Richard N. MacBain Pavilion, a 6-story $4.4 million hospital wing named to honor the College's former President, was dedicated. A bronze plaque near the front entrance of the building bears the following inscription:

The MacBain Pavilion

CHICAGO OSTEOPATHIC HOSPITAL

is a TRIBUTE to

Richard Norman MacBain
Physician, Educator, Administrator

In Grateful Acknowledgment for
Fifty Years of Service to This
Institution From His Student
Days to his Fruitful Years as
President

THE BOARD OF TRUSTEES A.D. 1970

The annual inpatient admittance potential was increased from 7,300 to 12,000 as the facilities of this much-needed addition to the institution's physical plant were made available.

The pavilion contained a full floor of pathology laboratories, a full floor for the radiology department, four floors for patient beds (increasing to 295 the total number of beds), an intensive care unit and recovery room. There were also a gift shop, business offices, and a new admitting and medical records department. Dr. Kawalek announced that within three months the employee total at CCOM would increase from 740 to 900.

The momentum generated by the construction of the MacBain Pavilion and the Peckham Basic Science Building stimulated the planning for two other facilities recommended in the master plan of the College: a new outpatient clinic and satellite hospital.

As early as March, 1968, the Board of Trustees had accepted the Phase II planning project submitted by Lawrence Lackey and Associates and Lester Gorsline Associates: construction of a new outpatient clinic on the Hyde Park campus. This would replace the long-used existing clinic with a facility that reflected entirely new perspectives for a neighborhood health center. It would provide an outstanding facility for training additional physicians as well as the necessary offices, research, examination and treatment rooms.

For 55 years the College had been forced to confine its out-patient services to an obsolete, overcrowded, antiquated and totally inadequate building. From time to time attempts had been made to renovate it, and the structure was periodically remodelled to ease the pressures of the moment. But the time had now come when such temporary make-do adjustments were no longer possible. Student enrollment was frozen at a level far too low for a growing and expanding institution. Clinical facilities remained hopelessly deficient. There was a critical need: (1) to increase student enrollment; (2) to provide a more effective teaching environment; and (3) to have adequate offices and research facilities for existing faculty. Most critical of all was the need for a larger, comprehensive health center and teaching clinic in a densely populated zone where every health problem of the inner city was present.

Early in the 70's a formal application was made to the Department of Health, Education and Welfare for a Government construction grant of $7,285,998 to be used toward defraying the cost—estimated at nearly $18 million—of constructing the new outpatient clinic. Another $930,545 was requested from the State of Illinois through the Hill-Burton Act. The College would generate the remaining balance.

The application for government financial help was accompanied by information and data of no little significance. Not only would the new outpatient clinic represent the first college-sponsored outpatient clinic to be constructed in Chicago in thirty years, it would increase by a full fifty percent the outpatient health care services the College could offer the community. Additionally, it would permit an increase in student enrollment from 94 to 124, an increase in the number of patients per day from 350 to 524, a boost in the faculty from 80 to 125, and a hike in the number of employees from 125 to 275. The number of patient visits annually could rise to 125,000 or even 150,000, a tremendous asset with which to meet the health needs of the community.

Actually, the services offered by CCOM extended far beyond the immediate Hyde Park area. CCOM was serving a region consisting of no less than ten communities with a total population of more than 500,000. These communities included Oakland, Grand Boulevard, Fuller Park, Kenwood, Washington Park, Woodlawn, Englewood, Greater Grand Crossing, Hyde Park, and South Shore. Approximately 88.9 percent of the population was non-white. At the time the application for funding was filed, the Clinic was handling 97,000 outpatient visits annually, 98 percent of which were non-white; 45 percent of all visits represented patients on public welfare. The communities served by CCOM were characterized by substandard housing, infant mortality, male unemployment, juvenile delinquency, families with income below $3,000, and other significant sociological and economic factors. This was surely strong evidence pointing out the need to construct a new health care center!

The application for the HEW construction grant was submitted to the Health Manpower Division. In October 1971 President Kawalek announced that the Federal government had approved a grant of $8,947,191 for the new Clinic. Unfortunately, in January 1972 all Federal funds for grants were frozen and by July the Federal statute provisions had to be reenacted, hence a new funding application was filed. Once again the College program for construction was approved and a new grant for assistance in the construction of the family health care outpatient clinic was offered. A grant in the amount of $6,544,618 was awarded CCOM. Concurrently applications had been filed with the State of Illinois for Hill-Burton funding for the Clinic. President Kawalek announced that the State of Illinois and the Federal government had approved a grant under the Hill-Burton Act for an amount of $930,391. The green light was on.

On Nov. 16, 1973, ground was broken for the new clinic as several hundred officials, administrators, civic leaders, students and friends of the College looked on. Located on the north side of 53d Street between Ellis Avenue and Berkeley Street, directly east of the old clinic, the new facility would be built on land already owned by the College and involve no displacement of people.

The 6-story clinic will have a 225-seat auditorium on the ground floor, plus a patient processing center, audiovisual facilities, seminar and conference rooms. The basement will accommodate clinical support facilities for radiology, kidney, diabetes and pulmonary care; also nuclear medicine and cardiology. Space will also be allocated for a pharmacy dispensary, and for student activities, lockers and vending machines.

The second floor will be given over to physical examination and treatment offices and seminar rooms. The third floor and half of the fourth will be used for examination and treatment offices. College administrative offices will occupy the other half of the fourth floor, along with offices for the President and Board of Trustees. The fifth floor will provide offices for all clinical department chairmen and teaching staffs.

The sixth floor will replace one of the most inadequate facilities of all: the library. In place of the currently cramped quarters on the third floor of the old building will be a new library seating 168 people and having a stack capacity for 77,000 volumes. A staff of nine professional and 17 non-professional employees will service the library needs of students and faculty. A facility that for many years was woefully limited by space and other restrictions will now offer far more efficient aid to those needing its help.

The new Outpatient Clinic represents the fulfillment of Phase II of the 15-year Master Plan. What of Phase III?

Here, too, the news was good.

The objectives of Phase III had been spelled out clearly by the faculty committee working with the two professional planning consulting firms. High on the priority list was the need for CCOM to graduate a larger number of osteopathic physicians each year—from 94 to 124 by 1980. It was also recommended that the number of Illinois resident osteopathic physicians graduated from CCOM be increased so as to account for at least four percent of all practicing physicians in the State of Illinois. To reach such a goal, the College must supply approximately one-half of the osteopathic physicians entering practice in Illinois each year. This objective did not appear un-reasonable when it is recalled that CCOM graduates already accounted for 47 percent of the Illinois osteopathic physician population.

Behind the statistics were incontestable realities. CCOM must break out of its constricted location in the inner city and broaden the learning experience of students in their clinical years (but by no means abandoning any of the values inherent in the Hyde Park location). CCOM also faced the task of recruiting young and dynamic faculty members, while at the same time retaining the teaching staff it already had.

One of the best means for reaching such objectives, it was agreed, was to build a *new* health center—a satellite hospital that would be under the control of the College and offer vastly expanded teaching and health care services.

The prospect of building a new hospital was quickly acclaimed by the planning and development committee of the CCOM Board of Trustees headed by John L. MacBean, who urged that the trustees pledge at least $1 million toward its construction. He told his associates: "We need to be on the line ourselves. We have to search it out ourselves—how are we going to do this—where do we stand? What will we commit? How will we generate it?" Andrew A. Athens, Chairman of the Board, replied: "All of us can help through various areas, through people we know or foundations that we are close to. We must help in any manner possible. We have committed ourselves to go ahead." As a parting thought, Dr. Kawalek reminded them that metropolitan Chicago and the rest of the state needed from 600 to 800 additional hospital beds—and needed them urgently.

There were serious concerns for the College in all this. They were pointed out by Dr. Kawalek at the annual meeting of the Board on October 25, 1972. If, he said, more osteopathic physicians do not set up practice in the state, the school will, by 1992, be in serious jeopardy. Many osteopathic physicians were nearing retirement, and if these practitioners were not replaced and increased in number, CCOM faced an inadequate pool of potential teaching physicians and practitioners for the college and hospital, and the profession a similar shortage for the osteopathic hospitals throughout the state. It was a sobering prospect.

As talk of a satellite hospital increased, the Woodland General Hospital of Chicago Ridge, through its Board of Trustees, presented CCOM more than $15,000 with which to conduct a thorough survey. The gift made possible the compilation and publication of a report entitled "The Satellite System: A Concept for Osteopathic Health Training and Care in Illinois." It contained a blueprint for a satellite hospital system that looms large in the future plans of the College.

In the meantime, Dr. Kawalek appointed a satellite hospital planning committee to develop and implement the concept of such a hospital. Appointed were Dr. Seaver A. Tarulis, Professor and Chairman of Obstetrics and Gynecology, as chairman, and the following as committee members: Robert A. Davis, Board of Trustees; Dr. Wilbur J. Downing, Jr., Instructor in Medicine; Dr. Richard L. Jensen, Assistant Professor of Surgery; Dr. Robert A. Kistner, Dean of the College; George V. Malmgren, Jr., Board of Trustees; Dr. William C. McCarty, Associate Professor of Otorhinolaryngology; Dr. David Robinson, Assistant Professor of Medicine; Dr. Thomas J. Szwed, Assistant Professor of Medicine; Dr. Leo K. Bishop, Assistant to the President; Earl C. Kubicek, Vice President, Planning and Development; Harold E. Green, Associate Director, Planning and Development; and Hans Kleyn, Comptroller. The last three were named as ex-officio members.

To assist the planning committee in finding a suitable site for the hospital, the firm of Realty Research, Inc., was engaged. As sites were selected and evaluated, acceptable locations were finally reduced to four: (1) Calumet-River Oaks; (2) Park Forest South; (3) Route 30, between Olympia Fields, Richton, and Park Forest; and (4) Intersection of Routes I-80 and I-57. After careful review, Dr. Tarulis, chairman of the satellite hospital planning committee, informed the trustees on May 10, 1972, that a site had been chosen: a 40-acre segment of a 78-acre plot located in the Olympia Fields-Flossmoor area [2]. The site extended from 203d Street north on Crawford Avenue and had a frontage of approximately 1,322 feet. It was easily accessible from Hyde Park, Palos, and northern Indiana, and would cost about $500,000. Dr. Tarulis announced that members of the professional staff of the Chicago Osteopathic Hospital were so enthusiastic over the prospects of a satellite medical center that 63 of the 80 active men on the staff had pledged $500 each to help raise the down payment!

A financial feasibility study was subsequently initiated and the architectural firm of Schmidt, Gardner & Erickson was engaged to prepare plans and specifications. The hospital was to be designed to meet the medical teaching program needs and space configurations as developed by the planning committee and the planning consultants.

At a meeting on Aug. 15, 1974, the executive-finance committee of the Board of Trustees approved plans for the hospital and authorized Dr. Kawalek to file an application with the Illinois State Department of Health for a permit to construct the building on the selected site on Crawford Avenue and 203d Street. The application specified that the hospital would contain 255,000 square feet, have a bed capacity of 198 [3], and cost an estimated $18,000,000. The permit was granted, and on September 25th the Board of Trustees of the Village of Olympia Fields voted 5 to 0 to annex the property so that sewers, water mains and other necessary service facilities could be installed [4].

In May, 1974, came the happy news that financial help for constructing the hospital was on the way. A letter directed to Dr. Kawalek by Dr. Joyce L. Lashof, Director of the Illinois State Department of Public Health, announced that the Illinois Advisory Council had recommended that CCOM "be allocated Hill-Burton assistance in the amount of $9,500,000.00 loan guarantee with interest subsidy for its proposed building program of a satellite teaching facility in Olympia Fields, Illinois."

Earlier in the year, a formal request was filed with the U.S. Department of Health, Education and Welfare, asking for Federal help in financing the $24.9 million project. Once again, impressive statistics accompanied the appeal for construction aid. The application was approved, but unfortunately, not funded. A letter from HEW on July 29, 1974, stated that the "application for construction grant assistance in the development of a teaching hospital was determined to be acceptable by the National Advisory Council at its June 10–12 meeting, but was not recommended for placement on the Active Funding List. Therefore, no commitment for a grant award can be offered." The letter promised, however, that, "Should the Health Professions Education Assistance Construction Program be continued and funded in Fiscal Year 1975, you will be notified and given an opportunity to reapply."

Meanwhile, the appeal of the new satellite hospital remains undiminished. The hospital will be located only 23 miles from the Hyde Park osteopathic center, and will provide clinical education facilities for 256 third and fourth year students of osteopathic medicine, 14 interns, and 11 residents. It will serve the needs of osteopathic physicians and their patients in East Lake County, Indiana, and in Will and Dupage Counties, as well as South Cook County, Illinois. It will serve an area covering nine townships with a current population of more than 469,000 and a projected "target population" of more than 570,000.

Initially, the satellite facility will have a 198-bed capacity. Ultimately, this will be increased to 500 beds. The hospital will be owned and operated by the Chicago College of Osteopathic Medicine as parent corporation. It will be a full-service teaching hospital, including intensive care, obstetrics, pediatric, psychiatric, and medical-surgical units. It will have a skilled medical staff and faculty, teaching physicians, residents and interns. Staff membership will be open to all qualified osteopathic and allopathic physicians to fulfill its educational teaching needs. The hospital's outpatient department will be capable of accommodating 80,000 emergency and outpatient visits annually, and its range of health care is being anticipated eagerly by the communities it will serve.

While the College was involved with new building plans, significant social and economic trends continued to affect the institution and its policies. Among the most prominent was the movement to unionize hospital employees. Dr. Kawalek informed the executive and finance committee of the Board of Trustees that CCOM had been served notice by the Hospital Employees Labor Program (HELP) that a petition had been filed under the provisions of the National Labor Relations Act demanding that it (HELP) be recognized as the bargaining representative for the Hospital's nurses aides, orderlies, housekeeping, dietary, post surgical aides, X-ray aides, ward clerks, central supply, linen room, eye department, pediatrics department and maintenance personnel; excluded were supervisory, professional, technical, security, office clerical, registered nurses and licensed practical nurses (LPN'S).

The agreement with the Union was in effect less than a year when controversy developed. In February, 1972, a group of fifteen licensed practical nurses walked off their jobs and, after ignoring requests to return to their posts, were dismissed for abandoning their patients. Picket lines were quickly thrown around the Chicago Osteopathic Hospital and CCOM and Union representatives began a series of meetings to discuss the grievances and attempt to settle the issues. The situation was aggravated, however, by the threat of resignations from more than 100 RN'S if the dismissed LPN'S were reinstated, and the Hospital felt it expedient to suspend all patient admissions except emergency cases.

The matter was finally settled by restoring the dismissed nurses to their jobs and signing a special organizational agreement with representatives of the registered nurses, graduate nurses, licensed practical nurses, operating room and central supply technicians. The pact brought into existence the Chicago Osteopathic Hospital Nursing Association, the first nursing association in CCOM's history.

A few months later, Dr. Kawalek announced that contracts had also been signed with the Hospital Employees Labor Program (HELP) of Metropolitan Chicago, Local 743; the International Brotherhood of Teamsters, Chauffeurs, Warehousemen and Helpers of America; and with Service Employees, International Union, AFL-CIO, Local 43.

While these internal problems were confronted and solved, the College continued to extend its range of services and influence far beyond its campus borders, at the same time strengthening its academic programs so as to better cope with constantly growing needs. Faculty and staff members were participating in increasing numbers in related organizational and group endeavors. The President of the College accepted membership in the Advisory Council of the state's health planning agency, and he is active in the health care planning activities of metropolitan Chicago. Four staff physicians represent the osteopathic medical profession in one of the eleven technical input groups of the Comprehensive State Health Planning Agency. Dean Robert A. Kistner is vice president of the Board of Governors of the Illinois Regional Planning Group. Also actively involved in the state's regional health care planning are Drs. Ward E. Perrin, Director of Medical Education; George T. Caleel, Director of Clinics; Jacklyn B. Melchior, Ph.D., Professor of Biochemistry; and Albert F. Kelso, Ph.D., Professor and Chairman of the Department of Physiology.

The College proudly acclaimed one of its graduates, Dr. Charles E. Ross (Class of '63), flight surgeon for the recent Apollo 16 mission.

Academically, the College strengthened itself by departmental reorganizations, curriculum changes, and additions to the teaching staff. New faculty appointments, all of them on the Ph.D. level, were announced for the microbiology, chemistry, anatomy, and the physiology-pharmacology departments. All have the rank of full or associate professor. Similar faculty expansion occurred in clinical education, anesthesiology, pathology, radiology, pulmonary function, pediatrics, ear-nose-and-throat, cardiology, surgery, psychiatry, obstetrics, gynecology and medicine. Faculty additions have also been announced for the Department of Osteopathic Principles and Practice.

A new program of audio-visual education has been adopted. A full-time librarian has been appointed and more staff help added in the clinic outpatient and social service departments. In all areas, instructional and service programs are being expanded. CCOM has been a teaching institution from the day of its founding; its emphasis on medical education remains its Number One objective.

One of the important sources of funds for the College's ambitious expansion program was the State of Illinois. The state, however, had made it clear that grants could be expected for certain purposes only if the College increased its enrollment of students who were residents of Illinois. The state legislature enacted programs which provided compensation for Illinois residents enrolled in private institutions for medical education. Under the program, the state agreed to contribute a sum of $50,000 toward capital construction for medical education for the first 20 students representing an *increase* in the number of Illinois residents enrolled in CCOM, and $20,000 for each additional student enrolled over and beyond the initial increment of 20, provided that the total enrollment increased by the same number of students. The program also provided operating dollars of $1,000 per Illinois resident enrolled in a professional school curriculum as of June, 1970, and stabilization dollars of $6,000 per increased Illinois resident medical student.

Dr. Kawalek reported that the College had received $2,500,000 from the State under this program and that CCOM now had 113 Illinois residents in its student body of 331. He added that the College would make every effort to increase the proportion of Illinois students so that by 1976 at least 175 students out of a potential student body of 366 would be state residents. Furthermore, beginning in 1974 the College expected an average minimum of 35 graduating Illinois residents qualified and ready to open general practice in the state and who would be available for the Chicago Osteopathic Hospital and, when built, the proposed satellite hospital.

At this time a number of important steps were taken in the field of allied health education with other educational institutions. These included agreements with the City Colleges of Chicago whereby CCOM provided clinical education experience for students registered in the LPN O.B. programs. An agreement was reached with the Moraine Valley Junior College to accept students for training at CCOM to qualify them as technicians for operating rooms, medical records, and medical laboratory. Similarly, agreements were signed with the Kennedy-King College and the Olive-Harvey College to establish nursing education programs for students working for Associate Degrees and R.N. licensure. The College also effected an agreement with the Thornton Community College to assist with the school's radiological technology program. All of these alliances are indicative of CCOM's cooperation in the community to help train nurses, medical technicians and other paramedical personnel, and illustrate the expanded educational development of the College as an established health care and education center constantly extending its range of educational programs and health services.

While the new outpatient clinic and the satellite hospital are the two major projects scheduled for completion in the 1970's, other, though lesser, expansion proposals and undertakings are under way. A student housing center for both married and single students that will also serve as a community center for those associated with the work of CCOM is high on the list of priorities. So is the enlarged library which will be known as the CCOM Alumni Memorial Library and occupy the entire sixth floor of the new outpatient clinic. Alumni have pledged to raise $1 million for the library which will be a Learning Resource Center capable of accommodating 152 users at one time as compared with 32 in the old library quarters.

Acquisition of property goes on as the College continues to grow and its campus broadens. Small parcels of land adjoining property already owned by the College have been added to the total holdings. Recently purchased through the City of Chicago Urban Renewal Program were 84,000 square feet at 54th Street and Ellis Avenue for student housing purposes; a lot at 52nd Street and University Avenue for automobile parking; a private residence at 5200 South University Avenue—the last privately owned property on the west side of University Avenue (in the College's immediate neighborhood)—to be used for the College's psychiatric clinic; and—the largest recent acquisition of neighborhood properties—Boucher Hall, formerly known as the George Williams College—located in the block bounded by 53d and 54th Streets, Ingleside and Drexel Avenues [5]. The

George Williams College building is being evaluated for potential use; meanwhile the property provides parking space for 341 cars.

In the immediate future the College must add at least 20 new faculty members to strengthen its academic program, for it is estimated that by 1978 student enrollment will reach a total of 496. The College must also recruit a house staff of 60 residents and interns as the services of its clinical teaching facilities expand.

Budgets are now mammoth by former standards, running to $17.7 million for the 1974–1975 academic year. Salaries, now far over the million dollar mark annually, account for 66 percent of the total budget and assets are valued at $18 million. Administering the Chicago College of Osteopathic Medicine of the 1970's is indeed "big business," and no less than six permanent committees meet regularly to direct the College's operations [6].

From a small suite on West Washington Boulevard with a student body of four and faculty of five, the Chicago College of Osteopathic Medicine has grown into an osteopathic teaching center with assets of $18,000,000, a faculty and staff of 144, a student enrollment of 376, and an alumni body of 1,850. It is an institution whose graduates account for nearly 13 percent of all osteopathic physicians practicing in the United States, an impressive figure for a college still modest in size, yet one which will continue to grow and influence osteopathic medicine wherever it is practiced.

Envisioned for 1985, only ten years following the institution's 75th anniversary, are a student body of 740, more than 200,000 visits a year in the family care outpatient clinic, approximately 2,500 full and part-time employees, a bed capacity of 650, a communications center, substantially increased student housing, additional research and extended care facilities. The future looks as beckoning as it must have appeared to the Littlejohn brothers some seventy-five years ago when they pioneered the study and practice of a new healing art in the rough and tumble Chicago of the 1900's. Far back in 1913, Dr. J. Martin Littlejohn wrote: "From the field of my rest in the far-away I shall look with eagerness to see the prosperity of this movement for the perpetual upbuilding of osteopathy, that we all love." He would be gratified, indeed, to see the modern dimensions of osteopathic education and range of health services provided by the institution he founded and loved so much.

### REFERENCES

1. As the 1970's got under way, CCOM had in operation no less than 17 departments to provide the professional education and training for its students: Anatomy; Anesthesiology; Biochemistry; Dermatology; Medical Jurisprudence; Pediatrics; Pathology;

Medicine; Microbiology and Bacteriology; Obstetrics and Gynecology; Ophthalmology and Otorhinolaryngology; Osteopathic Theory and Practice; Physiology and Pharmacology; Physical Medicine and Rehabilitation; Radiology; Psychiatry and Mental Health; Surgery.

2. The property was situated in an unincorporated area and would permit the construction of stores, office buildings and residential apartments.

3. This capacity can be expanded to 500 beds if needed. The height of the building is currently limited to 45 feet. A high school, which adjoins the property, will remain; sidewalks for students passing the hospital to and from school will be provided by CCOM. Since the site was originally zoned for single-family dwellings by Cook County, zoning regulations had to be modified to permit construction of the hospital.

4. The acquisition of hospitals already in operation, such as the Ottawa General Hospital in Ottawa, Illinois, was considered by the CCOM trustees but rejected in favor of the Olympia Fields facility.

5. Boucher Hall was purchased from the University of Chicago; the property at 54th and Ellis from the City of Chicago; and the residence at 5200 South University and 1119 East 52nd Street from private owners.

6. A number of committees within the structure of the Board of Trustees help the Board meet its responsibilities. These include the Executive Committee, By-Laws Committee; Joint Conference Committee, Finance Committee, Education Committee and, if occasion requires, an ad hoc committee to handle specific matters. The College activities are administered by four governing groups: the Chicago Osteopathic Hospital Corporation; the Board of Trustees of the Chicago Osteopathic Hospital; the Chicago College of Osteopathic Medicine Corporation; and the Board of Trustees of the Chicago College of Osteopathic Medicine. Annual meetings of these four groups are held consecutively on the same day, since members of one group belong to the other three as well.

*Spartan classrooms and laboratories were not uncommon at CCO in the early years and were typical of the facilities used in the fields of healing and education three-quarters of a century ago as contrasted to the highly sophisticated procedures and methods used today. Yet these sparse facilities produced some of the nation's leading osteopathic physicians.*

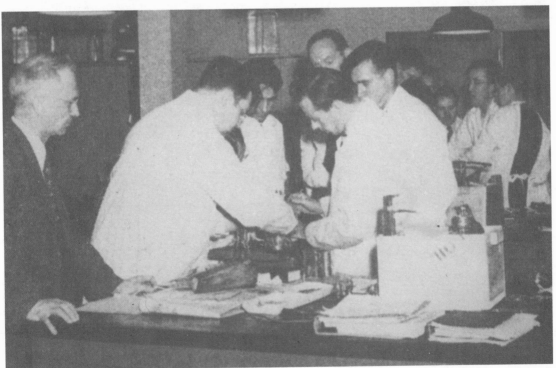

*An early-day laboratory scene at CCO. Dean Walter C. Eldrett oversees laboratory technicians running tests in the pathology laboratory which served both the College and the Hospital. The CCO Woman's Auxiliary provided much equipment during the College's early years by sponsoring fund-raising events.*

*Civic and educational leaders attended groundbreaking on April 9, 1962, for the new addition to the Chicago Osteopathic Hospital. Participating in the ceremony were, left to right: George Wells Beadle, President of the University of Chicago; Dr. Richard N. MacBain, President of CCO; Dr. Floyd F. Peckham, Chairman of the CCO Board of Trustees; and Richard J. Daley, Mayor of the City of Chicago.*

*Seventy-five additional beds for inpatient care were provided with the opening of the new Hospital wing in August, 1963. The new six-story structure (left in photo) contains a surgery floor with operating suites; a maternity floor with delivery wing; a pediatrics department; X-ray, outpatient laboratories, and sterilizing plant.*

Dr. Ward E. Perrin, Pfizer Professor and Chairman of the Department of Osteopathic Medicine, has been associated with the College since 1943, has held many administrative positions at CCOM.

Dr. Robert A. Kistner, Dean of the College since 1958, is a 1941 CCOM graduate and the holder of an M.D. degree from Loyola University. He is active in many educational and professional organizations.

Dr. Norman J. Larson, Chairman and Professor in the Department of Osteopathic Medicine, holds the chair, "The Mabel Campbell Professor of Osteopathic Principles and Practices" at CCOM. This chair was made possible through a bequest from the late Mabel Campbell.

Dr. George T. Caleel, Associate Dean and Professor of Medicine at CCOM, has been a faculty member since 1956. He graduated from CCOM in 1955 and is a recognized authority in the field of Nuclear Medicine.

Conditions in the CCOM library are crowded and book capacity is limited. The present site permits no expansion. The new Alumni Memorial Library which will occupy the top floor of the new outpatient clinic will have a stack capacity of 77,000 volumes and accommodate 168 people. A staff of 26 full and part-time employees will help service the library needs of students and faculty.

Student orientation program under way in the 186-seat auditorium of the Floyd Peckham Science Building. The building, dedicated in 1968, is named after Floyd F. Peckham, D.O., long-time CCO administrator and physician. Located in the building are the Departments of Biochemistry, Physiology, and Pharmacology.

*Attractive malls, drives and landscaping mark the approach and entrance to the Chicago Osteopathic Hospital on the CCOM campus. Out of the photographer's range at lower left will be erected the new six-story outpatient clinic, a facility which will again increase the range of patient services offered by the Chicago Osteopathic Medical Center.*

*The south end of the original college and hospital building on Ellis Avenue will soon be closed to clinic patients when the new facility now being constructed is completed in 1975. For many years the entrance shown here was a familiar one to patients arriving for medical treatment. The number of clinic patients has increased steadily since CCOM moved to Chicago's south side in 1918.*

*Another view of the entrance to the Chicago Osteopathic Hospital. The four-story wing shown here was completed in the 1950's, contains administrative offices as well as rooms for patients, conferences and lectures.*

*Located just north of the Basic Science Building on University Avenue is the Ashmore Apartment Building for CCOM married students. The three-story walk-up building was purchased in 1965 (negotiations began in 1963) from the Naomi Lois Gorham estate, and contains 23 efficiency and one-room units. Additional student housing must be provided as CCOM enrollment increases.*

The three-story Floyd F. Peckham Science Building in the 5200 block on University Avenue. The handsome building, opened in 1968 and a unit in the $15 million long-range building and development plan, is another dramatic achievement in the College's continuing effort to add to its physical plant, broaden its teaching programs, and thus provide even greater service to the community.

CCOM's preclinical medical program is administered in the Basic Science Building, shown here, at 53d Street and University Avenue. Adjoining the newer Floyd F. Peckham Science Building, it contains the Departments of Anatomy and Microbiology, and administrative offices. The College book store is on the ground floor.

*Another view of the six-story Hospital wing which was completed in 1970.*

*Service van for the Chicago Osteopathic Medical Center in front of Hospital entrance.*

Scale model of CCOM's new Outpatient Clinic, now under construction, is the center of interest for this group of administrators. The model was made by Lee Brooke (second from left), Director of CCOM Libraries. At his right is Lawrence J. Harrison, partner, Schmidt, Garden and Erickson, Architects and Engineers, Inc. At his left are Thaddeus P. Kawalek, President of CCOM; Andrew A. Athens, Chairman of the CCOM Board of Trustees; George V. Malmgren, Jr., Chairman of the CCOM Building Committee; and the Rev. Arthur O. Olson, Dean of Student Services, Lutheran School of Theology, Chicago.

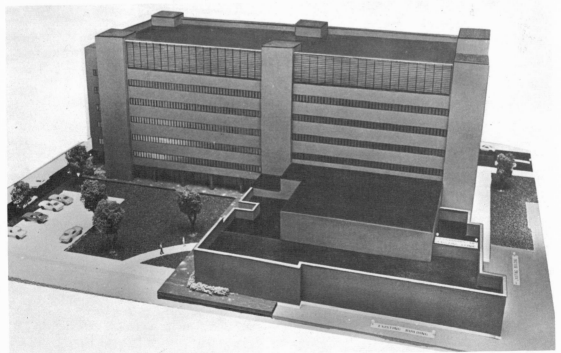

Closeup of the new Outpatient Clinic scale model. The new building will contain 220,000 gross square feet. Five of the six floors and the basement will contain facilities for teaching and patient care, while the entire top floor will be used for the CCOM Alumni Memorial Library. The building will have three banks of elevators, each with separate passenger and service lifts.

*Interior view of the majestic Rockefeller Memorial Chapel on the University of Chicago campus where CCOM Commencement exercises are now held. Photo was taken as a recent graduating class awaited the coveted D.O. diplomas.*

*Academic procession at the annual CCOM Commencement presents an impressive pageant. Photo shows CCOM faculty members leaving Rockefeller Memorial Chapel at the conclusion of graduation ceremonies in 1974.*

*A historic event in CCOM's long-range planning and development program was the groundbreaking for the new Outpatient Clinic on Nov. 16, 1973. Fred Browne, seven-year-old pediatrics outpatient and one of his chums, assist President Thaddeus P. Kawalek turn the first shovel full of earth. Many government representatives and community leaders attended the ceremonies.*

*Early stage in the construction of the new CCOM Outpatient Clinic. In background at the left is the present entrance for clinic patients, and at the right, the main COH wing. The new building will culminate more than ten years of planning and effort, and will be capable of accommodating 175,000 outpatient visits annually, compared with the peak capacity of 112,627 during a recent fiscal year.*

# ROAD TO VICTORY

*The Fight by the Chicago College of Osteopathic
Medicine and the Illinois Osteopathic Association To Win
Recognition and Equality for
Osteopathic Medicine!*

# ROAD TO VICTORY

WHEN Dwight D. Eisenhower, thirty-fourth president of the United States, signed H. R. Bill 483 on July 24, 1956, one of the last barriers in the way of full recognition and equality for osteopathic physicians was breached. The stroke of the Chief Executive's pen granted D.O.'s full rights for appointment as commissioned officers in the medical corps of the nation's armed forces—Army, Navy and Air Force—by the President with the advice and consent of the Senate (a courtesy which had long governed the commissioning of officers in the military).

A crusade spanning more than half a century thus scored another significant victory and brought closer the day when the profession would win complete equality [1].

For the State of Illinois and the Chicago College of Osteopathy, the struggle for recognition began in the closing year of the 19th century when, in 1899, the state legislature passed the Medical Practice Act, a legislative enactment that was to be an object of constant attack by the osteopathic physicians on the one hand, and a document for vigorous defense by the medical practitioners on the other.

For osteopathic medicine, the nub of the matter lay in the manifest discrimination which the Act contained. The Act permitted the graduates of a medical school to obtain a license to practice without the formality of passing an examination, but specified that all those "practicing other systems of treating human ailments" must take an examination; yet it prohibited them to practice or even take qualifying examinations to perform surgery unless they had graduated from a medical school in good standing.

The 1899 Act did provide that those who wanted to practice osteopathic medicine could take an examination, but that the examination would be given by the state medical board. No provisions whatsoever were made for examining the candidate in the principles and practice of osteopathy. Moreover, there was no requirement that the candidate be a graduate of a school of osteopathy or, for that matter, that he had studied in any school at all.

In classifying osteopathic applicants with "Other Practitioners", as opposed to medical school graduates, the osteopathic candidate found himself in the company of chiropractors, faith healers, massage specialists, midwives, and a nondescript assortment of rascals who eyed the treatment of man's physical ills as an irresistible means for making a fast dollar. Many who were ignorant of even the most basic principles of osteopathy were able to obtain licenses and open business as a "Registered Osteopath." The Act did little to separate the true from the false, and it is small wonder that the thoroughly qualified and reputable osteopathic practitioner lamented the toleration of these unprincipled so-called healers.

There were other inequities in the 1899 Medical Practice Act. It forbade osteopathic physicians to call themselves "Doctor". Many of those who did were hauled off to court, fined, and given stern warnings not to repeat the offense. They were not permitted to sign birth and death certificates, to practice obstetrics, or to enjoy the rights and privileges given to physicians of other schools. In fact, the osteopathic practitioner was not really licensed to practice osteopathic medicine at all as such, but merely to do business as one of the "Other Practitioners" which included the wide assortment of all those without benefit of sanction by the medical profession.

In 1901 the Illinois State Association of Osteopaths passed the following resolution and forwarded it to the State Board of Health:

> Gentlemen:
>
> The Illinois Association of Osteopaths in annual convention assembled at Chicago, May 4, 1901, respectfully call your attention to an unfortunate condition in the legal status of the osteopathic profession in Illinois, by which persons are authorized, under the license now issued to all who practice other systems than drug medicines, to represent themselves as osteopathic physicians, who have never qualified themselves to practice this system by attendance at and instruction in osteopathic colleges, and who therefore have no right to pretend to be Osteopathists.
>
> This situation works an injustice to the profession of Osteopathists in that it permits persons, in no way qualified, to use the name and make it a trademark for methods illegitimate, unprofessional, and unfortunate; and this situation works an imposition, and countenances repeated outrages, upon the public who have not the means of discriminating between the graduates of reputable osteopathic colleges and those who are not but who yet can show licenses from the State of Illinois to call themselves such if they please.
>
> We, the organized Osteopathists of Illinois, therefore, petition that your honorable body will join hands with us to correct these abuses by such measures as will prevent all but graduates of recognized colleges of Osteopathy from using the name of, and pretending to practice, the system of Osteopathy [2].

Two years later, the Illinois society proposed a new section as an addition to the 1899 Act, an adjustment that would permit osteopaths to be examined by osteopaths for obtaining licenses to practice. The proposal read as follows:

> For an act to amend "An act to regulate the practice of Medicine in the State of Illinois, and to repeal an act therein named," approved April 24, 1899; by adding thereto a new section to be known as section 2a.
>
> SECTION 1. Be it enacted by the People of the State of Illinois represented in the General Assembly: That "an act to regulate the practice of medicine in the State of Illinois, and to repeal an act therein named," approved April 24, 1899, in force July 1, 1899, be and the same is hereby amended by adding the following section, number "2a":
>
> SECTION 2A. That licenses to practice Osteopathy shall be granted by the State Board of Health to all applicants of good moral character who pass the regular examination of such board, in anatomy, histology, physiology, obstetrics, gynecology, pathology, urinalysis, toxicology, hygiene and dietetics, diagnosis, theory and practice of Osteopathy and present to said board a diploma from a regular college of Osteopathy maintaining the standard of the associated colleges of Osteopathy in its requirements for matriculation and graduation and requiring personal attendance for at least four terms of five months each. The fee for examination and for a certificate shall be fifteen dollars ($15.00); ten dollars ($10.00) for an examination and five dollars ($5.00) for a certificate if issued.

The State Board of Health shall appoint an examiner who shall be a graduate of a recognized college of Osteopathy and who shall examine applicants upon the theory and practice of Osteopathy. He shall receive therefor five dollars ($5.00) and the State Board of Health the balance of the fee. All reputable graduates of regular colleges of Osteopathy who were practicing in this State prior to March 1, 1903, and who shall be recommended to said Board by the executive committee of Illinois State Osteopathic Association, shall, upon application, without examination, be granted a license to practice Osteopathy, Provided, Such application for such license is made within ninety (90) days from the passage of this act, Provided, further, That a physician's certificate issued by a reputable college of Osteopathy after an attendance of not less than two terms of five months each, may be accepted by the Board on the same terms as a diploma and the holder be subject to the same regulation in all other respects as other applicants before the Board: Provided, further, That the Board may in its discretion dispense with an examination in the case.

First—Of an Osteopath duly authorized to practice Osteopathy in any other state or territory or the District of Columbia who presents a certificate of license issued after an examination by the legally constituted Board of such state, territory or District of Columbia, accorded only to applicants of equal grade with those required in Illinois. The fee for the issuance of such certificate or license shall be ten dollars ($10.00).

Second—An Osteopath who has been in actual practice for the period of five years, who is a graduate of a reputable college of Osteopathy, who may desire to change his residence to Illinois, and who makes application on a form to be prescribed by the Board, accompanied by a fee of twenty-five dollars ($25.00). Osteopaths when so licensed shall have the same rights and privileges, and be subject to the same statutes and regulations as other physicians, but shall not have the right to give or prescribe drugs or to perform surgical operations.

Section 2. All acts and parts of acts inconsistent with this act, are hereby repealed.

The proposed changes by the Illinois Osteopathic Association were not destined to have early approval by the state legislature.

Typical of the continued opposition of the Illinois state board of health to any osteopathic physician calling himself "doctor" was the following form letter set out in 1905 to D.O.'s who violated this injunction:

John Smith, Esq., Osteopath, Pedunk, Illinois

Dear Sir:

The attention of the state board of health has been called to the fact that you are using the title of "doctor" in connection with your practice, in violation of the law. You are directed to discontinue this at once. It is also charged that in the treatment of women you give local applications of medicine. It is unnecessary to inform you that you are exceeding your authority in this connection. Should further complaint be received concerning your practice and advertising yourself as "doctor" it will be my duty to bring the matter before the board.

Very Respectfully,
J. A. Egan, M.D., Secretary

*The Osteopathic Physician,* which published the letter, termed Mr. Egan's warning a political maneuver and advised D.O.'s to tell him "to go chase himself [3]."

Illustrative of the determined refusal of the state to grant D.O.'s the right to sign death certificates was the case of a Quincy, Illinois, osteopathic physician who signed a death certificate involving Mrs. Ella Jordan, wife of the Rev. Walter Jordan of that city, who had died of typhoid fever. The Quincy board of health expressed doubt that it had the right to issue a burial permit in such a case and reported the matter to the state board of health. Mr. Egan, board secretary, promptly wired:

UNDER THE LAW OF ILLINOIS, A DEATH CERTIFICATE CAN NOT BE SIGNED BY ANY PERSON EXCEPT A PHYSICIAN AUTHORIZED TO PRACTICE MEDICINE AND SURGERY IN ALL THEIR BRANCHES, OR A MIDWIFE.

A coroner's jury was finally summoned to determine the cause of Mrs. Jordan's death and to rule on the validity of the osteopathic physician's pronouncement. It is presumed the minister's wife was finally permitted burial with appropriate ceremonies.

The osteopathic profession in Illinois steadfastly continued its struggle for obtaining the state's official blessing. In 1907 the state's attorney ruled that an osteopath was indeed a "doctor" and had the right to so call himself. It was a small victory, to be sure, but nonetheless a hopeful omen.

Early in 1909 the state legislature at Springfield was again faced with proposals by the osteopathic physicians to win recognition. The Illinois Osteopathic Association had succeeded in having one of its legislative supporters introduce a bill creating a board of osteopathic examiners. The board was to be self-sustaining and only osteopathic physicians who had graduated from osteopathic colleges requiring the completion of a course of three years of nine months each (in three different years) for graduation would be eligible to serve on it. The bill was introduced in the House and Senate on February 24, passed the Senate handily, and reached a third reading in the House. But on May 29 the bill was stricken from the calendar "in the rush of business" before adjournment.

The reasons for the bill's demise, however, were only too apparent. Although the severest critics of the bill to authorize a separate examining board admitted that the proposal was "bullet proof as to its constitutionality," the behind-the-scenes activity by the bill's opponents was vigorous.

Chief protester to granting any further liberties to the Osteopathic profession was the Chicago Medical Society which had forwarded a letter to every member of the state legislature. It read:

Hon. (Senator or Representative)
Springfield, Illinois

Dear Sir:

In the interest of Public Health and speaking for the 2,400 members of the Chicago Medical Society, I desire to enter the most emphatic protest against the passage of House Bill No. 173, known as the Osteopathy Bill, by the House of Representatives.

These men, calling themselves "osteopaths," seek your sympathy by asking you to license them in order to protect them against unqualified rubbers and masseurs. If they come with clean hands and ask honest protection they should have it. But they do not. Their REAL desire is to engage in the PRACTICE OF MEDICINE without passing the state board examinations which physicians and surgeons must pass. Read Sec. 4 in which osteopathy is made to cover such subjects as obstetrics, gynecology and minor surgery.

These concessions carry with them by implication the use of certain necessary medicines such as anaesthetics, stimulants, styptics and antiseptics. These men say they are OPPOSED to the use of MEDICINES, are required to give no evidence or any knowledge of medicines, yet come seeking the privilege of doing certain things in which the use of medicines is unavoidable.

Again, Sec. 6. Note the words "The same as PHYSICIANS of other SCHOOLS OF MEDICINE." How is that for a joker? If they are qualified to pass the same examination as others MUST, who use physic, why don't they pass it and become PHYSICIANS? Why do they try to sneak into MEDICINE under cover of asking protection against masseurs? This measure is intended to establish as a SCHOOL OF MEDICINE a class of men who claim to treat disease WITHOUT medicine, pretending to believe one thing, while seeking in an underhanded manner the right to do the opposite. What do you call that?

These men claim disease is due to faulty adjustment of joints. Absolutely right scientific investigation has PROVED that most diseases are due, directly or indirectly to the activities of bacteria, minute organisms which live in our bodies and feed themselves upon our tissues as cattle graze upon the fields. Why DREAM in the face of positive knowledge when life, and death, happiness and disease are at stake.

The osteopaths as a body have NOT done and DO NOT DO scientific work in the investigation of disease.

THEY DREAM. THEY DO NOT PROVE.

This bill is not an honest bill.

Very truly yours,
M. Z. Albro, Secretary [4]

After such a flurry of mail, even the most optimistic knew that for the time being the effort was doomed, that they must reorganize and try again next year. And try again they did.

The Illinois state society in 1910 once more went on record as favoring a separate board of examiners and thus end the prevailing policy whereby the State Board of Health served as the examining group. In striving for a separate board, the osteopathic physicians obtained unsolicited help from the Illinois Medical Society which wanted a single licensing board in order "to prevent medical or religious sects from using the name physician or doctor [5]." The osteopathic physicians suspected, however, that the establishment of such a board would be accompanied by guidelines dictated by the medical profession which would still serve to keep the osteopathic physicians at bay.

J. Martin Littlejohn, president of the Littlejohn College and Hospital, took up the battle. In a letter to *The Osteopathic Physician,* he pleaded that there be no compromise with the medics, that while he favored a single independent examining board, he nevertheless felt that the espousal of such a board by the medics and their probable consent to permit an osteopath to serve on the board (but in an inferior role), was largely an attempt to *absorb* the osteopathic physicians and thus put an end to their annoying and persistent appeals for legislative relief. Nevertheless, Dr. Littlejohn announced he would continue to battle for an independent board of examiners—but a board that would recognize the interests of the osteopathic system and would help to achieve a complete separateness of the osteopathic system from all others.

He warned that an examining board must establish equality of qualification, both in preliminary education and in professional curriculum, and in establishing the rights, privileges and status of the osteopathic practitioners with other practitioners. Only a qualified board of osteopathic physicians, he insisted, was qualified to examine osteopathic applicants for licenses. He urged osteopathic colleges to become "better colleges than theirs" [medical schools] and that osteopathic standards of education be more thorough than those of the medical schools. "Let us," he pleaded, "stand shoulder to shoulder on the platform of independence, equality, and the highest standard of efficiency in educational qualification [6]."

In 1913 another bill to bring about the establishment of an independent examining board was introduced into the state legislature, this time by Thomas N. Gorman of Peoria, Illinois. Tabbed H.R. Bill No. 229, it died, predictably, for it was never brought up for a vote after a third reading and numerous attempts to modify it.

In the meantime, official state refusal to permit D.O.'s to sign birth and death certificates continued. In 1915 a 65-year-old woman in Springfield, Illinois, died from pneumonia and heart complications in the city hospital. She had been under the care of Dr. Emery Ennis, a well-known Springfield osteopathic physician. But as had happened on so many previous occasions, the state held that an osteopath was not qualified to sign a death certificate, and again a coroner's inquest was held to resolve the dilemma [7]. The case, highly publicized, once again called attention to the plight of the osteopathic physicians and helped speed the day when such inequalities were banished.

As a matter of fact, it was only a year later that the Illinois state's attorney general reversed the decisions of several municipal boards of health which had ruled that death certificates signed by osteopathic physicians were invalid. The Illinois official decreed that such certificates were indeed valid, but had to be signed by an osteopath as a D.O., not as an M.D. The ruling was only a partial victory, for the state's attorney general still forbade an osteopath from signing birth certificates unless he also held a certificate as a midwife [8].

The full right of D.O.'s to sign both birth and death certificates in Illinois was won in 1917 when Dr. Fred W. Gage took his case to the state supreme court and won a momentous decision not only for himself but for the entire osteopathic profession [9]. Dr. Gage, a Chicago osteopathic physician and a 1900 graduate of the American School of Osteopathy in Kirksville, Missouri, had received a certificate from the Illinois state board of health in August, 1900, authorizing him to "treat human ailments in the State of Illinois without the use of medicine and without performing surgical operations." The Chicago Bureau of Vital Statistics, however, refused to register him as being one authorized to sign birth and death certificates.

Dr. Gage appealed to the Cook County circuit court, which ruled against him, and the case eventually reached the Illinois supreme court. The state's highest judicial body reversed the lower court's ruling and awarded Dr. Gage a significant triumph. The court ruled that "A physician is one versed in or practicing the art of medicine, and the term is not limited to the disciples of any particular school." Thus, even though Dr. Gage as a practicing osteopathic physician did not use medicine on patients nor perform surgical operations, he did "treat and operate on patients for physical ailments."

The term "medicine," the court held, was not limited to substances supposed to possess curative or remedial properties but must be interpreted to include also the "science of preserving health and treating disease for the purpose of cure, whether such treatment involved the use of medical substances or not." The court explained that "anyone whose occupation is the treatment of diseases for the purpose of curing them is a physician, and this is the sense in which the term is used in the Medical Practice Act." Moreover, the requirement that a death certificate be signed by a "legally qualified physician" can truthfully be met by an osteopathic physician who is by the very definition of the term "physician" legally qualified to sign such documents. The same, of course, held true with regard to birth certificates. Thus for the first time, Illinois osteopathic practitioners won the right to be called physicians and the authority to sign birth and death certificates with official sanction [10]. It was an important milestone on the road to equality.

But there was even more good news for the osteopathic profession in 1917. The Illinois 50th General Assembly, in its closing session, passed a "consolidation" or "medical compromise bill," a legislative enactment that not only provided increased stature for osteopathic medicine but implied that further inequities, if they existed, would be reviewed in future years and settled by additional legislation [11]. The bill was actually supported by both the medical and the osteopathic camps, for it aimed a telling blow against the quacks still practicing with impunity throughout the state. It prescribed higher educational standards governing both preliminary and professional education for practitioners of "drugless healing."

The bill provided that, as a condition prerequisite to examination, the candidate shall have completed an approved four-year high school course; that the professional course shall be four years in length and consist of four sessions extending over at least four calendar years; with a minimum requirement that forty months shall have elapsed between the date of matriculation and the date of graduation. This was another great step forward.

The 1917 "consolidation" bill also permitted members of the so-called "drugless healing" classifications to use antiseptics under the direction of the Department of Public Health together with the right to use antidotes. It further provided that, in cases where a practitioner has taken a course in obstetrics equivalent to that taught in a medical college, the candidate may, at his request and at the same time he is being examined in general subjects, also be examined in the subject of midwifery. The bill stipulated that candidates in this group be given examinations similar to those given candidates seeking licenses to practice medicine and surgery, but that questions pertaining to materia medica, therapeutics, surgery and obstetrics be excluded. Moreover, the osteopathic candidate would be examined in osteopathic therapeutics by a special committee of osteopathic physicians selected in accordance with the provisions of the "consolidation" bill.

The bill had teeth in it. It made it a crime for any person to call himself an osteopath who was not licensed as an osteopath; anyone convicted of so doing faced a fine, imprisonment, and license revocation. All in all, the bill seemed a good one and its provisions were rightfully hailed by the state's osteopathic physicians as tremendous improvements in their beleaguered profession. Nevertheless, as late as 1920, the practice of obstetrics by osteopathic physicians was, in general, forbidden.

On April 2, 1920, Dr. Louis C. Hanavan, a member of the faculty of the Chicago College of Osteopathy who later became professor of obstetrics at the college and head of the Chicago Osteopathic Hospital's obstetrical services, received a letter from the Illinois department of registration and education downgrading the school's teaching of obstetrics and refusing Dr. Hanavan the right to take a midwife's examination to qualify him for the practice of obstetrics [12]. The letter, signed by F. C. Dodd, Superintendent of Registration, read:

Dear Doctor:

At a meeting of the Professional Committee for Medicine held in this office yesterday, April 1, 1924, it was determined that the subject of Obstetrics as taught in the Chicago College of Osteopathy is not deemed equal to that taught in an approved Medical College. Therefore, you are not eligible under the law to make application for the midwife examination.

Officials of CCO immediately pointed out that the committee which had investigated the school's obstetrical department was composed of three medical doctors, and that the real objection to the school's obstetrical department was that the departmental teaching staff of five listed only one graduate of a medical college, the other four faculty members being graduates of an osteopathic school. In addition, school officials pointed out, one of the members of the committee had for years been known to oppose any attempt by the osteopathic profession to obtain fair and adequate legislative regulation.

Dr. Blanche M. Elfrink of CCO's obstetrical department, looking for a way to make the best of a bad situation, appeared before the college trustees and recommended that, in order to meet the state's clinic requirements, four or five osteopathic physicians who were also M.D.'s be added to the hospital's obstetrical staff. The Board quickly accepted her recommendation [13].

Opposition by the medical profession to osteopathy remained so distressing that one of the staff members of the Chicago College of Osteopathy even asked that his name be omitted from the college catalogue. The reason: he was working for his Ph.D. degree at the University of Chicago and the head of the anatomy department was not only antagonistic to osteopathy in general but strongly opposed any student of his even working in an osteopathic institution. The trustees, with a baleful eye, recommended that the Dean grant the student's request for anonymity [14].

In 1921, further significant events took place. Early in the year, Dr. E. B. Waters of Winchester, Illinois, was brought to trial on a charge of practicing surgery and midwifery without a license, that is, "to practice midwifery and surgery in all their branches" as specified in the Medical Practice Act. After the pro's and con's of the case had been heard, the jury returned a verdict of *not guilty.* It was the first case of this nature to go to trial in the State of Illinois and ended as a signal victory for osteopathy [15].

In mid year, gains which had been won in 1917 through the "medical compromise bill" and which had revised many of the undesirable clauses of the 1899 Medical Practice Act, were suddenly nullified. In June, 1921, the Illinois supreme court ruled that the 1917 revised Medical Practice Act was unconstitutional. The decision involved a Danville chiropractor who had been urged to practice without a license in order to test the legality of the 1917 legislation. The *Chicago Tribune* published a news dispatch from

Springfield, dated June 22, outlining the case and the reasons for the court's action. It read as follows:

> The Illinois medical practice act as revised in 1917 was found unconstitutional in the State Supreme Court today. The decision was handed down in the case of Lucius J. Love, a chiropractic of Danville, who refused to take out a license.
>
> The court's opinion holds that the revisions of requirements for chiropractics are unreasonable and discriminatory. The court's decision restores the old medical practice act in effect prior to the revision.
>
> It was announced tonight that a motion for a new trial will be filed. In the meantime numerous prosecutions instituted by the state department of registration and education will be held up until this motion is disposed of.

### Verdict is Unanimous

> There is little hope that the revision will be saved, however, as the opinion of the court, which was prepared by Justice Duncan, was concurred in by the full membership of the bench.
>
> The decision is a blow to the state medical society, which spent much time in preparing the revision of 1917, but it brings joy to the heart of President Palmer of the Des Moines (Iowa) Chiropractic School, who has been protesting against the act ever since its passage. Love, who made the fight in the Supreme Court, is a graduate of the Palmer School.
>
> The revision of 1917 was prepared by Charles E. Woodward, now president of the state constitutional convention. Its one weak spot, it seems, was the section which revised the law relating to osteopathy, chiropractics and practitioners other than medical doctors.

### Qualifications Unstated

> The old law provided for an examination and the licensing of these practitioners, but did not undertake to specify the qualifications required of applicants for licenses.
>
> In making the revision, applicants for licenses were required to pursue a course of study equivalent to that of the medical practitioners and in addition qualify in their own school. The educational qualification contemplated a period of four years in college.
>
> Love took a two years' course at the Palmer school and then asked to be examined for a license. This was denied, and on the advice of his attorney he began to practice for the purpose of testing the constitutionality of the law [16].

Thus the gains which had been made by the osteopathic profession in 1917 were wiped out and the profession once again found itself operating under the original Medical Practice Act of 1899.

Reaction was swift. Dr. Oliver C. Foreman, professor of osteopathic theory and practice at the Chicago College of Osteopathy, and a member of the school's Board of Trustees, wrote to the *Journal of the American Osteopathic Association* as follows:

> . . . Now comes Illinois: With the killing by the chiros of the 1917 Medical Practice Act the "Other Practitioners" are operating under the old law of 1899. The medics must pass a new law this next legislation, and they are going to try and pass one of their own trying to control all other schools of therapy. Already it is rumored that they are going to ask a two-year premedical requirement for the Osteopaths. Now as the Chicago College of Osteopathy, in order to meet up with all the requirements already laid down by the other states, has been forced to put in practically a one year premedical or pre-freshman year, it is a question whether or not less can be asked for or expected than is already required by the Chicago College of Osteopathy. This practically would mean the elimination of the graduates from all other Osteopathic schools in Illinois, unless schools come up to this requirement. Neither could we have reciprocity. This should not be, as it is just one more blow to our institutions and to the profession. The Chicago College of Osteopathy with its limited capacity cannot possibly supply all the needs Osteopathically of the profession in these states of high requirements, neither are all of our schools turning out the numbers we desire. The cost of an Osteopathic education is so increased, it becomes more and more difficult to meet it. And when the student has graduated, he feels it has cost him so much he cannot afford to give of his time or means for the good of the profession or its schools. This has been evident in recent years. Our institutions, the majority of which are attempting to operate on a non-profit basis, with no endowments, are depending solely upon the generosity of a few of the Osteopathic Physicians. Under increased requirements, our institutions cannot continue in a healthy state, let alone develop as they should. The Osteopathic Physicians in Illinois and elsewhere should stand against anything more than the A.O.A. plan of four years high school or its equivalent and four years of Osteopathy. Either those states requiring more will have to change their laws or die Osteopathically; our colleges will cease to function to the best advantage of the profession. The selfishness or indifference of a few have worked to the detriment and the harm of numbers. Our profession must have numbers, true to the faith, for there is much work to be done, too much for the too few of those who are doing it [17].

The generally chaotic situation in which osteopathic medicine found itself at this time stimulated the state osteopathic association to vigorous activity. It denounced certain practitioners for "practically purchasing their licenses from the Department of Registration and Education" and proclaimed:

> We are opposed to the granting of licenses under any circumstances to graduates of colleges giving courses by mail, of colleges which do not enforce reasonable entrance requirements, or of colleges which give courses with lower requirements than those demanded by the American Osteopathic Association (A.O.A.).

We recommend that steps be taken to rectify the condition which has resulted from the efforts of the A.M.A. to "standardize" hospitals, whereby most of the hospitals in this state have been closed to the members of our profession, and even to a large percentage of medical doctors. We believe that every licensed physician should be given access, under just restrictions, to all hospitals which derive any part of their funds from charity or to the state, and which are free from any tax burden [18].

In the meantime, the Chicago College of Osteopathy was having its own problems with the State of Illinois. In October, 1922, Dean Jerome Raymond reported to the College trustees that seventeen of the school's graduates had taken the Illinois state board examination, but only four had been given passing marks and "these only after much persuasion on the part of the superintendent of the Board of registration and education, Mr. Michels [19]."

The dean further explained that the examining board had requested the CCO graduates to write the designation "Other Practitioners" on their examination papers. Later, reasoning that since the students were permitted to reply to only 80 percent of the questions (queries on obstetrics, surgery, and materia medica were ruled out for osteopathic candidates), the board had deducted 20 percent from the grades made by the students and thus handicapped them from scoring passing grades. Dean Raymond personally appeared before the Illinois board of registration in November and requested a rereading of the examination papers (with instructions from the trustees to institute a mandamus proceeding if the board refused to reappraise the examination papers). Later in the month he reported that the papers had been reconsidered [20].

A year later, Dean Raymond again appeared before the College trustees and reported that on August 28, 1923, a delegation from the state board of registration and education had visited the college, granted its graduates the right to take the examination to practice obstetrics, but recommended that the College require a two-year premedic program instead of a one-year program then in effect; that a year of internship be required; and that the school teach materia medica or pharmacology. If these requirements were met, the visiting committee pointed out, CCO graduates would be permitted by the state to take the examination to practice medicine in all its branches, including surgery.

What the delegation did not spell out in so many words, of course, was that the acceptance of their recommendations would virtually do away with osteopathy as a separate practice and integrate it completely with general medicine.

The perils of their recommended program were apparent at once to Dr.

Oliver Foreman, the CCO faculty member and trustee who a year earlier had written to the *AOA Journal* concerning the pernicious effect resulting from the state supreme court's nullification of the revised 1917 Medical Practice Act. He took up the cudgel immediately to hold off any attempts to ambush the progress of osteopathic medicine in its effort to maintain itself as an independent profession, and sternly warned that the profession might indeed be swallowed up by that branch of the medical profession dominated by the holders of M.D. degrees.

Joined by Dr. Jessie O'Connor, well-known Chicago woman osteopathic physician and associated with Foreman on the CCO faculty, he directed a letter to all members of the College Corporation, calling on them to join the fight for osteopathic independence. A letter dated September 22, 1923, signed by Drs. Foreman and O'Connor, asked:

> Is our college to become a Class "C" medical college and later relegated to the discard, or are we going to be an osteopathic institution? Because we have lost in our legislative fights, are we going to sacrifice our college to the dictation of the American Medical Association, whether it is through the Association directly or through their instrument, the Board of Registration and Education of the State of Illinois?
>
> By the flattery they are handing us, are they to steal our institution, or are we going to continue to be independent? Are we going to be Osteopaths because of our special system of therapy—adjustment—or do we wish to be Osteopaths because we can give a dose of castor oil, operate, prescribe aspirin or what not? Is Osteopathy to continue as a separate science or be just a tail to the medical kite?
>
> The proposition of the Board of Registration and Education of the State of Illinois that we require a two-year pre-medical course, a year's internship, and include materia medica in our curriculum, and they then will license our graduates to practice MEDICINE IN ALL ITS BRANCHES in the State of Illinois, means the downfall of Osteopathy and the eventual destruction of our institution by the American Medical Association [21].

A year later, in 1924, osteopathy in Illinois won a major triumph when the Illinois Supreme Court, in a 7 to 1 decision, affirmed the complete equality of osteopathic practice with that of "regular" medicine in the state and granted qualified osteopathic physicians the right to practice surgery without hindrance or interference.

The Supreme Court's decision centered around Robert E. Schaeffer, D.O., a Chicago osteopathic physician who had performed an operation on a Mrs. Blanche Mehlen. Dr. Schaeffer had been brought to court on the charge of practicing surgery without a license and thus being guilty of violating the 1899 Medical Practice Act. He was fined $100 in Municipal Court.

Dr. Schaeffer took the position that the 1899 Act was void because of its discriminations against physicians who had graduated from osteopathic colleges as against those who had been educated in medicine and surgery in medical colleges. He insisted that his position was substantiated in 1917 when the Medical Practice Act was declared void (the People vs. Love).

The State countered that the case involving the chiropractor Lucius J. Love in 1917 was dissimilar and that the Supreme Court's decision on that occasion affected only cases where physicians treated human ailments without the use of drugs or medicine and without operative surgery.

Dr. Schaeffer then took his case to the Illinois Supreme Court where his stand was upheld and the Municipal Court's decision reversed. The Illinois Supreme Court spelled out clearly the reasons for its significant decision:

> We think there can be no question whatever that this statute discriminates against appellant as an osteopathic physician and in favor of the graduates of the medical school as contended by him. It requires him or a graduate of his school [he had graduated from the American School of Osteopathy in Kirksville, Missouri], after spending four years in such graduation, to continue his college education for a further time, and perhaps four years longer until he has become a graduate of a medical school, before he can ever be permitted to be examined for license to practice osteopathy and surgery, while a graduate of a medical college is permitted without further study, to practice medicine and surgery.
>
> In the second place, he is required to study the therapeutics of the allopaths or other medical schools which he does not desire to use in his practice before he can practice osteopathy and surgery, while the graduate of a medical school is not required to graduate in osteopathy or to study osteopathic therapeutics, and yet he may be licensed to practice, and may practice, osteopathy.
>
> In the third place, if an osteopath attends a medical college for the purpose of graduation, the probabilities are that he will be required to repeat in the medical college the study of all those subjects, including surgery, midwifery and gynecology, and all the other studies that we have above enumerated as having been passed by him in his own school, before he can begin the practice of surgery.
>
> The very great prejudice existing among many physicians of the medical schools against the osteopaths, and of the osteopaths against those of the medical schools, is well known. This statute recognizes both systems as meritorious because it allows both to treat human ailments according to their system, and it discriminates against the osteopath and seems to place the examination of osteopaths to practice osteopathy entirely at the will and discretion of a medical board, as no one other than those educated in the medical system are qualified, under the act, to conduct the examination provided for by it. This statute therefore tends to deprive the osteopaths of their constitutional right to practice surgery who are, so far as this record shows, just as efficient and as well prepared by college and hospital training to practice surgery as are the physicians of the medical schools. The act is therefore void.

[ 197 ]

We are only concerned with the question whether this act is unconstitutional by reason of unlawful discrimination, as charged. As we have previously said in other cases, we have no leaning for or against either system or either practitioner. It has been demonstrated over and over again that there is merit in both systems, and neither should be unjustly penalized by statutes which permit unlawful discrimination.

This statute is in contravention of the fourteenth amendment of the Federal constitution, which provides that no State shall make or enforce any law which shall abridge the privileges or immunities of citizens of the United States, nor shall any state deprive any person of life, liberty or property without due process of law, nor deny to any person within its jurisdiction the equal protection of the law.

It also violates the provisions of our bill of rights that no person shall be deprived of life, liberty or property without due process of law, and that no law impairing the obligation of contracts or making any irrevocable grant of special privileges or immunities shall be passed.

In the passage of this statute the legislature evidently overlooked the fact that it discriminates against the osteopaths, as already shown.

It is a fundamental principle of this government that its people have the right to make constitutions that will guard them against the tyranny of statutes that permit unlawful discrimination, however innocently or inadvertently made, and courts are required to regard their constitutional oaths and declare every such statute void when it conclusively appears that such act is unconstitutional.

For the foregoing reasons the judgment of the municipal court is reversed [22].

The Illinois Osteopathic Association, which had been in the thick of the legal jousting for years, was jubilant and mailed to each of its members the following letter:

Dear Doctor:

The decision of the Supreme Court in the case of People vs. Schaeffer, No. 14738, is one of the most signal victories for osteopathy ever won in the courts of any of the states. Briefly, the opinion is accomplished by the following results:

1. Re-affirms the case of People vs. Love and holds the entire Medical Practice Act of 1917 invalid.
2. Holds the entire Medical Practice Act of 1899 invalid because of its manifest discriminations against osteopaths and schools of osteopathy, particularly with reference to surgery and obstetrics.
3. Makes it clear that no Medical Practice Act will be held valid if it confers a monopoly of surgery or obstetrics on so-called medical schools or systems of healing [23].

*The Osteopathic Physician* called the decision "a monumental victory" and predicted that it would be "quoted many times in the future in the legislative and court battles of other states," and that it would "help to get justice for Osteopathy in every state where medical politicians seek to surround the practice of our profession with embarrassments and inhibitions [24]." Added satisfaction was obtained by Illinois osteopathic physicians when the State's request to have the Schaeffer case reopened was denied by the Supreme Court and the final verdict reaffirmed: "The decision stands."

Nonetheless, the legal sparring was far from over. In 1931 the Illinois attorney general ruled that osteopathic physicians could not vaccinate or administer toxin, since smallpox vaccination involved "a slight surgical procedure" as well as "an injection with a syringe." The attorney general reasoned that, since osteopathic physicians supposedly treated human ailments without the use of drugs or medicine and without operative surgery, they were not qualified to administer vaccination. He added, however, that the Department of Public Health had no right to refuse biologicals to osteopathic physicians even though they were forbidden to use them [25]. This interpretation was strange, indeed, and did nothing to clarify the situation.

Later in the year, additional warnings were issued to the state's osteopathic physicians by the attorney general. He ruled that a practitioner of osteopathy was not permitted to administer an anesthetic; to "take blood tests"; to "take blood transfusions"; to "treat varicose veins by injecting liquid solutions into the body"; "treat rectal troubles by injecting medical compounds and properties"; nor "to treat asthma by injecting a sedative drug into the system [26]."

In Ottawa, eight osteopathic physicians appealed to the Circuit Court for an injunction to prevent the Ryburn-King hospital in that community from interfering with their caring for patients at the hospital [27]. In Decatur City, the attorney general reversed a ruling giving osteopathic physicians the right to practice in the city's public hospital [28]. These cases indicated clearly that much remained to be done.

In 1934 the wall of discrimination crumbled a bit more. Largely through the efforts of Dr. H. Willard Brown and two CCO physicians, Drs. Chester H. Morris and Ernest R. Proctor, the Federal Emergency Relief Administration (FERA) ruled that osteopathic physicians were fully qualified to serve on its rolls; that the sick could choose their own personal physicians; and that osteopathic physicians would be paid for their services by the state relief authorities on the same basis that the M.D.'s were paid. The *Forum of Osteopathy* commented, "Osteopathy in Illinois is closer to recognition compatible with its position with the people [29]."

Two decades later, the Chicago College of Osteopathy, which had campaigned tirelessly to achieve full recognition as an osteopathic institution, at last reached an objective it had sought for many weary years. On June 22,

1954, the Appellate Court of Illinois, First District, ruled that graduates of the College had the right to take state board examinations in ALL fields of medicine and that a Doctor of Osteopathy who passed the examination, could practice his profession without limitation and on the same basis as any other well-trained physician [30]. For this legal victory, much of the credit must go to Dr. Richard N. MacBain, CCO's president, who pleaded the school's case in court after court.

The chain of events leading to the important Appellate Court ruling in 1954 began in 1943. For many years the state's Medical Examining Board had not only ignored the College's requests for inspection in order to obtain state approval but had, even after many formal pleas, refused to specify just what requirements the college must meet in order to win the Committee's blessing.

In 1943, the Illinois Osteopathic Association, by means of a writ of mandamus, compelled the state Department of Registration and Education to have its examining committee outline the requirements which must be met by any school applying for approval as an institution qualified to train physicians and surgeons under the 1923 revised Medical Practice Act. The requirements were hurriedly drawn up and the Illinois osteopathic forces charged that the requirements "showed a lack of knowledge of even the simplest procedures in modern medical education on the part of a committee whose business it is to pass on the educational qualifications of physicians and surgeons practicing in Illinois [31]."

During the next five or six years the Examining Committee continued to reject the College's requests for approval. The Illinois Osteopathic Association charged that many of the medical colleges approved by the committee during these years failed to comply with a number of the provisions in the rules; that of 80 schools approved between 1943 and 1949, forty-nine failed to comply with requirements which had led specifically to the refusal to recognize CCO; and that, in practice, the Medical Examining Committee showed itself reasonable in dealing with medical colleges but most strict in dealing with the Chicago College of Osteopathy [32].

Nevertheless, the Chicago College of Osteopathy made vigorous preparations to win accreditation. Between 1943 and 1949, the College conducted fund-raising drives and was able to raise more than $500,000 for expanding and increasing its facilities in its attempts to win approval both for its teaching branch and its affiliated Chicago Osteopathic Hospital(COH).

In 1949 the College once more applied for inspection and after weeks of waiting, a five-man examining committee visited the school. As had happened so often in the past, the committee reported unfavorably to the Department of Registration and Education in Springfield. The committee alleged that the College had not met minimum requirements for approval. The State accepted the report.

The Chicago College of Osteopathy had solid reasons for protesting the Committee's and the State's actions. Although the revised Medical Practice Act specifically pointed out that there must be no discrimination "against any system or method of treating human ailments, or against any medical college, or against any professional school, college or institution teaching any system or method of treating human ailments," the Medical Examining Board arbitrarily continued to discriminate and withhold approval of CCO.

To make matters even worse, the Examining Committee declared that osteopathic physicians could be adequately trained in osteopathic colleges only by Doctors of Medicine, not by Doctors of Osteopathy. CCO officials lamented that the Examining Committee "refused to accept the qualifications of our faculty—men and women of twenty to thirty years teaching experience, certified in their respective specialties by qualified examining boards, people whose qualifications have been evaluated and approved by every evaluating agency, except the Medical Examining Committee of Illinois! [33]"

In 1950 another examining committee visited the College campus. This committee consisted of five doctors of medicine; two of them were national officers of the American Medical Association. Once again the Committee rejected the College's bid for approval.

The College responded to these rebuffs by claiming that the Examining Committee had shown discrimination and pointed out that forty states had given the Chicago College and the five other osteopathic institutions in the United States full recognition. Illinois, the College stated, was the only major state in the Union still refusing to recognize osteopathic education and the right of osteopathic physicians to offer the full medical services they had been trained to provide.

The College took action against the state Medical Examining Committee by filing its plea with the Cook County Superior Court. This body, however, upheld the Examining Committee's verdict. Dr. Richard N. MacBain, CCO president, filed an appeal. On June 22, 1954, the Illinois Appellate Court completely reversed the Superior Court's decision and, in a 7 to 1 decision, stated:

> It is our conclusion based on the record that with respect to schools which grant the degree of Doctor of Medicine, the department has considered as substantial compliance with its rules the same or even a lower measure than that which it has applied to the plaintiff.
>
> We are of the opinion that this has been done with the intent to discriminate and that to deny plaintiff the relief sought would be to condone an evasion of the statute (Section 20 of the Medical Practice Act). . . .

The plaintiff has substantially complied with the requirements in accordance with the standards which the department in practice has applied, and the department should approve its application.

The judgment of the trial court is reversed and this cause remanded with directions to refer the matter back to the Department of Registration and Education for the entry of an order approving plaintiff's application [34].

It was a gratifying victory, and a forerunner of an equally satisfying Supreme Court decision just a year later!

The Illinois Department of Registration and Education did not accept the Appellate Court's decision without remonstrance. The Department filed a motion in the Appellate Court asking that the mandate of the court be revoked. At the same time, it also filed a petition asking for the right to appeal to the Illinois Supreme Court in hopes of getting former court decisions reversed.

The answer to this maneuvering came on April 19, 1955, with another momentous victory for CCO and the osteopathic profession in the state. In a unanimous decision, the Illinois Supreme Court reaffirmed the decision handed down by the Appellate Court on June 22, 1954, and ordered the Department of Registration and Education to approve the Chicago College of Osteopathy as a school "whose graduates are eligible to take the examination for a license to practice medicine in all its branches [35]."

After more than thirty years, CCO graduates were at last declared eligible to take the examination for a license to practice medicine in all of its branches and to offer the services which they were qualified to give.

For the College's administration, faculty, students, alumni and friends, the Supreme Court's decision was immeasurably gratifying, for the ruling centered exclusively on the Chicago College of Osteopathy, highlighting it as an institution approved for the training of graduates for the *full examination* given by the Medical Examining Committee. This meant that the school's graduates had the right to be examined in the subjects of materia medica, therapeutics, surgery, theory and practice. The Court noted that CCO had been active since 1913 [when the Littlejohn College name was discontinued as a result of reorganization] and that its facilities included class rooms, laboratories, library, outpatient department, together with a 100-bed hospital. It noted further that the College had a faculty of 64 trained in all branches of medicine and surgery; that it operated on an annual budget of some $700,000; that its educational program had been accepted by every agency, both Federal and State, to which it had applied (with the exception of the Department in Illinois); and that its instruction in all subjects paralleled that given in approved medical institutions. In its concluding paragraph, the Supreme Court stated:

The grounds for denying recognition to the plaintiff college are all invalid; therefore, at the time of said order by the Department the plaintiff was qualified as a college reputable and in good standing whose graduates are eligible to take the examination for a license to practice medicine in all its branches in Illinois. The judgment of the Appellate Court is affirmed and the cause is remanded to the Department with directions to expeditiously determine whether any changes have occurred subsequent to that time which justify withholding approval. Said determination is ordered to be made with the object of effectuating the manifest intention of the legislature as elaborated in this opinion.

Judgment affirmed, and cause remanded, with directions [36].

One of the happiest over this newest triumph, of course, was Dr. MacBain. He, however, saw new challenges ahead and said: "The granting of full professional recognition by the State of Illinois to the College and its graduates comes at a time when the osteopathic profession has had to reexamine its place in medicine. The larger and older school of medicine has rejected proposals for even a minimum degree of collaboration with osteopathy. We must continue to grow and develop as a separate school of practice—independent and self-sufficient [37]."

The year 1955 was indeed a turning point in the history of the College!

In April, 1955, when the Supreme Court ordered that the Chicago College of Osteopathy be fully accredited, seven graduates of the College had applications on file for the state medical examination scheduled for June 21. Just prior to the time of the examination, Dr. MacBain received the following letter from Vera M. Binks, Director of the Illinois State Department of Registration and Education:

> I am today advising you of the accreditation of the Chicago College of Osteopathy and the Chicago Osteopathic Hospital. The minutes have just been signed by the members of the Committee and the Director.
>
> In response to your inquiry and your letter of June 10, the applicants for examination to practice medicine in all of its branches will be required to take the subjects on which they have not been previously examined—materia medica, therapeutics, surgery, theory and practice. . . .
>
> The Department will accord the same privilege to your graduates . . . as is accorded to other medical students [38].

The final chapter in the long, long battle for osteopathic equality in the State of Illinois was written in 1959 when an amended Medical Practice Act was signed into law by Governor William G. Stratton. This bill gave the state's 350 osteopathic physicians the right to practice medicine in all its branches *provided* they complete a 248-hour refresher course in the areas where they had been restricted in practice and pass the subsequent examination. These requirements applied to all D.O.'s who held an Illinois license and who had been in resident practice in the state for a period of not less than one year prior to July 9, 1959. These practitioners were given until July 1, 1963, to complete the post-graduate course in a college of good standing in Illinois [39].

The bill which Governor Stratton signed also created a composite medical examining committee. Added to the five medical doctors on the committee were a Doctor of Osteopathy and a Doctor of Chiropractic, thus boosting the membership to seven and giving *all seven* full voting rights (For several years, an osteopathic physician had served on the board, but had held no voting privileges).

Safeguarding the provisions of the bill was the statement: "The provisions of this ACT shall not be so construed nor shall they be so administered as to discriminate against any system or method of treating human ailments. . . . [40]"

The long battle was won!

## REFERENCES

1. In 1973 the State of Mississippi became the 50th state to grant full privileges to osteopathic physicians, thus completing the roster of states where osteopathy is on an equal footing with all branches of the healing art.
2. *The Boston Osteopath,* June, 1901.
3. *The Osteopathic Physician,* July, 1905, p. 11. Further evidence to indicate the widely varying views held concerning osteopathy is found in the *Naturopath Magazine* for April, 1905, which classified osteopathy as a branch of naturopathy, along with dietetics, hygiene, and suggestive therapeutics.
4. *The Osteopathic Physician,* May 1909, p. 8 (Vol. 15, No. 5).
5. *Ibid.,* July, 1910, pp. 1–2. (Vol. 18, No. 1).
6. *Ibid.*
7. *Journal AOA,* November, 1915, p. 170. (Vol. 15, No. 3).
8. *Ibid.,* July, 1916, p. 593. (Vol. 15, No. 11).
9. *Ibid.,* June, 1917, p. 1226. (Vol. 16, No. 10). Dr. Gage was a prominent member of the CCO faculty during the years 1913–1920. He was one of the early osteopathic physicians in the Chicago area, one of the chief CCO protagonists in the school's early courtroom struggles, and a tireless worker for the Illinois Osteopathic Association. He was a member of the CCO Board of Trustees (treasurer for a number of years), and he served on the school's finance and hospital committees. He was also active in the Chicago Association of Commerce and the Kiwanis Club. In February, 1920, Dr. Gage resigned because of ill health and he died later in the year.
10. *The Osteopathic Physician,* June, 1917, pp. 10–11. (Vol. 31, No. 6).
11. *Ibid.,* pp. 13–14.
12. CCO Board of Trustees Minutes for April 2, 1920.
13. CCO Board of Trustees Minutes for June 16, 1920.
14. *Ibid.*
15. *Journal AOA,* May, 1921. (Vol. 20, p. 532).
16. Published in *The Osteopathic Physician,* July, 1921, p. 29 (Vol. 40, No. 1).
17. *Journal AOA,* November, 1922, p. 161. Dr. Foreman's reluctance to boost educational

requirements was not, of course, shared by all osteopathic physicians nor by the full membership of the college's Board of Trustees.

18. *Journal AOA,* July, 1922. (Vol. 21, p. 729).
19. CCO Board of Trustees Minutes for October 12, 1922.
20. *Ibid.*
21. Letter from CCO files.
22. *The Osteopathic Physician,* February, 1924, p. 7. (Vol. 45, No. 2).
23. *Journal AOA,* February, 1924. (Vol. 23, p. 448).
24. *The Osteopathic Physician,* February, 1924, p. 7.
25. *Journal AOA,* March, 1931. (Vol. 30. p. 290).
26. *Journal AOA,* April, 1932. (Vol. 31, p. 316).
27. *Ibid.*
28. *Ibid.*
29. *Forum of Osteopathy,* May, 1934. (Vol. 8, p. 333).
30. *Ibid.*
31. CCO Pamphlet, 1950.
32. *Ibid.*
33. *Ibid.*
34. *Forum of Osteopathy,* August, 1954, p. 571.
35. *Journal AOA,* June, 1955. (Vol. 54, pp. 648–651).
36. *Ibid.*
37. *The President's Report* for 1954–1955.
38. Evidence that relations between the American Medical Association and the Chicago College of Osteopathy were improving is found in a report submitted by an AMA investigating committee after it spent three days in February, 1955, looking over CCO facilities. The Committee reported that physical facilities were grossly inadequate, that the College provided no instruction in Psychiatry, that salaries were inferior to those in regular medical schools, and that research was negligible (a deficiency due, no doubt, to the limited income on which the school was operating).

Yet the Committee found much to praise: the high academic standards and quality of students, the many departments which were "identical to those in medical schools", and the excellence of the overall curriculum. The concluding sentence of the report was especially noteworthy: "It may be stated that the one thing which was outstanding and striking in the Chicago College of Osteopathy was the fact that in spite of the handicaps imposed by lack of financial resources, space, equipment, etc., there was in evidence such a spirit of dedication and devotion to his work on the part of everyone concerned as to be an inspiration to every member of the visiting team."

Although the investigation was made early in 1955, the report was not submitted until several years later, since CCO was given full recognition by the State of Illinois in April, 1955. In 1958, President Richard N. MacBain wrote Dr. J. Murray Kinsman of the University of Louisville School of Medicine [who had headed the investigating committee], informing him of the new CCO Basic Science Building, of the many improvements that had been made, and assuring him that many of the shortcomings, pointed out by the Committee were being eliminated. Nevertheless, Dr. MacBain sadly reported that "we have found no solution to the financial stringency which seems to affect all colleges training doctors."
39. In October, 1959, the Chicago College of Osteopathy began offering a full-range refresher course so that Illinois D.O.'s would be qualified to take the state board examination leading to full practice rights. This post-graduate course was given on Saturdays and Sundays over a 16-week period.
40. *Forum of Osteopathy,* September, 1955, pp. 33–34.

[ 207 ]

*To Teach, To Heal, To Serve!*

ROBERT A. KISTNER, D.O., M.D., F.A.C.O.S., *Vice President—Medical Education Affairs, Dean of Faculty*

WARD E. PERRIN, B.S., D.O., F.A.C.O.I., *Associate Dean Clinical Education (Acting) Medical Director—Chicago Osteopathic Hospital*

GEORGE T. CALEEL, B.S., D.O., F.A.C.O.I., *Associate Dean Clinical Education*

HAROLD L. HAKES, PH.D., *Dean of Students and Director of Admissions*

VIRGINIA I. COSTELLO, *Registrar*

SHAFER A. GROSS, B.S., *Controller*

W. LEE BROOKE, A.B., M.A.L.S., *Director of Libraries*

HARVEY H. ACTON, M.A., *Administrator Hyde Park Osteopathic Medical Center*

## COLLEGE DEPARTMENTS AND CHAIRMEN

| | |
|---|---|
| *Anatomy* | FREDERICK J. JULYAN, PH.D. |
| *Anesthesiology* | CHRISTIAN C. LYNGBY, D.O. (Acting) |
| *Biochemistry* | JACKLYN B. MELCHIOR, PH.D. |
| *Family Medicine* | HOWARD H. HUNT, D.O. |
| *Medicine* | WARD E. PERRIN, B.S., D.O., F.A.C.O.I. |
| *Microbiology* | AARON ALEXANDER, PH.D. |
| *Obstetrics and Gynecology* | SEAVER A. TARULIS, D.O., F.A.C.O.O.G. |
| *Ophthalmology and Otorhinolaryngology* | SOL R. KAUFMAN, B.S., D.O. |
| *Osteopathic Medicine* | NORMAN J. LARSEN, D.O., F.A.A.O. |
| *Pathology* | DAVID L. STURDIVANT, A.B., D.O. (Acting) |
| *Pediatrics* | THOMAS E. JARRETT, D.O., F.A.C.O.P. |
| *Pharmacology* | VENKATRAY G. PRABHU, PH.D. |
| *Physiology* | ALBERT F. KELSO, PH.D. |
| *Psychiatry and Mental Health* | JOHN C. LEE, M.D. |
| *Radiology* | HAROLD KATZEN, D.O. |
| *Surgery* | P. ROBERT LOMBARDO, B.A., D.O., F.A.C.O.S. |

# CLASS OF 1975

Amon, Joseph
Arko, Gregory

Bailey, Gary
Beaty, Richard
Bertin, Anthony
Birse, Gregory
Bowen, James
Breitzer, Gerard
Bush, John

Cadamagnani, Paul
Ciemiega, Robert
Clearfield, Michael
Cook, Edwin

Daly, Gregory
Davies, Richard
Dettman, Archie
Dickason, Robert
Dieterich, David

Engelmann, Theodore
Eubanks, Robert
Eutzler, James

Franckowiak, Charles
Friedman, Richard
Fung, Fred

Geimer, Paul
Geissler, Evan
Goodall, Thomas
Guthrie, Robert

Huelsing, Joseph

Johnson, James

Kolb, Gary
Kolb, Melvin

Litchfield, Robert
Love, Terry

MacGregor, Douglas

Mall, Ronald
Mandel, Ronald
Marcowitz, Stewart
Matheu, Frank
Maxvill, Charles
McLeod, Kenneth
Mechelke, Craig
Medina, Francisco
Meyer, Donald
Miceli, Louis
Michels, Victor
Mihalo, Daniel
Miko, Theodore
Mitrick, Michael
Moore, David
Moore, Thomas A.

Naim, Candace
Neumann, Charles

O'Donnell, James

Papp, Louis
Parsons, Robert
Pelton, James
Pintal, William
Plesich, Stephen
Potocki, Joseph
Prechel, William

Sacha, Robert
Schreck, Edward
Senatore, Peter
Shaw, B. Frank
Sheldon, Stephen
Shoemaker, Russell
Skora, Alan
Stanek, Michael
Steininger, Louis
Streeter, W. Cal
Strnad, Richard
Sun, Din-on
Syperda, Glenn
Syperda, Virginia

Troutman, Monte

Tupa, Robert

Vander Putten, Carl
Varas, Theodore
Vogler, James

Waitzman, Thomas

Walton, Frank
Warnowicz, Mary Anne

Young, Stephen

Zych, Gregory

## CLASS OF 1976

Adams, Clinton
Aprahamian, Ashod

Babcock, Howard
Bakotic, Raymond
Barbara, Louis
Baymiller, James
Bender, Lawrence
Benson, Jack
Bielfelt, Bruce
Bischof, Michael
Blumenthal, James
Bochucinski, Phillip
Bowman, Philip
Brophy, Edward
Brown, Russell

Capone, Edward
Carney, Michael
Casey, Robert
Castillo, Thomas
Cirone, Ronald
Collins, John
Curry, Lawrence

Daros, E. James
Davis, Terry
DeBlander, Richard
Dicillo, Patrick
Duckles, Edward
Dunker, William

Egol, Andrew
Enich, Nadine

Gentleman, James

Green, Robert
Guernsey, Charles
Gulick, Peter
Guthrie, Roger

Halpin, Maurice
Harney, Michael
Hegyi, Douglas
Heyer, John
Hillman, John
Horvath, G. Dennis

Jones, J. Louis

Keer, Michael
Kelly, Thomas
Kiefer, Karen (Spencer)
Kiefer, Richard
Kikoler, David
Kovachevich, Martin
Kozlowski, Joseph
Kravitz, Howard
Krejsa, Richard

Lacey, Roy
Lemanski, Dennis
Lennox, John
Little, William
Lynch, Michael

MacNealy, Mark
Mazeika, Bart
McNamara, Brian
Moore, Thomas H.

Nelezen, Gerald

O'Connell, Michael

Podzamsky, John
Pohlman, Anthony
Ponitz, Kenneth
Posuniak, Edward
Putman, John

Reiner, Mark
Roden, Wayne
Ronan, William
Rubin, Bernard

Sams, Michael
Sargeant, William
Sartori, Roy
Saydel, Kenneth
Scarnati, Richard
Schamaun, Gregory
Shepherd, Dane
Shoolin, Joel

Sims, P. Scott
Sloka, Karlis
Soffa, Jeffrey
Stabler, Gary
Stevens, W. Craig
Strampel, William
Syvertsen, Guy

Thiel, John
Thompson, Harold
Trusewych, Timothy

Wagner, Joan
Wagner, William
Waller, Leon
Williams, James
Wilson, James
Woodworth, John

Zato, William

## CLASS OF 1977

Adler, Paul
Albrycht, Diane
Alderson, Thomas
Allen, John W.

Baggerly, Gregory
Bajpai, Kamlesh
Bathrick, Thomas
Bedingfield, Bruce
Bell, Thomas
Bescak, George
Boes, David
Boes, James
Bright, John
Burick, Joseph

Christiansen, Lance
Chumley, H. Don
Conley, Charles

Daly, Jerome
deGroh, David
Doyle, Michael

Economan, Dale
Elsasser, Stephen
Eubanks, Theresa
Evans, Richard
Everingham, Craig

Farres, Evans
Fitzpatrick, Richard

Giger, Anton
Giordano, Joseph
Gorczynski, Michael
Green, John
Growney, James

Herbig, Merrie

Imler, David

Kalamaris, John
Kasenberg, Thomas
King, Gerald
Komara, Frank

Laakso, Lisa
Lee, Lois Bic
Lehman, John
Livingston, Bruce

Malachinski, Leon
Malen, Paul
Mann, Dennis
Marcotte, Gary
Marks, William
Martin, Paul
Matrick, Henry
Matthews, Philip
McKeigue, Mark
McKenney, Edward
McNeilis, Thomas
McVay, Mark
Meli, James

Natarelli, Joseph
Nelson, Craig
Nicholson, Edward
Niemiec, Michael

O'Mara, Karen
O'Mara, Michael

Page, Billy Joe
Peplow, Ronald
Pera, Abraham
Peters, Ray E.
Piaskowy, Frank
Pietsch, Robert

Raymond, Frank
Rearick, David
Ripple, Stephen

Russell, Robert

Schaefer, Christine
Schellin, Richard
Schmidt, Glendon
Smith, Robert
Spyridakis, Andreas
Starsiak, Casey
Stover, Roland
Stynowick, Jeffery
Sutton, Michael

Taylor, David
Thomas, Gordon
Thomas, Katherine
Tischler, Jeffrey
Tupik, Ronald

Uchman, Stanley
Utt, James

Vander Velde, Lawrence
Vlcko, Vladimir

Walsh, Ronald
Wassef, Rodney
Weinstein, James
Weiss, Randy
Wells, Larry
White, Stephen
Wong, Wai Yan
Wright, John

Yeager, Ricky

Zubres, Mark

## CLASS OF 1978

Adams, Richard W.
Athens, Aris T.

Bartasis, Dennis L.
Bartolone, Robert S.
Baxter, David W.
Bernhard, Mark D.

Blanchard, David E.
Blumenthal, Kenneth
Borenitsch, Kenneth A.
Boss, Sheila M.
Boyer, R. Michael
Burger, James P.
Burlas, Regis P.

Chilton, Richard
Cianciolo, Kirk D.
Cichon, Joseph J.
Ciemiega, Gerald J.
Currier, Robert M.

Delliquadri, David R.
De Mattia, Frances C.
Dennis, John Scott
Dick, Lou Anne
Donoghue,   Kathryn
  Mary
Dunn, Timothy A.

Eubanks, Douglas Lyle

Foreman, Larry W.
Foreman, Syd Alan
Foutch, Philip G.

Gemma, Ronald L.
Goeller, Scott A.
Goldstein, Mitchell
Goldstein, Scott B.
Goodman, Bonita Ann
Gore, Steven D.
Gormsen, David L.

Habryl, Louis S.
Haggenjos, Jeffrey J.
Harkness, Charles L.
Harrell, Jon F.
Heigerick, Glenn C.

Ireland, Mark L.

Johnson, James R.
Jolitz, Brian K.

Kalesperis, George S.
Kalish, Steve B.
Kanrich, Stephen G.
Karl, Gary A.
Kiester, Jesse D.
King, Dennis E.
Koepke, Richard A.
Kovachevich, Robert
Kroll, Gregory Donald

Kuhlmann, Bruce William

LaFond, Lawrence H.
Lagoski, Charles W.
Leestma, Eric Jon
Losure, Thomas A.

Manakas, Michael F.
Manoogian, Robert H.
Miota, Daniel
Molesky, John D.
Mueller, Craig R.
Multack, Richard F.

Nanes, Richard

Oster, Michael H.

Perich, Larry M.
Pope, Leslie Anne
Poplar, Melvin L.
Powell, Ronnie W.
Pyka, Paul A.

Raftery, Patricia A.
Randolph, William O.
Reed, John R.
Russo, Martin T.

Seltzer, James E.
Skinner, James R.
Small, Samuel D.
Smith, Eric H.
Starsiak, Janettee T.
Steigerwald, John G.
Storey, Diane
Strauss, Mark D.
Sullivan, Michael W.
Surek, Christopher L.

Teolis, Matthew B.
Trevor, Marie Ellen
Turk, Richard C.

Ulmer, Lawrence A.
Utes, Frank A.

Van Greuningen,
Celeste
Vrable, Thomas D.

Watson, Philip D.

Wooldridge, Carl W.
Wyatt, Lewin

Zeller, Charles J.
Zweiban, Bruce E.

# ALUMNI OF THE
# CHICAGO COLLEGE OF OSTEOPATHIC
# MEDICINE

Abadi, Joseph, '68
Abbey, Thomas E., '70
Abbondante, Richard, '59
*Abbot, Lynn Stratton, '27
Abend, Morton, '57
Abrams, F. Barry, '69
Abrams, Josephus D., '66
Abretske, John L., '54
Abshire, Paul L., '45
Adams, F. R., '22
Adams, Harry L., '40
Adams, John E., '72
Adams, Roy H., '45
Adams, William Lynn, '52
Adamson, Stanley J., '35
Adler, Leonard D., '51
Affhauser, Robert M., '23
Agbabian, Vahagn, '56
*Agnew, Rachel E., '23
Agostinelli, John A., '65
Agustsson, Ann Hudson, '63
*Aho, Toivo John, '49
Aillaud, Andre, '27
Ajlunt, Peter B., '69
*Albee, Mary E., '26
Alexander, Ethelyn, '24
*Alexander, Russell G., '25
*Allegrett, Angelus, '37
Allen, Max M., Jr., '60
Allen, Paul van B., '24
Allen, Russell, '58
Allen, Thomas W., '64
*Allen, W. Burr, '03
*Allison, Walter T., '20
Allum, Thomas H., '68

Alpert, Barnet I., '67
Alshan, Norman, '49
Ambrosecchia, D. F., '45
Amster, Norman H., '67
Amundson, Gerald A., '53
Anable, Wayne R., '74
Andenno, A. Joseph, '56
Anderson, E. G., '32
Anderson, John O., '60
*Anderson, L. A., '22
Anderson, Lillian H., '19
Anderson, Melvin J., Jr., '56
*Anderson, Otto L., '26
*Anderson, Ruth A., '23
Andres, O. E., '25
*Andrews, Gemma Ferrari, '51
Andrews, Otho V., '51
Angiulo, Patrick J., '51
Antell, Morton F., '69
*App, John M., '29
Appleyard, Arthur N., '55
*Appleyard, Esmond C., '38
Appleyard, F. Douglas, '36
Aprahamian, Edward, '61
Arden, Bernard S., '61
Arfstrom, Harold G., '34
Arkush, Allan M., '72
Armaly, A. Michael, '55
Arminski, Charles, '46
Armoudlian, Vaughn M., '67
Arner, Wayne A., '61
Arnold, Ervin R., '24
Arnold, Homer J., '15
Aronson, Donald, '51
Aronson, E. I., '51

*Denotes deceased.

NOTE: This directory has been compiled from the records available to the CCOM Office of
Planning and Development.

Asbury, Stanley E., '73
Asorian, Nazareth V., '65
*Aspley, R. William, '22
Athens, William A., '53
Atkins, Maylon C., '26
Atwood, Eldridge D., '15
Ausmus, James C., Jr., '56
Austin, Charles E., '43
Axtell, S. W., '42

Babb, Emily A., '20
Back, Joseph M., Jr., '48
Bacon, G. S., '26
Bacon, Robert J., '66
Baggerly, Charles E., '33
Bailey, A. Eugene, '26
Bailey, Albert W., '23
Bailey, Hannah W., '35
Bailey, Ruth, '41
Bakeman, Robert E., '56
*Baker, Frank, '03
Baker, John T., '43
Baker, Leo M., '51
Baker, Ross B., '41
Balabanian, Henry G., '52
Balas, Robert M., '55
Baldridge, R. Wayne, '44
Baldwin, Paul E., '24
Bamel, Solomon, '49
Banasa, Emmanuel S., '74
Bania, Andrew J., '55
Barany, William C., '68
Baratti, Carmen P., '62
Barbachym, Donald R., '56
*Barber, Eileen B., '34
Barber, Norman D., '59
Barden, John H., '73
Barkay, H. John, '56
Barker, Barry L., '73
Barker, Edward, '63
Barkhouse, Charles K., '24
Barnes, Margaret W., '36
Barnett, Keith, '61
Barnett, Louis, '56
*Barnum, Lyle R., '25
Barrett, Thomas E., '70
Bartels, Richard R., '24
*Bartlett, Maud E., '17

Bartowiak, J. E., '48
Bashline, H. Woodrow, '48
Bates, C. A., '36
Bauer, Herbert G., '41
Baur, Marie E., '28
*Beach, Benson H. S., '26
*Beal, Birdice, '16
Beal, Clarence J. W., '16
Beal, Myron C., '45
Bean, George, '43
Beard, Jared L., '73
Bearden, Donald G., '63
*Beauchamp, Calvin C., '34
Beck, Daniel B., '50
Beck, Milton, '49
Becker, Alan H., '54
Becker, Carl G., '53
Becker, Philip A., '68
*Beckwith, C. Gorham, '31
Beckwith, Robert L., '38
Beechnau, Louis H., '53
Beilke, Martin C., '28
Belen, Jack E., '72
Bell, Elizabeth, '43
Bell, Harold A., '43
Bell, John R., '46
Bellone, Jack D., '69
Belsito, Joseph E., '56
Beltram, John C., '35
Ben, Walter T., '60
Benaderet, Gerald L., '59
Benson, Dewey C., '62
Benson, John R., '43
Benteen, Harold D., '37
Berg, Albert J., '60
Berg, David J., '70
Berger, Owen J., '56
*Berk, Morris, '23
*Berlijn, Gerard J., '35
Berlin, Alan R., '71
Bernhardi, Ernest F., '23
Bernhardi, Ernest F., Jr., '51
Berry, Clyde A., '31
Bershas, Marvin, '55
Bethune, Richard C., '32
Bethune, Richard H., '45
*Biddle, Isabell, '05
Bielak, Daniel M., '73

Bifano, George M., '71
Bigman, Ronald L., '66
Billings, Donald W., '49
Billman, Bernard D., '55
Bingham, Rolan J., '65
*Bircher, Ralph L., '40
Birk, Allan, '56
Birnhak, Sheldon E., '67
Biscotti, Louis J., '71
Bishop, Peter J., '58
Bishop, Reginald O., '32
*Bixler, Mina L., '40
Bizer, Wayne F., '72
Black, Florus R., '40
Black, Robert B., '67
Blackburn, Gerald W., '73
Blaha, Robert J., '58
Blaik, Robert E., '72
Blain, James L., '55
Blair, Robert J., '68
Blakeman, Lloyd J., '59
Blakesley, Roy J., '30
Blamey, William E., '55
Bland, Coburn C., '54
Blanke, James K., '58
Blanzy, John E., '60
Blau, Larry L., '66
Blixt, James K., '67
Bloch, Bernard, '43
Blok, Robert J., '69
Blonder, Ronald D., '72
Bloom, R. Lee, '65
Bloom, Stuart L., '66
Boccia, Raphael J., '65
Bock, Daniel H., '64
Bocknek, Marc P., '72
Bode, Robert F., '70
Body, John, '25
Boehm, Alfred C., '21
Boehm, Gerhard W., '52
*Boggan, Joseph R., '25
Boggan, Peter A., '36
Bok, Arthur B., '54
Bok, Frank J., '56
Bonanno, Joseph P., '64
Bonham, Robert P., '39
*Boone, Harry F., '55
*Booth, Paul E., '18

Boozer, Stotts C., '64
Borenitsch, Robert L., '74
Boris, Henry C., '58
Borrow, Irene, '46
Borton, Everett C., '38
Boskin, Melvin, '60
Bour, James M., '59
*Bowen, H. M., '21
Bower, Jean Suffern, '51
*Bowman, E. Ruth, '24
Boyd, C. M., '17
*Boyle, William J., '45
Brand, Burton, '51
*Brandenburg, Frank C., '30
Bradley, Gertrude, '30
Bradley, Horace S., '30
Brandwine, Warren I., '71
Brant, Leonard A., '60
Brasseur, James K., '60
Braunfeld, Robert J., '69
Braunstein, David B., '73
Braunstein, Sara Griner, '74
Brdlik, Otto B., '73
Breckenfeld, Robert B., '72
Brenner, Sheldon L., '66
Brenz, Ronald W., '67
Brewer, Darl R., '30
Brewer, Nelson, '53
Brickner, Gerald, '53
Briner, B. Biddle, '44
Briner, Barbara Jo, '74
Briski, Robert J., '58
Broadnax, Gary B., '73
Brochu, Robert Wayne, '67
Brockington, Walter K., '60
Brockway, David, '52
Bronikowski, John A., '64
Brooker, Ronald E., '62
*Brooks, Burton C., '45
Brooks, Edward M., '71
Brooks, John C., '68
Brooks, Robert A., '53
Brostman, John R., '57
*Brott, Wilson L., '40
Brown, George R., '52
*Brown, H. L., '18
Brown, H. Willard, '26
Brown, J. M., '33

Brown, John W., '71
Brown, Michael G., '71
Brown, T. Gordon, '51
Brown, Virginia K., '63
*Browning, L. A., '40
Brozen, Benjamin A., '47
Brueckman, Joseph R., '70
*Bruer, Walter P., '25
Brusso, Gordon W., '27
*Bruxer, Lawrence H., '23
*Bryant, Arthur L., '31
Brysacz, Stanley P., '71
Brzezinski, Stanley E., '53
Buccini, Ernest J., '51
Buckholtz, Charles D., '67
*Buckler, William G., '14
Buckler, William M., '43
Buckley, Vernon C., '56
Budnick, John S., '73
Buller, William Earl, '25
Bullis, Harvey R., '23
*Burbank, Jesse Y., '21
Burbidge, N. A., '32
Burd, James A., '25
Burk, Ronald E., '60
Burke, Joseph W., Jr., '57
Burke, Stanley E., '67
Burns, Raymond J., '31
Bush, Richard E., '67
*Busse, Clara, '18
Butler, Robert, '51
*Butler, Ruby L., '24
Butrey, Peter A., '59
Buttars, Jack A., '65
Buziak, Chester J., '60
Byrd, Roger C., '67

Cacilo, Peter, '27
Cade, Walden L., '51
*Cain, C. N., '12
Caldwell, Neil R., '54
Caleel, George, '55
Caleel, Richard T., '61
*Calkins, W. C., '23
Callton, Samuel, '58
*Cameron, H. Dallas, '40
*Campbell, Lloyd R., '34
Campbell, Paul E., '71

Campbell, William M., '68
Capling, Robert D., '51
Cappitelli, Dennis W., '71
Captain, James S., '66
Captain, Spiro J., '66
Capuson, Carlton G., '59
Caputo, Anthony J., '60
Cardellio, Anthony, '67
Cardellio, Jesse J., '63
Carey, Thomas R., '57
Carey, Wesley S., '28
Carl, James M., '72
*Carlisle, Vernon R., '22
Carlos, Perry G., '74
Carlson, Constance E., '74
Carlson, Don H., '65
Carlson, Loren S., '74
Carnegie, Dorothy E., '54
Carnegie, W. B., '33
Carney, Thomas J., '63
Carpenter, Richard C., '42
Carr, David G., '68
Carr, Larry L., '65
Carroll, Loyd D., '52
Carter, John E., Jr., '63
Catalano, Peter A., '59
Cataldi, William G., '67
Catapano, Gerard A., '59
Catron, Lee R., '22
*Catron, Murray A., '29
Chaltry, Richard R., '68
Chamberlain, Darrell H., '53
Chambers, Sadie B., '25
Chance, Charles W., '73
Chandler, Jerry J., '69
Chapello, Isabelle, '55
Chapin, Ella I., '25
*Chapin, Ralph M., '23
Chapman, Lyle F., '54
Charlip, Edward S., '70
Charochak, Richard P., '60
Chase, Charles A., '27
Chatterley, Daniel J., '57
Chauvin, John H., '53
Cheney, Jerome F., '53
Chesky, Stuart B., '68
Chestnut, Julian S., '74
Chinen, Masahide, '60

Christianson, Steven W., '73
Chroniak, Raymond A., '40
Chugay, Nikolas V., '71
Chuprevich, Joseph W., '72
Chuprevich, Thomas W., '70
*Chval, Charles A., '33
Chwierut, Thomas J., '70
Cincala, Robert P., '69
Citrin, Paul H., '66
*Clark, Albert B., '19
Clark, Arthur J., '23
Clark, Carl G., '31
Clark, Darrel C., '51
Clark, Elvin L., '22
Clark, George L., '72
Clark, Jack A., '57
Clark, Robert A., '69
*Clarke, Robert, '25
Clarke, Shirley C., '62
Clarke, Warren M., '52
*Claverie, Jean B., '22
*Cleaves, Ernest R., '29
*Cleland, Albert, '11
Cleveland, Edward W., '16
Clough, Robert G., '61
*Clouse, W. E., '41
Clunis, Grace E., '29
Coan, James E., '50
Coates, Marion Ray, '28
*Cobb, Emma, '17
Coffey, William M., '26
Cohen, David L., '72
Cohen, Jay M., '57
Cohen, Norman H., '53
Cole, Raymond E., '74
Colletti, Jacob S., '56
Collier, Michael F., '53
Collins, Archie, '53
*Collins, H. L., '41
Collins, Meldon G., '29
Colman, Richard J., '69
Compher, Arthur M., '54
Comstock, Jack D., '49
Cone, Robert R., '60
Congdon, James E., '72
Conklin, Monroe K., '36
Conley, Charles R., '53
Conley, Robert, '52

Conlon, Justin W., '60
Conner, W. Keith, '62
Connor, Walter G., '28
Constantinides, Angelos G., '59
Cook, Clara R., '20
Cook, James L., '68
Coombs, Leroy, '22
*Cooper, Benjamin, '41
Cooper, Earline, '42
Cooper, William R., '59
*Corbin, Billy Lee, '43
*Corliss, T. C., '17
Cornish, Gregory, '71
Cortese, Anthony J., '52
Costin, J. Richard, '49
*Couch, Clarence H., '21
*Coulter, Lawson B., '25
Courah, Mohammad S. A., '60
Courtney, B. B., '37
Cover, Evelyn Rawles, '47
Cover, James E., '47
*Covolus, John J., '49
Cox, William H., '70
Craig, Celia S., '32
*Craig, Ralph B., '32
Crandall, Max, '65
Crandell, B. Robert, '44
Crane, Roger H., '56
Crase, Bertram E., '30
Craske, W. Don, '23
Craske, W. Don, Jr., '62
Craske, William J., '62
Cratty, Walter, '53
Crenshaw, Langston, '35
Crismond, Joseph J., '37
*Critchfield, David E., '38
Croak, James M., '68
Cronan, Roy F., '34
*Crosby, Clifton A., '18
*Crosby, Leslie L., '49
Crossley, Richard P., '52
Croushore, John H., '74
Crowner, Nyles D., '36
Crowner, W. L., '29
Cucchi, Donald D., '66
*Cullom, Sidney A., '27
Culver, Robert E., '59
Cuneo, Peter W., '71

*Cunningham, Paul J., '48
Cunningham, Raymond J., '65
Curley, Robert R., '63
Curry, Homer B., '30
Curtin, John M., '73
Curtiss, R. G., Jr., '57
Cyman, Frank T., '41

Dalby, George N., '54
Dalessandro, Angelo, '60
Dalinka, Jerome F., '67
D'Amico, Paul, '61
D'Anconti, John S., '74
Danny, Peter, '53
Darling, Francis D., '66
*D'Armond, B. J., '39
Darnall, Eugene C., '28
Daros, Lester J., '67
Dashow, Edward E., '72
*Davenport, Mary C. M., '30
Davidson, Maurice A., '64
Davies, Allen D., '69
Davies, Edmund, '56
Davis, H. D., '23
Davis, Lowell B., '49
Davis, Lyle, '55
Davis, Marion W., '24
DeAngelis, John, '59
DeByle, Kenneth W., '66
Decker, Almeda A., '53
Decker, Lawrence A., '72
*DeCourcey, Giles W., '45
*Deeming, James D., '64
DeJong, Alex C., '74
Delaverdac, Claude L., '70
DeLuca, Michael, '61
DeLuise, Frank A., '53
DeMattia, Michael D., '64
*Denker, Merle J., '31
Dennis, Lawrence A., '38
Dennis, Ray J., '41
Dennis, Wallace L., '50
DePizzo, Nicholas P., '59
Derbabian, O. John, '58
DeRouin, Gael L., '72
Desnoyers, John A., '54
*DeVilbiss, Bernard C., '21
DeVivo, Joseph M., '57

DeWitt, Eugene L., '61
Diamond, Steven M., '70
DiBlasio, Leo F., '52
Dickinson, Frederick T., '71
Diebold, Wendell, '16 & '25
Dierdorff, John T., '63
DiFilippo, Nicholas M., '74
DiGiovanna, Anthony M., '68
DiGiovanna, Eileen L., '59
DiGiovanna, Joseph A., '59
DiPierro, Rocco W., '73
DiRito, Vincent J., '60
Dixon, Cletus L., '36
Dobbes, Joseph F., '61
Dobson, Harry F., Jr., '43
Dohren, Lester G., '38
Dohren, Walter J., '36
Dole, Leslie M., '42
Doll, Oliver B., '51
Doll, Thomas J., '55
*Domke, Edward P., '27
Donalson, Brinton C., '58
Dorfner, Philip A., '58
*Dorn, Norman H., '31
Dosh, Don L., '54
Dott, Raymond N., '53
Dougherty, James F., '70
*Dovesmith, Edith E., '21
Dow, Raymond B., '42
*Dowd, W. T., '16
Dowling, J. Gordon '66
Downing, Allene C., '52
Downing, Bradley C., '24
Downing, Donald D., '52
Downing, Wilbur J., Jr., '53
*Downing, Wilbur J., Sr., '25
Doyle, James P., '69
Drabecki, Thomas A., '70
Drake, Richard C., '49
*Dressler, Daniel L. E., '27
Drumheller, Glenn W., '73
Dubin, Howard, '65
Ducsay, Zolton, '49
Duda, L. Joan, '54
Duda, Richard M., '67
*Duffee, Paul E., '27
*Duffel, Richard E., '30
*Duglay, Howard A., '13

Dukes, Dennis G., '73
Dunlop, Richard M., '57
Dunning, Helen M., '25
Dunseth, Roy C., '20
Dunworth, Leonard L., '52
*DuPuis, Ernest M., Jr., '54
DuRall, James R., '60
Durkee, Joseph B., '41
*Dygert, C. W., '27
Dyrud, James P., '70

*Eagan, John H., '16
Ebert, Allan M., '69
Ebert, John P., '73
*Eckerson, Hubert H., '22
Eckert, Richard R., '53
Eckhouse, Arnold M., '67
Ecoff, Arthur, '56
Edelman, Eugene J., '46
Edwards, Jack L., '68
Edwin, E. S., '17
Efrusy, Mark E., '70
Egglesfield, William T., '70
Eisenberger, Darryl L., '66
*Ekbom, A. R., '17
Eldrett, Walter C., '27
Elkowitz, Edward B., '60
Ellias, Andrew R., '72
*Ellicott, George W., '24
Elliott, Alfred C., '39
Elliott, J. Lyman, '35
*Elliott, William D., '39
Ellis, Charles M., '58
Ellis, Melville H., '53
Elloway, Peter S., '42
*Elsea, E. Deane, '27
Emerick, Myron R., '65
Emmerson, Richard, '40
Emmett, Steven M., '68
*Engeldrum, H. C., '15
Engstrom, Robert E., '56
Ennis, B. K. '20
*Ensinger, W. B., '23
Epsten, Robert, '49
Erbe, Henry H., '30
Erlandson, Anna T., '29
Eschtruth, Paula L., '64
Esmail, Zulfikar K., '71

*Esser, A. C. H., '12
Everingham, Donald J., '53
*Evers, J. Harold, '22

Fabaz, Anthony G., '74
Fabian, Adelaide P., '31
Fadool, George P., '56
Falcone, Robert E., '54
Falkenburg, Louis, '43
Falknor, David E., '34
Farmer, Edward C., '28
Farnham, Arthur B., Jr., '61
Farnham, G. M., '43
Farrar, J. Marvin, '35
*Faulkner, Wolford R., '40
Federico, Andrew, '50
Felch, Richard A., '68
Feldman, Erwin E., '66
Feldman, Herbert O., '56
Feldstein, Herbert S., '59
Fenton, Roger B., '71
Ferguson, Howard W., '29
Ferlito, Armando C., '45
Fernandes, John J., '68
*Ferrill, H. Ward, '48
Ferro, Gregory M., '73
Fidler, Robert S., '41
Field, Noble W., '32
Field, Samuel H., '27
*Fielding, Anne M., '22
Finazzo, Salvatore J., '57
Fineman, Bill L., '55
Fineman, Morris, '61
Fingerman, Alan N., '68
*Fink, Charles A., '11
Finkelstein, Albert, '46
*Finley, John H., '16
Finley, John H., Jr., '53
Fiorella, Edward J., '51
Fischer, Calvin H., '69
Fischer, John T., Jr., '54
Fish, William H., '56
*Fisher, Albert C., '24
*Fisher, Harry, '28
*Fisher, Nadine, '40
*Fisler, Arnold H., '32
Fitz Gibbon, Arleen W., '39
Fitz Gibbon, Errol E., '40

Fleischner, J. R., '60
Fleiss, Paul M., '61
Flemming, Albert E., '64
Fletcher, Frederic A., '62
Florio, Richard, '46
Foellner, Richard P., '69
*Fogarty, Joseph A., '27
*Foote, Delevan M., '27
Foreit, Claude, '59
Foreman, Stewart B., '69
Forster, H. E., '20
Fortier, Clarence W., '61
Fossler, Van H., '23
*Fossler, W. C., '09
Foster, Maude E., '25
Foster, Melvin E., '62
Foster, Will P., '60
Franczyk, Thaddeus, '71
Frank, Jane L., '69
Frank, Peter, '68
Frank, Terrence R., '68
Frankel, Jerome H., '59
Franklin, James J., '61
*Frankosky, Erich, '17
Frantz, Edgar G., '29
Fraser, Donald L., '64
Frazier, Roger L., '59
Frazzini, Henry V., '71
Freed, Nathan, '69
*Freehafer, Eric E., '67
Frew, Dennis L., '74
Fried, Gerald, '63
Friedman, David, '39
Friedman, Ronald H., '74
Friedman, Sherwood E., '70
Frisbie, Earl F., '32
Fritz, John A., '69
Fritz, Melvin M., '61
Fritz, William J., '56
Froeschle, H. B., '20
Frost, Jerome H., '52
*Fry, Robert A., '24
*Fryette, H. H., '03
*Fuher, Joseph B., '57
Fuller, Ethel Truax, '21
*Fuller, Marion D., '20
Fuller, W. S., '25
Funk, Ernest M., '25

Gabelman, Omer P., '48
Gabier, Wendell V., '64
Gable, James T., '67
*Gaddie, Charles E., '35
*Gaddis, Alvin R., '29
Gadowski, Gerald A., '74
Gadowski, Raymond F., '69
*Galbreath, C. V., '14
Gallo, Louis M., '73
Gamrath, James H., '55
*Gandy, Preston B., '22
*Ganoom, Richard, '61
Garber, Paul A., '73
Gardiner, Edward S., '30
Gardner, Robert J., '68
Garling, Arthur M., '58
Garney, Thomas J., '63
Garvin, William V., '56
Gary, Clifford M., '71
Gastman, Marvin, '63
*Gawel, Walter, '52
Geller, Robert J., '71
George, Frank W., '53
Gerber, Melvin D., '68
Gerhard, Roland C., '63
Gerig, Dean A., '59
Gibaldi, Andre V., '63
Gierke, Louis W., '57
Gifford, Richard Otis, '40
*Gilbert, Lucy, '17
Gilbertson, David L., '67
*Giles, Herman C., '20
*Gilliand, Harry C., '26
Gilroy, Gerald L., '69
*Gingerich, L. E., '24
Gipe, James F., '43
Gladish, Ronald L., '74
Gladstone, Leonard, '63
Glanz, Franklin, '54
*Glass, Oscar R., '27
Glassman, Richard I., '74
Glazer, Howard S., '63
Glinski, Leonard T., '66
Glinski, Robert G., '74
Gloeckler, Carl H., '27
Glover, Frank C., '66
Gobel, John W., '72
Goddard, Francis D., '37

Gohn, Charles J., '57
Gold, Sheldon S., '65
Goldberg, Marvin, '58
Goldblum, Warren C., '63
Goldman, Michael S., '67
Goldner, Malvin A., '52
Goldsmith, Jonathan L., '71
Goldsmith, Lawrence C., '69
Goldstein, Joseph B., '74
Goldstein, Martin B., '59
*Goncharoff, Bernard, '55
Goodman, Raymond E., '64
Goodstein, David, '61
Gordon, Garry F., '58
Gordon, Irving M., '54
Gordon, Michael A., '69
Gordon, Nathan L., '65
Gordon, Ross B., '56
Gore, George J., '24
Gosenfeld, Lawrence F., '71
Goss, Charles B., '70
Gotbaum, Irwin, '59
Goulding, Wesley P., '38
Graeser, Ronald E., '70
Graesser, Otto W., '60
Graham, Arnold A., '39
Graham, Lyle W., '41
Gramm, Gary A. B., '72
Grana, Arthur J., '62
Grant, Jack H., '37
Grant, Thomas H., '70
*Grant, Watson L., '52
Grasska, William J., '45
*Graves, Millicentev, '05
Gray, E. Kenneth, '28
Green, George K., '45
Greenbaum, Michael H., '61
Greenleaf, Dodd K., '59
*Greenspan, Joel A., '66
Greenspan, Reynold S., '49
Greenwald, Herbert L., '69
*Greenway, John A., '54
Gregory, Margaret K., '44
Gren, Ronald E., '64
Gretkierewicz, Paul R., '66
Grice, Harry M., '17
Griesemer, Gerald, '59
Griffith, Hazel, '17

Griffiths, William S., '53
Grigg, W. B., '58
Grimaldi, Anthony M., '71
*Gripe, Otto H., '16
Gross, George A., '61
Gross, Warren T., '52
Grossman, Jay S., '71
Grosso, Frank, '57
Grove, Richard, '63
Grove, Ronald E., '62
Gruber, Leonard, '62
Gruman, Fred I., '31
Gudelis, John R., '64
Guernsey, Alexander S., '30
*Gueslee, Christian B., '22
*Gulmeyer, Calla L., '10
Gunn, Johanna M. D., '24
Gushwa, Richard L., '59
Gustin, George V., '31
Guthiel, Byron W., '25
*Gutmann, Linus W., '22
Gutridge, George H., '21
Guttridge, Randall J., '61
Guzzi, Loretta, '67

Haas, William G., '67
Hackenberg, John C., '71
Hagan, Michael E., '74
Hagle, Betty J., '61
Hagmann, H. Charles, '36
Hahn, Terry M., '72
Hailer, William L., '55
Hajjar, Raymond T., '59
Hall, Jay E., '51
Hall, Willard K., '60
*Hammond, R. Barton, '25
Hammons, James W., '58
*Hanavan, Louis C., '17
*Hanavan, Louis M., '48
Haney, James E., '65
*Hannah, R. H., '20
*Hanney, H. P., '23
Hansen, William J., '60
*Hapke, Bertha L., '23
*Harman, Daniel C., '32
Harnden, Richard L., '53
Harned, J. J., '29
Harned, Lewis B., '19

Harned, Virgil W., '19
Harnish, E. Thomas, '49
Harper, Dwain L., '63
*Harris, Elmer W., '51
Harris, H. Elton, '17
Harris, James D., '67
*Harrison, Edward H., '30
Hartl, Harold W., '64
Hasbrouck, Melvin B., '22
Haselby, Ray C., '69
Haspel, Lawrence U., '67
Hassin, Ian B., '68
Hatch, Loren L., '51
*Hatthorn, Mary M., '20
Haughton, Harold J., '52
Haverty, Gary F., '70
*Hayden, James R., '20
Haynes, Edith, '23
Hayosh, Donald J., '74
Hays, Russell B., '49
Hazzard, Robert C., '71
Heatherington, Earline E., '42
Hebblewhite, Jon G., '70
Heberle, Clement K., '30
Heck, E. Hugh, '54
Hecker, Earl T., '64
Hecker, Gustave E., '21
Heckert, William F., '71
Hedeen, Carter B., '69
Hedeen, M. Sidney, '37
*Heffelfinger, Daniel B., '32
*Heffelfinger, Howard M., '25
Hefka, Robert N., '56
Heigerick, Glenn L., '41
*Heiner, Frank J. G., '26
Heller, Harold R., '51
Heller, Harry A., '54
Heller, Richard E., '53
Hendricks, Frank J., '50
Hendricks, Larry D., '68
Hendrickson, Donald W., '49
Hensley, John R., '20
Herbert, Richard A., '71
Herbold, William C., '38
Hersberger, Kenneth L., '67
Hess, Alfred, '58
Hess, Robert L., '23
Hewson, Herbert R. S., '34

*Hickey, George W., '23
Hierlwimmer, Ulf R., '72
*Higgins, Effie E., '17
Hilbrick, Joan M., '70
Hill, Albert S., '53
Hill, Doyle B., '64
*Hill, William F., '13
Hillier, Harry H., '71
Himes, George E., '45
Hinsperger, C. V., '27
Hinsperger, Wilfred A., '27
*Hinton, Herbert L., '23
*Hiscox, William, '46
Hoeffleur, Norman A., '64
Hoefner, Victor C., Jr., '49
Hoeft, Irwin F., '52
Hoersting, Leo H., '36
Hoersting, Louis J., '36
*Hoff, C. B., '17
*Hoff, Perla, '17
*Hoffman, C. W. W., '25
Hoffman, Lynn V., '54
Hoffman, Michael D., '68
*Hoffman, Roy, '55
*Hogue, William A., '17
Hojnacki, Irene J., '63
Holappa, Frederick C., '66
Holderman, Raymond H., '69
Hole, William N., '54
Hollis, James, '58
Holt, James L., '41
Holt, James R., '61
Holtz, Richard A., '68
Holzworth, Arthur B., '39
Holzworth, David G., '73
Hommes, Philip M., '72
Honeckman, Charles, '68
*Hooe, Carroll William, '39
Hoopingarner, Doyle A., '56
*Hoover, H. V., '27
Hoover, Larry C., '56
Hoover, Lon A., '56
*Hoover, Mary Alice, '33
Hopkins, Richard E., '52
Hormavirta, Hilkka O., '36
*Hornberger, Otho E., '39
Horne, Carroll V., '43
Horowitz, Arnold, '49

Horowitz, Gary R., '71
Horton, Bruce D., '66
Horton, E. Randall, Jr., '40
Horton, John G., '73
Hoshour, Thomas E., '73
*Hoskins, E. J., '17
Hoste, Ruth M., '61
Hostetler, M. A., '26
Hostetler, Max P., '70
Hough, David B., '74
Housel, Leslie J., '21
*Houser, Harold R., Jr., '66
Houser, W. H., '56
Hover, Robert J., '62
Howe, Paul F., '53
*Howe, Stanley D., '23
Howell, Richard K., '74
Howlett, J. Maurice, '40
Huber, Edward A., '70
*Hudson, Julia, '17
Huette, John A., '74
Hughes, John B., '67
Hughes, William J., '71
Hugus, Charles E., '68
Hulett, Arthur S., '24
Hull, Helen F., '22
Hunter, Richard M., '52
Hurd, Douglas B., '56
Hurt, Howard F., '60
Hurwitz, Ronald J., '66
Huycke, Daniel S., '71
Hyatt, Clarence E., '23
Hyatt, James E., '42
Hyman, Howard, '55

Imbesi, Joseph T., '69
Imhoff, David E., '53
Ingaglio, Richard P., '51
Irving, B. Lee, '54
Irving, Walter L., '73
Isaac, Clifford W., '60

Jablonski, Richard A., '74
Jackman, Norman, '57
Jackowski, Lawrence M., '63
Jacobs, Bernard, '46
Jacobson, Lawrence E., '62
Jaeblon, Frank E., '66

Jaffe, Gerald A., '64
*Jakubowski, Robert V., '67
James, Michael J., '69
Jamieson, Austin L., '59
Jamieson, Thomas K., '69
Jaminet, Robert A., '64
Janicke, John L., '63
Jarrett, Lawrence M., '37
Jarvis, Ernest L., '48
Javery, Herbert A., '50
Jen Kin, James H., '61
Jenkins, Rachel E., '37
Jenniches, Jan Philip, '60
Jensen, Fred J., '57
Jensen, Richard L., '58
Jesani, Mirza G., '71
Jessup, Charles E., '64
*Johnsen, Martin R., '56
Johnson, Charles L., '72
Johnson, D. E., '26
Johnson, Elsa L., '43
Johnson, Eugene M., '45
Johnson, James E., '70
Johnson, Jeffrey T., '73
Johnson, John W., '33
Johnson, Quincy A., '62
Johnson, Sydney J., '56
Johnson, Terry L., '74
Johnson, Thomas R., '60
Johnson, V. G., '30
Johnson, William W., '43
Johnston, A. Reid, '41
Johnston, Donald W., '32
Johnston, Douglas H., '72
Johnston, Hilda L., '32
Johnston, William L., '43
Jones, Alice R., '17
*Jones, Wilger L., '23
Jordt, Dorothy K., '31
Jordt, Edward W., '30
Josell, Edward, '66
Judge, Alfred, '38
Juliano, Leroy J., '63

Kadish, Sol, '60
Kadwell, Lynn A., '69
Kahn, Gerald S., '65
Kalash, Daniel, '63

Kalchthaler, Thomas J., '71
Kallett, Charles C., '53
*Kamlay, Thaddeus P., '41
Kani, Dorothy M., '50
Kani, E. Edward, '50
*Kanouse, Allen M., '32
Kantor, Stanley B., '73
Kantzler, George W., '51
Kaplan, Martin R., '64
Kaplan, Robert P., '73
Kaplus, Albert, '50
Kappler, Oscar C., '30
Kappler, Robert E., '58
Karibian, Charles, '57
Karibo, David F., '69
*Karr, George, '24
Karrat, John J., '68
Kasovac, Mitchell, '63
Kasper, Robert, '63
Kasperowicz, Leonard, '62
Kata, John M., '70
Katz, Allen M., '58
Katz, Paul M., '72
Katz, Robert, '56
Katzen, Harold, '57
Katzowitz, Abraham L., '57
Kaufman, Ronald B., '57
Kaufman, Solomon R., '63
*Keckley, Paul J., '46
Keefe, Michael T., '67
Keefer, R. A., '54
Keener, Marie A., '29
*Kegerreis, A. E., '24
*Kehr, John D., '24
*Kelager, J. D., '25
Kelce, Matthew E., '61
*Kellam, L. J., '20
Keller, Ralph J., '54
*Kelley, Dorsey M., '25
Kelley, Robert R., '40
Kellman, Milton, '49
*Kelly, Ann Koll, '28
Kelly, Robert H., '55
Kelly, Thomas P., '73
Kelz, Arnold, '59
Kemmler, Florence, '30
Kendrick, Ronald M., '67
Kenneweg, Edward W., '56

Kent, Michael C., '63
Kern, Arthur, '49
Kerr, Harold E., '34
Kerschen, Joseph G., '71
Kessler, Howard S., '72
Kessler, Wilmer C., '23
*Kettner, Earle H., '43
*Kettner, J. Henry, '39
Keyes, Richard F., '60
Keyes, Robert V., '55
Kidder, Alice G., '39
Kiester, Winfield Scott, '57
Kik, Richard, Jr., '53
Kiley, Harvey C., '62
*Kimball, John T., '45
Kimball, Stanley W., '43
King, Chancey D., '25
King, Monroe J., '63
Kinn, Edward J., '61
*Kinney, Kenneth F., '04
Kinslow, J. Lowell, '48
Kistner, Robert A., '41
Klak, Kenneth J., '73
Klein, Donald R., '63
Kline, James M., '72
Klingel, Leo F., Jr., '51
Klingelsmith, Gerald G., '63
Klopfer, Urich G., '71
Knapic, William S., '66
Knauff, Ronald E., '61
*Knecht, P. E., '22
Knowles, C. Richard, '71
*Knox, Claire D., '22
Knox, Robert M., '57
Kodama, Richard Y., '56
Koenig, H. Harvey, '65
Koepke, Charles F., '48
Kolbe, William, '43
Komasara, Eugene T., '61
Kontos, Peter G., '74
Kopelman, Fred M., '60
Kopp, Stewart E., '66
Koprince, Daniel, '52
Korrol, Charles R., '64
Korten, Frank V., '32
Koscielski, Stanley M., '62
Koskela, John I. A., '68
Kosley, Milton, '49

Kosta, Andrew P., '63
Kostka, Helen M., '17
Kotoske, Donald E., '68
Kovach, Alexander J., '57
Kovachevich, Thomas, '69
Kovan, Charles D., '61
Kovan, Robert, '55
Kozma, Anthony P., '64
Kragor, Hugh F., '60
Krahan, Erwin G., '44
Kraker, Ralph F., '41
Kramer, Eugene P., '57
Kramer, Stephen W., '56
Krates, George N., '53
Kratz, Arthur W., '52
Kratz, Charles G., '55
*Kratz, J. Collin, '17
*Kratz, W. J., '17
Kraus, Irvin M., '70
Krieg, Eugene J., '53
Kronstadt, Herbert S., '62
Kronstadt, Richard A., '69
Kroot, Frederick D., '70
Krug, James R., '53
*Kruse, Charles A., '11
*Kruze, Jacobine, '23
Kubek, Carl J., '68
Kubilius, Martin, '54
Kuchynka, John F., '59
*Kuehn, Edwin W., '56
Kuhn, Gloria J., '70
Kulichenko, Victor, '72
*Kulik, Stephen, '43
Kull, Albert F., '39
Kull, Robert J., '68
Kulus, John J., '74
Kurjan, Kenneth H., '74
Kurn, Samuel P., '54
Kurt, Kenneth J., '63
Kush, Aloysius W., '73
Kushner, Edward K., '23
Kushner, Roger M., '71

Laderman, David, '54
Lagerveld, Ronald H., '68
*Laidlaw, H. W., '36
*Laird, John H., '23
Lamb, Leonard H., '56

*Lambert, A. G., '34
Landberg, George E., '58
Lande, M. K., '53
Lande, Richard L., '64
Landgraf, Donald J., '65
*Landis, Elmer, '29
Landis, Joel J., '45
Landsdorf, Robert M., '67
Lane, Donald J., '58
*Lange, Kenneth D., '58
*Langford, Robert H., '57
Langseth, Jerry E., '71
Lapins, Peter J., '54
Lapp, Richard J., '67
Larsen, Wesley B., '45.
Larson, E. O., '23
Larson, George M., '41
Larson, George M., Jr., '71
*Larson, Kenneth A., '30
Larson, Norman J., '35
*Lasanen, William C., '64
Lasick, John C., '41
Lasick, Louis, '41
Laskody, Richard J., '68
LaTorra, Albert J., '61
*Lattig, B. B., '27
Lattin, Paul B., '71
*Latus, Leo F., '24
Latus, Thomas A., '58
Lau, Patrick H., '74
Lauffer, Warren G., '45
*Launt, Harry F., '25
Lavell, Louis W., '52
Lawley, George D., '57
*Leach, Acelia M., '24
Leach, George J., '71
*Leake, Lee S., '39
Leavitt, Clifford A., '53
Leavitt, Donald, '43
Lee, Maurice R., '45
Lehault, John C., '33
Lehman, Elton D., '63
Lehmkuhle, Joseph M., '62
Leland, Joel E., '70
Leleszi, Jimmie P., '70
Leng, Janet E., '27
*Lennon, Clifford J., '24
Lennon, Robert L., '67

Lentz, Roland, '56
Lenzi, Angelo V., '46
*Leonard, Herman N., '20
Leonard, Norman H., '57
Leonard, Willard W., '53
Leshner, Stanley B., '72
Levine, Arthur, '65
Levine, Neil M., '74
Levine, Sheldon A., '72
Levine, Stanley, '59
Levinson, Gerald J., '68
Levitt, Martin E., '63
Levy, Howard P., '74
Lewin, Steven M., '73
Lewis, Lloyd G., '42
*Lewis, Selwyn F., '23
Lewis, Seymour, '49
Lichwa, Edwin A., '58
Lieberwitz, Donald M., '62
Lief, Lawrence K., '65
Lighton, Jack E., '67
Like, Jerry L., '62
Limmer, Howard B., '70
Limond, Richard V., '65
*Lindberg, Ralph F., '24
Lindenmuth, John P., '71
Lindley, Donald E., '41
*Lindstrom, Sadie Banks, '21
Lipinski, Joseph W., '64
Lipon, John J., '71
Lippman, Mervin R., '49
Lipton, Nathan, '49
Listopad, Morris, '65
Liszewski, Lawrence J., '74
Little, Thomas N., '67
Lizik, Ronald S., '71
Lodish, E. Michael, '64
Lodyga, Ervin J., '63
Loeding, John R., '61
Lofman, Bernard S., '65
*Logan, James A., '25
Logue, Francis M., '49
Lo Iudice, Jean A., '72
Lo Iudice, Thomas A., '72
Lombardo, P. Robert, '52
Long, John W., '51
Long, Walter L., '62
*Loos, William, '33

Lossick, Joseph G., '64
Lovy, Andrew, '62
Lucas, Culmer C., '35
Lucas, Milton J., '44
Ludwig, Harry A., '64
*Luebke, Ottilie E., '17
Lundberg, Eunice, '20
Lustig, David, '65
Lutz, Jerrold W., '60
Lutzke, Wayne H., '63
*Lycan, John P., '23
*Lynch, B. G., '32
Lyne, James R., '64
Lyngby, Christian, '54
*Lyngholm, Thorvald, '21
Lyon, Thomas M., '41

*McBride, Robert A., '42
McBride, Roger W., '66
McCabe, George T., '25
McCabe, Gerald E., '59
*McCallin, Alfred D., '52
McCallion, William, '57
McCarthy, Jeanne E., '49
*McCarthy, R. L., '17
McCarthy, Thomas H., '55
McCarty, F. Timm, '66
*McCarty, Robert K., '46
McCarty, W. Kelly, '73
McCarty, William C., '49
*McCord, James C., '31
*McCormick, James H., '38
McCormick, William H., '43
McCullough, Lillian L., '29
*McDermott, Edward P., '63
McDevitt, Frank J., '55
McDonald, Bruce G., '73
McDonald, Malcolm H., '69
*McDonough, W. M., '24
McDougal, J. L., '39
McFadden, Donald K., '60
McFarland, Margaret, '40
McGinnis, Wesley F., '41
McGovern, Edward L., '61
McGovern, Leonard F., '74
McGuigan, Amy, '21
*McKay, Thomas A., '24
McKenzie, Michael, '71

McKissick, Douglas R., '34
McLain, Robert E., '60
*McLaughlin, Charles E., '38
McLead, Karl H., '50
*McLravy, Winifred E., '24
*McNabb, Lewis W., '61
McNaughton, Thomas J., '54
McNeill, Charles M., '32
McNutt, Rose McBride, '26
Mabilia, Joseph A., '63
MacBain, Richard N., '24
MacCullough, Martha, '41
MacDermid, John E., '59
MacDougall, Howard L., '54
MacGillivray, Ian D., '70
*MacGregor, George W., '10
Macioch, James E., '73
Mackenzie, A. S., '41
*MacKenzie, Allan A., '33
MacKenzie, D. Clyde, '57
*MacKenzie, William P., '40
Mackie, John D., '68
Madonna, John J., '69
Madorsky, Arthur, '57
Madziar, Roman J., '54
Mager, Raymond P., '69
Maggio, John J., '68
Magliocco, Robert R., '49
Makita, Victor K., '49
Makovec, Fred J., '32
Malcoun, Anthony J., '64
Malinowski, Robert A., '63
Mandell, William J., '73
Manikas, Steven G., '63
Mann, John E., '67
Manning, John E., Jr., '58
Mansfield, B. P., '19
*Mansfield, Robert I., '26
Manskey, A. V., '41
March, Jerome E., '63
Marchiano, Robert E., '59
Marcinkowski, Joseph J., '65
Marcus, Fred W., '74
Marcus, Henry F., '67
Marcus, Mary Donna, '73
Marjan, Edward J., '46
Marjan, George F., '45
Marks, Charles A., '54

Marohn, L. A., '43
Marquardt, Marvin C., '43
Marsales, Bernard R., '42
Marsh, Ella J., '71
Marshall, Donald B., '72
*Marshall, Frederick G., '27
Martin, Joel T., '73
Martin, Marvin, '67
Martin, Peter A., '39
Martin, Robert, '41
Martin, Robert L., '70
Martindale, Roger J., '71
Marting, Thomas E., '66
*Martwick, Horace A., '21
Marvit, Isarel, '39
Marx, Michael, '71
Marzolf, Mark N., '74
Mason, Nellie C., '38
Massau, Bruce A., '72
Massullo, Mario D., '49
Masten, Charles, '52
Matheu, Joseph M., '69
Mathews, Irving M., '54
Matlin, Milton, '51
Matlin, Saul, '44
*Matousek, John A., '40
*Matson, Wilfred A., '20
Mattera, Anthony, '63
Matzkin, William L., '54
Mauer, Floriene A., '18
Mauer, William J., '56
Maughan, Matthew J., '57
Maycumber, Robert R., '52
Mayer, Joel S., '56
Mayne, Merrill M., '41
Mazure, Christopher J., '60
Mazure, David J., '71
Mazzie, Albert F., '60
Meachum, Floyd T., '58
Meech, Wayne C., '63
Meeker, Jack F., '53
Meeuwenberg, Richard A., '73
Melnicoff, Ira L., '70
Menk, Rodney B., '57
Mercer, C. William, '62
*Merchant, Raymond F., '25
Mering, Fred B., '41
*Merrell, Willis R., '20

Merrill, William E., '41
Mertes, Stanley R., '66
Merwick, Robert R., '61
Messana, Anthony S., '61
Messana, Frank J., '66
Mester, Loretta G., '67
Meyer, Gary A., '67
Meyer, Robert C., '61
*Meyer, William A., '49
Meyers, Kenneth S., '65
*Meyran, Lawrence S., '11
Mianecki, Daniel J., '68
Mihalich, Stephen P., '51
Mikros, Zacharia C., '57
Miles, Tom R., '69
Milford, Albert F., III, '72
Milford, Creagh E., '74
*Miller, C. Earl, '16
Miller, Charles E., '39
Miller, David M., '68
Miller, Gary L., '71
Miller, H. Ross, '52
Miller, Horace M., '16
Miller, Jack M., '50
Miller, Marvin, '65
Miller, Stephen I., '74
Miller, William C., '68
*Mills, Anna Mary, '12
*Mills, Charles E., '18
Minkin, Harvey, '69
Minkin, Sheldon, '62
Minor, Bryan G., '69
Mintz, Samuel, '45
Minwer, George, '65
Miral, Leon R., '66
*Mischler, Paul E., '34
*Mitchell, Fred L., '41
Mitchell, Fred L., Jr., '59
*Mitchell, Frederick W., '38
*Mitchell, Otis W., '40
Mitchell, Robert B., '68
Mitros, Paul P., '57
Mittelstadt, W. W., '34
Mittner, Joseph J., '72
Mitzel, Robert D., '57
Modzinski, Leo, '60
Moffitt, Harry A., '73
Mohney, John L., '69

Molden, Ralph, '36
*Molden, Ronald S., '36
Molisky, Albert, '53
Montagino, Neil J., '67
Montague, Richard A., '39
Montgomery-Davis, Joseph, '74
Moore, Floyd, '24
Moore, Marcia A. L., '26
Moore, Robert L., '53
Moore, Thomas I., '43
Moore, Thomas R., '61
Moorton, Peter J., '69
Mora, Sebastian A., '72
Moretsky, Robert I., '64
Morgan, Carl, '58
*Morgan, Paul M., '23
Morrell, Howard J., '40
Morris, David P., '68
Morrison, John H., '37
Morrison, John H., Jr., '69
Morse, Ora, '24
Morse, Robert J., '68
Morse, Stephen R., '67
Mort, Gary L., '74
Mortola, Robert G., '59
Moser, Edward S., '17
Mosier, Eugene D., '33
Moss, V. I., '51
Mosteller, Robert E., '60
Mottice, James E., '59
Motyka, Daniel J., '64
*Mowry, Dean H., '28
Mruk, Arlene, '62
Muciek, Stanley J., '51
Murphy, Edward G., '64
Murphy, Edward W., '34
*Murphy, F. J., '32
Murray, James C., '70
Murray, Roger W., '61
Murray, Thomas V., '64
Murray, William K., '72
*Musial, Matthew, '54
Musselman, D. A., '28
Myers, Harold R., '41
Myers, Henry, '53
*Myers, Robert R. K., '29

Nagy, William J., '61

Najarian, Christopher B., '69
Nanni, Vincent J., '61
Nash, Ernest, '53
Nash, Norman C., '59
Nauman, Eric P., '37
Neer, Howard L., '54
*Neff, William A., '22
Negley, William H., Jr., '41
Nelson, Burton M., '71
Nelson, C. R., '38
Nelson, Calvin R., '55
Nelson, Clifford W., '41
Nelson, Donald E., '57
Nelson, Elmer T., '49
Nelson, Kenneth E., '70
Nemcok, Joseph C., '74
Nemeth, Richard E., '61
Nersesian, Andrew A., '57
Neuman, Harry M., '49
Neuman, Phillip, '67
Newberry, Frederick M., '59
Newell, John A., '57
*Newman, J. H., '33
Newman, James M., '73
*Newton, John W., '49
*Nichols, Thomas P., '42
*Nicholudis, Thomas N., '59
Nickle, C. John, '74
Nielsen, Martha D., '41
Niles, James E., '53
Niles, Wilbert P., '66
Nimmer, Wilbur A., '53
Nims, Dwight P., '45
Nitz, Albert J., '26
*Noben, Henry G., '24
Nooyen, Russell L., '63
Nori, John B., '70
Norman, Harold A., '58
*Norris, Fred, '15
Norton, Frank R., '65
*Norwood, James F., '61
Novotny, Carl J., '69
Nowak, Gerald J., '66
Nowak, Richard F., '63
Nowinski, Lawrence J., '66
Nowland, Robert G., '53
Nutt, Hiram R., '30
Nutt, James, '61

*Nye, Robert E., '14
Nyman, Daniel E., '23

O'Berski, Jerry W., '69
Obudzinski, John A., '74
Occhino, Frederick M., '70
*Odden, Loren H., '30
O'Donnell, Robert E., '66
Okrent, George M., '64
Olden, Michael R., '72
Olds, Frederick C., '20
Olini, Gilbert C., '55
Olson, C. Raymond, '56
*Olson, Kenneth N., '54
Olson, Robert W., '71
O'Malley, George G., '41
O'Neil, Dean M., '35
Opipari, Michael I., '64
Orum, Robert E., '53
*Osborn, Harry, '17
Ostrowski, Charles A., Jr., '62
Ostrowski, Joan M., '57
Otto, John R., '61
Overton, Melvin M., '32

Padeen, Thomas A. '64
Paesano, John N., '70
*Page, Forrest H., '24
*Page, Leon E., '17
Page, Paul E., '60
Paley, Albert E., '57
*Palmer, Harold R., '31
Palmer, James Duane, '54
Palzinski, Lawrence, '56
Panagon, Nicholas S., '57
Panars, A. W., '38
Pantovich, Ratibor, '64
Paolucci, Benjamin J., '64
Paolucci, Carmen A., '71
Pappenhagen, A. B., '23
Parenti, Francis J., '40
Paris, Robert G., '62
Park, Kenneth W., '71
Parker, Carlisle K., '27
Parker, Kenneth S., '69
Parrish, John W., '32
Parry, Frank J., '52
*Parson, Clifford S., '20

Parsons, Bessie B., '22
*Parsons, Elizabeth, '16
Passalacqua, Michael A., '73
*Patterson, Lawrence E., '45
Patterson, Robert M., '44
Patti, Gary J., '70
Patton, Larry S., '68
*Paul, Louis J., '26
Paul, Sherryl Kay, '73
Paver, John, '55
Pavlowich, Walter M., '58
Peckham, Arthur C., '29
Peckham, C. Fred, '26
Peckham, C. Fred, Jr., '57
*Peckham, Floyd F., '21
*Peckham, Russell R., '23
Pedinoff, Seymour, '55
Pelino, Carl J., '53
Pelino, Donald G., '55
Pelino, Thomas P., '65
Pence, Tom K., '67
Penn, William P., '68
Pennington, Ray A., '41
Peppard, Harold M., '25
Peppo, William, '69
*Perkal, Louis, '38
Perrin, James B., '22
Perrin, Leo L., '34
Perrin, Ward E., '43
Perrotta, Augustine L., '66
Perrotta, Richard C., '69
*Perry, Iris Adell, '23
Perry, Thomas W., '22
Pesta, Carl M., '63
Peterson, C. Gordon, '41
Peterson, Einer, '35
Peterson, Ernest R., '25
Peterson, Robert A., Jr., '46
Peterson, Sherman H., '41
Pettina, Samuel A., '72
*Pettit, Gladys F., '27
Pettycrew, L. William, '37
*Pfeiffer, Garland F., '34
*Pick, Frank E., '40
Pickhardt, Marylouise G., '23
Pierce, Carl W., '21
*Pierce, Everett L., '27
Pierce, Robert H., '62

Pietrangelo, Nicolas, '73
Pike, George, '30
Pike, John R., '25
Pike, Robert E., '60
Plotnik, Samuel M., '59
Poage, Alan J., '30
*Pockett, Gard A., '23
Podeszwa, Ted A., '63
Poehner, John, '44
Poel, Larry A., '73
Poel, Richard A., '61
*Pollard, C. E., '17
*Pontius, David H., '26
Popoff, Michael, '68
Porter, Antonio M., '64
*Porter, E. R., '23
Porth, Eli, '71
Portnoy, Irving, '63
Posevitz, Laszlo, '68
Posner, Michael H., '72
*Post, Irving R., '26
Pramstaller, George J., III, '71
*Pratt, Edward, '52
*Pratt, Gordon, '43
Pratt, Harrison W., '41
Preib, Faith B., '71
Price, Calvin U., '59
Printz, Sidney J., '49
Pristou, Walter, '57
Proctor, Howard D., '54
Prosen, Anna A., '47
Pruett, Everett W., '24
*Pryor, C. O., '27
Pryor, Robert A., '43
Puckett, James L., '69
Puig, Carlos J., '72
Purdum, Charles A., '27
Purdy, David L., '61
Purtzer, John C., '72
Pysh, Joseph J., '62

*Quinn, Bernice L., '23
*Quinn, John F., '31

Rabinowitz, Bert B., '62
Racher, Emanuel, '43
*Racicot, Antoinette M., '30
Rackliff, Herbert, Jr., '57

*Radel, Verena, '23
Rader, Daniel L., '51
Rama, Peter S., '62
Randazzo, Michael R., '51
Rasmus, Charles H., '53
Rasmussen, Chester M., '57
Raue, William T., '66
Rauscher, A. B., '43
Ravin, Sheldon J., '73
Raymond, John E., Jr., '58
Rea, Charles W., '38
Rea, Lee A., '65
Reagan, Walter N., '52
Reagles, Vernon J., '52
*Reder, Robert R., '22
Reeves, Cecile S., '24
Reider, Daniel R., '55
Reiff, James S., '61
Reiland, Bernard F., '56
Reimer, Herbert W., '43
Reinhard, Ronald N., '74
Remer, Lawrence S., '65
Remsberg, Harmon W., '28
Remsberg, Richard J., '55
*Remsburg, Emory R., '25
Rench, L. R., '19
Renders, Joseph R., '73
Rendleman, Donald G., '70
Renk, C. G., '33
Renn, Richard H., '54
*Rentschler, Truman, '24
Rentz, Louis E., '60
Retholtz, Joel S., '74
Reter, Dennis A., '71
*Reynolds, R. R., '23
Rice, John L., '59
Rich, Anthony J., '65
Rich, John R., '21
Rich, Patrick A., '62
Richard, Ronald J., '55
Richards, Thomas M., '72
*Richmond, William G., '36
Rickett, Robert D., '55
Ridgeway, Ken O., '72
Riley, Edward O., '64
Rinck, Larrie G., '71
Ringewald, Richard O., '65
Rinne, Toine M., '48

Ripple, Richard, '57
Rise, Noel L., '70
Rizzo, Vincent J., '64
*Robb, S. Edith, '19
Robbins, Albert F., '69
Roberts, John C., '71
Roberts, John H., '59
Roberts, Newal J., '42
Robertson, John D., '73
Robinson, David, '54
Robinson, Mary Hoffman, '33
Rocke, J. Ellryn, '62
Roeper, Ralph H., '57
Rogers, Burr M., Jr., '56
Rollins, Arlen J., '73
Roncskevitz, Joseph S., '61
Ronneau, Gerald A., '71
*Rook, George L., '30
Root, John D., '30
Ropp, Howard, '52
Rosbolt, Robert N., '54
Rose, Arvilla McCall, '32
*Rose, George O., '24
Rose, Howard J., '70
Rose, William L., '53
Rosenbaum, Jerry S., '66
Rosenthal, Margaret A., '74
Ross, Charles E., '63
Ross, Don C., '54
Ross, William M., '55
Rossiter, Lawrence, '64
Roth, Gilbert, '55
Roth, Harvey G., '67
Roth, Steven J., '71
Rothenberg, Ronald I., '65
Rott, Arthur O., '73
Roulier, Randolphe G., '57
Rubin, Michael N., '70
Rudnikoff, Peter, '49
Rudorfer, Alvin, '62
Ruehle, Henry E., '63
*Ruff, Jean H., '20
Ruffino, Gasper F., '59
Runyon, Sidney S., '53
Rusch, Leonard B., '49
Rusco, Ralph H., '64
Rusk, Leo A., '58
Rusk, Thomas J., '61

Russack, Neil W., '61
*Russell, Ray M., '23
Russo, Joseph J., '57
Ruthschow, Henry W., '57

Sabbota, Harvey P., '68
Sabo, Beverly, '73
Sabo, Samuel R., '65
Sachs, Barry, '61
Salach, Roderick C., '55
Salo, Arvo, '30
*Samblanet, H. L., '23
Samblanet, H. Louis, '54
Sampson, Michael A., '69
Sanders, Herbert L., '41
Sands, Eugene N., '50
*Sands, Henry C., '19
Sands, Maude B., '18
*Sannes, C. R., '27
Saperstein, David J., '68
Sargent, Paul R., '61
Saridakis, Manuel P., '74
Sauter, Robert B., '61
Savan, D. Beryl Mack, '44
Savoia, Anthony L., '56
*Scallan, J. W., '09
Scanlon, Terrence W., '74
Schachter, David S., '72
*Schafer, Frank M., '54
*Scharmach, Frank L., '57
*Schatzman, J. F., '40
Schecter, Harvey J., '72
Scheinfield, Samuel, '71
Scheller, Edward L., '58
Scherritti, Wallace W., '69
*Schildberg, E. O., '42
Schildberg, Harold R., '23
Schiller, Irwin, '64
Schilling, M. J., '49
Schillinger, J. Frederick, '60
Schimmoller, Richard E., '60
Schirs, Gary S., '63
Schlueter, Raymond W., '61
*Schmitz, Ann, '51
Schmook, Raymond J., '30
Schneiderman, Frank, '57
Schoelles, George J., '31
Schoen, Paul F., Jr., '53

Schoenhals, H. W., '42
Schofner, Robert M., '52
Schomaker, Thomas E., '62
Schonfeld, Alvin J., '72
Schoolcraft, Frank L., '55
Schooley, Thomas F., '38
Schorr, Robert B., '71
Schowalter, Norbert G., '36
*Schreck, H. Clay, '10
Schrimpf, Charles F., '58
Schroeder, Norman, '42
*Schuler, Jack E., '49
Schulman, Charles, '57
Schulte, Edward L., '69
Schultheis, Roland A., '61
Schultheis, William F., '66
Schultz, Allen F., '71
Schultz, Dale R., '70
Schussler, Irwin, '68
Schuster, Marshall S., '63
Schutt, Christine M., '23
*Schwab, Walford A., '21
Schwartz, Anthony, '73
Schwartz, Arnold, '58
Schwartz, David A., '71
Schwartz, Jerrold J., '65
Schwartz, Maurice K., '53
Schweig, Edward L., '56
Scorzelli, Jerome E., '71
Scott, Roger D., '73
Secontine, Richard D., '54
Seebass, James S., '65
*Seelye, Robert L., '40
Segall, Irwin, '59
Sehl, George S., '64
Sekera, Richard J., '64
Selitsky, Benson, '67
Sergeant, E. V., '30
Sevastos, John P., '56
*Sevison, Earl L., '26
Shaffer, L. S., '41
Shaftoe, L. C., '30
Shaheen, Samuel H., '52
*Shain, Fred B., '25
Shambach, Lawrence, '61
Shamus, Norman J., '63
*Shapin, Theodore, '23
Shapiro, Donald M., '68

Shapiro, Howard M., '70
*Sharp, F. A., '30
Shedler, Leonard, '58
Sheflin, Eric J., '67
Shepherdson, John D., '74
Sheremeta, Zoni, '54
Sherr, Julius, '43
Sherritt, Wallace W., '69
Shimmel, Robert G., '55
Shipon, Jacob A., '70
Shissler, William R., '70
Shomer, Gerald L., '72
Shoskes, Morris, '42
*Shostrand, Melvin L., '30
Shriner, Merlin L., '65
Shusterman, Margaret S., '73
Sibley, Harold O., '30
Siddall, John D., '62
Siefer, Ellis, '42
Siefer, James R., '73
Siegel, Berton, '64
Sievers, Richard J., '53
Silver, Allan J., '45
Silver, Richard S., '74
Silverman, Lee R., '72
Silvers, Howard R., '63
Silverstein, Arthur, '73
Simich, Robert L., '60
Simmer, John N., '49
Simmone, Arthur R., '24
Simmons, Dorothy M., '24
Simmons, Joan, '56
*Simons, Lester, '66
*Simpson, John H., '25
Simpson, Nelle Lucile, '24
Sinden, Dorothy G., '22
Singer, Ronald A., '74
Siniscalchi, Frank S., '51
Sirounian, Harry, '66
Siskosky, James A., '72
Siudara, Jerome E., '57
Skrzypek, Eugene W., '65
Slabaugh, Ronald C., '64
*Sliker, Walter A., '22
Sloan, John H., '63
Slowik, Edward M., '57
Small, Edward P., '40
Small, H. R., '40

*Smielding, Amelia H., '23
Smilek, Martin, '60
*Smith, Alexander, '17
Smith, Bill W., '64
Smith, Edward W., '70
*Smith, Floyd E., '58
*Smith, George H., '17
*Smith, Herbert J., Jr., '44
*Smith, Howard M., '23
Smith, James W., '56
Smith, Keith, '60
Smith, Kermit C., '66
Smith, Lloyd D., '20
*Smith, Milton E., '33
Smith, Richard K., '49
Smith, Robert F., '70
Smith, Walter J., '39
Smith, William G., '50
Smyk, Anthony, '59
Snow, Douglas H., '73
Snyder, Richard P., '70
Sokalski, Stephen J., '69
Solce, David, '72
Solyn, Richard J., '70
Somers, N. Louis, '40
*Somerville, Herbert B., '31
Sommerville, Eva W. Maggoon, '22
Sonesen, Marshall H., '41
Sorgenti, Robert L., '57
Sowerby, Delbert C., '60
Spagnuolo, Louis J., '49
Spavins, Walter R., '44
Speyer, Donald I., '68
Spiering, Neal, '64
Spilson, George C., '61
*Spirtos, George N., '46
Spoelstra, Paul C., '59
Spohn, Earle W., Jr., '67
Sprague, Margaret McFarland, '40
*Sprankel, Gerald R., '51
Springer, Robert E., '54
*Squier, Leon W., '27
Stach, Edward J., '48
Stack, E. William, '30
Staddon, Earl R., '69
*Standish, Louise A., '20
Stanley, Donald E., '67
Stanley, Douglass, '24

Stanley, Gerald N., '73
Stanley, S. Edward, '35
Starr, Robert M., '60
Stauffer, Charles W., '35
Steenkamp, Johannes C., '72
Steigerwald, William M., '63
Stein, Avrum M., '69
*Stein, Theron L., '22
*Steinhardt, Allyn M., '45
Steinway, David M., '72
Stenger, George S., '70
Stern, Milton, '71
Stevens, Everett N., '56
*Stevenson, George W., '20
Stevenson, George W., Jr., '58
Stevenson, Robert M., '52
*Stevenson, Stuart P., '31
Stewart, Harriette M., '37
Stewart, Jack D., '54
Stewart, Jerome R., '65
Stiger, John C., '73
Stillings, Shirley R., 443
*Stinson, James A., '30
Stirling, Marie S., '55
Stirling, Robert K., '55
Stoinoff, Kenneth R., '68
Stone, Dale H., '62
Stone, David A., '74
Stone, Irwin K., '43
*Stoneman, Anna B., '20
*Stout, James W., '51
Stout, Lorea DeVore, '51
*Stowell, Maude S., '22
Strachan, W. Fraser, '30
Strausberg, Stuart E., '73
Streeter, David R., '62
Streeter, Dennis L., '71
Strefling, John L., '58
Strefling, Michael R., Jr., '55
Strickler, Jack M., '54
Strinka, Andrew A., '54
Strobl, John J., Jr., '68
Strong, Leonard V., Jr., '20
*Stucker, John P., '54
*Sturgess, Chauncey B., '30
Suchyta, F. Robert, '73
Suffern, M. Grayle, '51
Sullivan, Daniel E., '74

Sullivan, John R., '59
Sullivan, Leigh R., '49
Sullivan, Terence P., '62
Superfon, Neil P., '64
Surloff, Arthur B., '66
Sutherland, Fordyce M., '42
Sutliff, Glenn F., '51
*Sutton, Benjamin R., '25
Sutton, Hubert L., '52
Sutton, Paul E., '26
Swainson, Weymoth L., '47
Sweeney, James W., '73
Sweeney, Walter L., '59
*Swengel, Flora Y., '08
Swetnam, Robert E., '74
Swiacki, Gerald R., '69
Swiatek, Thomas G., '73
Switzer, John G., Jr., '52
Szathmary, Jay D., '71
Szumiak, Roland F., '52
Szwed, Thomas J., '62

Tabor, Dannie L., '71
Talerico, Henry, '58
Tam, Robert, '64
*Tannen, Harry L., '43
Tappan, Russell G., '22
Taras, Joan E., '67
Taras, Richard J., '66
Tarulis, George J., '35
Traulis, Seaver A., '37
Tauber, Jerome B., '46
Tauber, Ronald M., '72
*Taylor, Arthur T., '34
Taylor, F. Hoyt, Jr., '51
Taylor, Frederick E., '74
Taylor, Harry W., '41
Taylor, Richard M., '69
Taylor, Robert L., '49
Taylor, W. H., '28
*Taylor, Yvonne I., '42
Teer, Norman H., '61
Teitz, Eric L., '61
*Temrowski, Valentine J., '52
Tengblad, Malcolm A., '36
Tenner, Charles H., '63
Territo, Joseph L., '67
Teune, Peter, Jr., '63

Thatcher, Wayne L., '53
Theobald, Paul K., '25
Thomas, James D., '29
Thomas, Paul G., '54
Thompson, Alford C., '30
Thompson, Curtis, '53
Thompson, Dennis S., '70
Thompson, Duane A., '62
Thompson, J. Thomas, '61
Thompson, K. R. M., '32
Thompson, Robert B., '69
Thompson, V. C., '22
*Thompson, W. C., '52
*Thompson, Wayne I., '43
*Thorburn, William F., '22
Thrane, Louise C., '33
Threlkeld, C. H., Jr., '53
Threlkeld, Colin H., '23
Thulin, James A., '38
Thulin, John A., '53
Thumim, Martin B., '67
Thurow, James A., '71
Tibbetts, Austin B., Jr., '53
*Tipton, Robert C., '27
Tischler, Irwin W., '71
Tobes, Harold J., '62
Toerge, John E., '74
Tokar, John T., '60
*Tom, Walter, '56
Tomchuck, Robert J., '70
*Toohey, James J., '51
Tookoian, Hagop, '60
Torreano, Sharon A., '73
Torres, Manuel, '53
Tower, Gladys L., '28
Townsend, Alexandra A., '67
Toy, William G., '59
Trader, Margaret M., '65
Trager, Gerald M., '64
Trapp, Weber C., '24
Treadwell, Bryce B., '64
Treadwell, Dale G., '32
Trent, David M., '70
Trimper, Donald P., '62
Tripi, Vincent J., '57
Tripp, Arthur F., '60
Trombetti, Louis J., '63
Trostel, Franklin A., '61

Troub, Donald L., '74
Troutman, Bruce W., '73
Truax, W. B., '23
Tsang, Pui Lam, '60
Tucek, Ladd T., '61
Tucker, Harry E., '44
Tucker, Wayne L., '58
Tuinstra, Theodore J., '64
Tull, Jean Lishness, '44
Tull, Thomas R., '41
Turkish, Verna J., '59
Turner, Donald F., '70
Turner, James P., '24
Turner, Kenneth E., '53
Turner, Lucile A., '22
Turowski, Jacek F., '49
Turton, Robert L., '55
*Twigg, William J., '22
Tyska, Edmund R., '64

Ufkes, Herbert C., '54
Ulbrich, Carl J., '74
Ulbrich, Paul W., '70
Ulmer, John L., '35
Ungerleider, Arthur C., '62
Usher, Lawrence J., '65

Van Andel, Claude A., '51
Vanator, Douglas P., '63
Van Boven, Melvin J., '.9
Van Campen, Josephine, '36
Van de Grift, J. J., '33
Vanden Daele, Marie D., '49
*Vander Roest, William, '52
Vanderschot, M. Louis, '64
Vandervort, Paul G., '59
*Van de Wege, James W., '34
Van Dyke, A. B., '36
Vanneman, John W., '45
Vargas, John E., '67
Vastola, David L., '69
Vastola, Frank, '49
Vaughan, James A., Jr., '51
Vaughan, Robert G., '52
Veen, James P., '62
*Vekert, Charles E., '41
Venanzi, Enzo J., '56
Ven Huizen, George R., '70

Verbovsky, John R., '73
Verhalen, John J., '24
Verrastro, Thomas R., '56
Vilkins, Peter I., '69
Vincent, Roger D., '64
Vinci, Joseph L., '63
Violand, Thomas E., '59
Vogelgesang, George W., '68
Volz, Max, '58
Vos, John F., '37
Voss, Fred A., '32

Wagner, James P., '73
*Wagner, Lydia L., '27
*Wagner, Ruth A., '27
*Waid, C. Paul, '38
Waine, Burton H., '51
*Waitley, Douglas D., '25
*Walcott, Etta R., '17
Walczak, Vern M., '62
Waldron, Maxwell E., '60
*Walker, Alex E., '17
Walker, Alfred J., '49
*Walker, Walter J., '41
Walling, Ronald D., '31
*Walstrom, Borther E., '28
*Walstrom, May L., '28
Walstrom, Richard E., '39
Walther, Robert C., '22
Walton, Mark W., '70
Walton, William J., '40
Ward, James C., '50
Ward, Robert G., '45
Warn, James D., '54
*Warner, Alois L., '47
Warner, Francis E., '22
Waronker, Alan D., '59
Warren, Reginald J., '70
Waruszewski, Paul A., '74
*Waschke, Harold G., '28
*Waskin, Edmund W., '41
Waskin, Robert R., '71
Wasserstein, Jerome C., '74
Watkins, Bob W., '60
Watson, Mark F., '74
Waugh, William W., '72
*Waybright, K. O., '28
Wayne, James C., '54

*Webb, Millard D., '25
Wehrum, Paul A., '56
*Weil, George L., '27
Weiner, Gilbert R., '66
Weiner, Glenn L., '74
Weiner, Kenneth A., '70
Weingarden, Michael A., '64
Weingarden, Terry L., '65
Weingart, Bernard S., '68
Weingarten, Michael P., '71
Weinstein, David S., '73
*Weisjahn, William H., '22
*Weisner, John M., '23
*Weiss, Melvin V., '47
*Weiss, Paul J., '59
Weiss, Stanley, '52
Weller, Ronald J., '58
Wendorff, Flora K., '15
*Wendorff, H. A., '15
Wendorff, Robert H., '48
*Wensley, Clarence A., '45
Wesley, Adelin M., '53
Wettlaufer, R. H., '41
Wexler, Jerome, '57
*Wharton, John D., '53
Wheeler, Avis, '39
Wherrit, Paul H., '26
*Whipple, Robert L., '30
*White, Edward T., '23
White, Herbert C., '64
White, Lawrence W., '67
White, Richard T., '72
Whitlow, Francis F., '64
Whittington, Rodgers, '73
Widdows, H. C., '29
*Wieland, Clara, '17
Wiersma, Jay A., '52
Wilde, Perry C., '44
Wildt, Robert, '52
Wiley, Kenneth W., '43
Wilk, J. Ronald, '64
Willcox, Elizabeth A., '24
*Willet, Harry R., '26
*Willett, Francis J., '27
*Willia, V. Emerson, '25
*Williams, A. C., '38
Williams, Basil B., Jr., '70
*Williams, E. R., '43

Williams, Jack L., '66
Williams, John H., '38
Williams, T. Clif, '42
Williams, William M., '57
Willis, B. E., '68
Willis, Robert M., '41
Willman, Donald E., 73
Willman, Wallace S., '38
Wilmot, Geraldine W., '25
Wilson, Rendall R., '55
Wineman, Bruce A., '72
Winkler, Martha V., '57
Winkworth, Harry H., '68
Winstanley, H. William, '66
Witt, John R., '58
Witte, Albert A., '64
Witte, Henry W., '53
*Witty, Drake R. A., '54
Wolbart, John C., '57
Wolfe, George P., '66
Wolfe, Robert R., '64
Wolfe, V. B., '25
Wolfer, George K., '58
Wolfson, Paul M., '70
Wolski, John D., '59
Woltebeek, J. C., '39
Wonder, H. Harpster, Jr., '52
Wong, Roger Y., '74
Wood, David L., '74
Wood, Lloyd R., '39
Wood, William, '33
Woods, Edward R., '57
Woods, Kenneth D., '71
Woodworth, Robert M., '70

Wooster, Ralph L., '22
Wooster, William E., '52
Work, Thomas A., '72
Wortman, Reginald R., '70
Wygant, Thomas, '60

Yacavone, David W., '74
Yee, Hyman, '70
Yee, Jerry N., '73
Young, Claud, '60
Young, Evan C., '65
Young, Morris H., '49

Zachem, C. R., Jr., '62
Zager, A., '57
Zager, Lawrence M., '65
Zandstra, Benjamin, '55
Zarewych, Bohdan N., '69
Zaring, G. Franklin, '41
Zawol, Leopold T., '49
Zettel, Robert H., '51
Ziegler, John W., '51
*Zielinski, Raymond L., '45
Zilvitis, Bruno J., '41
Zima, Thomas E., '74
Zimmerman, Ronald R., '70
*Ziontz, Harold J., '41
Zobel, George J., '62
Zurack, Robert A., '63
Zuzga, John J., '42
Zuzga, John J., Jr., '70
Zweifel, Thomas J., '74
Zwerin, Marvin B., '70
Zweissler, Chester J., '40

TO TEACH, TO HEAL, TO SERVE!

*Book design by Anthony C. Principato
and David Johnson*

*Cover and jacket design by Erwin Weirather*

*Composed and printed by
The University of Chicago Printing Department*

*Composition on the
Mergenthaler Variable-Input-Phototypesetter
in Garamond*

*Printed by offset on
60 lb. Opaque Natural Vellum Finish
Book Jacket by offset on Lustro Gloss Enamel*

*Binding by Engdahl Bindery of Chicago
using Joanna-Arrestox B6800 cloth and
80 lb Cardinal Rotunda Text for endsheets*

3